The Royal College of Surgeons
of Edinburgh

The
Royal College of Surgeons of Edinburgh

Historical Notes from 1505 *to* 1905

BY

CLARENDON HYDE CRESWELL
F. S. A. (Scot.)
Late Officer and Sub-Librarian of the College

PRIVATELY PRINTED FOR THE COLLEGE BY

OLIVER AND BOYD
EDINBURGH: TWEEDDALE COURT
LONDON: 33 PATERNOSTER ROW

1926

PRINTED IN GREAT BRITAIN BY
OLIVER AND BOYD, EDINBURGH

PREFATORY NOTE

WHILE Mr C. H. Creswell acted as Officer and Sub-Librarian to the College from 1899 to 1918 he indulged his antiquarian bent by collecting from the Records of the College and from documents in its archives, as well as from other original sources, facts bearing upon the history of the Craft of Surgery in Edinburgh from the earliest times.

His investigations were interrupted when he was recalled to the Army in 1914, and his lamented death on 29th October 1918, while on service, prevented their completion.

The part of the work that remained to be done was the arrangement of the collected material so as to form a consecutive record of the development of the College and of its various activities. Certain sections had, in fact, been so arranged by Mr Creswell and had appeared in the pages of the *Edinburgh Medical Journal* before his death, and it was his intention to deal with the rest of the material on similar lines.

The President's Council, in whose hands the MS. was left, feel that this contribution to the History of the College is worthy of preservation in a form readily accessible to Fellows of the College.

In preparing the work for the press, certain sections have been rearranged and condensed and connecting paragraphs have been supplied where these seemed necessary. No additions and but few deletions have been made.

As Mr Creswell's notes were not fully documented, it has not always been possible to authenticate the literal accuracy of extracts and quotations or to verify dates.

A. M.
A. L. T.

Fellows of the College who Subscribed
to the Volume

Bindiganavale Garudachanja Srinivas Acharya, India.
William Ainslie, Hereford.
Reginald Alcock, Hanley, Staffs.
Robert Marshall Allan, Australia.
Frederick Thomas Anderson, Cheltenham.
William Anderson, Aberdeen.
Hirjee Nowroji Anklesaria, India.
Edward Archer-Brown, South Africa.

Joshua Isadore Baeza, Straits Settlements.
Simon Alexander Ballantyne, Coventry.
William Dodgson Barrow, Lancaster.
Ralph Campbell Lindsay Batchelor, Edinburgh.
Joseph Beard, Carlisle.
Lewis Beesly, Edinburgh.
William Bruce Bell, Manchester.
Harold Graves Bennetts, Australia.
William Charles Bentall, Southport.
Henry Norman Bethune, Michigan, U.S.A.
George Bidie, London.
Edward Jocelyn Bilcliffe, Lincoln.
Robert Bertram Blair, Hull.
Ernest Dykes Bower, Gloucester.
John Macaulay Bowie, Edinburgh.
Edwin John Bradley, Stafford.
William Henry Eden Brand, Banchory, Kincardineshire.
Edward Stanley Brentnall, Manchester.
Robert Charles Espinasse Brodie, Melbourne, Australia.
Keith Paterson Brown, Edinburgh.
John William Burns, Liverpool.
Harry Haward Bywater, Liverpool.

Charles John Caddick, Kenya Colony.
Francis Mitchell Caird, Edinburgh.
Duncan Macnab Callender, Kent.
Thomas Marshall Callender, Kent.
Ernest Hugh Cameron, Edinburgh.
Andrew Campbell, South Africa.
Walter Waddell Carlow, Edinburgh.
Oliver Carlyle, Dumfries.

George Lyall Chiene, Edinburgh.
Percy John Chissell, Ceylon.
Sir James Richardson Andrew Clark, Maidenhead, Berks.
William Alexander Cochrane, Edinburgh.
James McMurray Cole, New Zealand.
Thomas Colley, Dorset.
Henry Anstey Cookson, Sunderland.
Harold Keith Corkill, Edinburgh.
Francis James Coutts, London.
Alister Forbes Cowan, New Zealand.
John William Crerar, Cumberland.
Andrew Croll, Canada.
David Cromie, Malmesbury, Wiltshire.
Robert Crothers, Brighton.
John Cumming, Edinburgh.

Arthur Dangerfield, Streetly, Staffs.
Pares Chandra Datta, India.
Hugh Stevenson Davidson, Edinburgh.
Norman Grenville Walshe Davidson, Glasgow.
Frank Inglis Dawson, Droitwich.
Charles William Dean, Lancaster.
James Adam Dick, Australia.
John Kolbe Milne Dickie, Canada.
Alexander Don, Kent.
Hugh Donovan, Birmingham.
Norman McOmish Dott, Edinburgh.
Charles Edward Douglas, Cupar-Fife.
John Wheeler Dowden, Edinburgh.
Alfred Duke, Newcastle-on-Tyne.
Ethelbert William Dyer, South Africa.

Henry Hawes Elliot, Southsea, Hants.
Alfred Moore Elliott, Co. Tyrone, Ireland.
Louis Daniel Englerth, Philadelphia, Pa., U.S.A.
William Everett, Barry, Glam.

Ernest Chalmers Fahmy, Edinburgh.
James Haig Ferguson, Edinburgh.
James Fitzgerald, New Zealand.
John Fraser, Edinburgh.
William James Fraser, London.
Augustine Sargood Fry, India.
Charles Knowles Fuller, Canada.

George Edward Gabites, New Zealand.
Arthur Alexander Gemmell, Liverpool.
Robert Alexander Gibbons, London.
John Herbert Gibbs, Edinburgh.

Arthur Horace Gibson, Western Australia.
Ernest James Gibson-Berkley, London.
Andrew Graham, China.
Charles William Graham, Edinburgh.
Robert Balfour Graham, Leven, Fife.
John Parlane Granger, Glasgow.
David Middleton Greig, Edinburgh.
Alexander Hill Griffith, Surrey.
George Gunn, Birkenhead.
James Turner Gunn, Auchterarder.
John Donald Gunn, Edinburgh.
Charles Cowen Gurd, Canada.
Douglas James Guthrie, Edinburgh.

John Basil Hall, Bradford.
Reginald Dalton McKellar Hall, London.
Thomas Watson Hancock, Norwich.
George William Hardie, India.
Robert Bloomer Hare, Canada.
Rowland Hill Harris, Michigan, U.S.A.
James Norman Jackson Hartley, Edinburgh.
Sydney Lawrence Harke, New Zealand.
Frank Harvey, Yateley, Hants.
Charles Henry Hayton, California, U.S.A.
Thomas James Henry, Australia.
Norman Hodgson, Newcastle-on-Tyne.
Sir James W. B. Hodsdon, Edinburgh.
Richard Cranshaw Holt, Buxton.
John Fletcher Horne, Barnsley.
David Huey, Co. Antrim, Ireland.
John Brown Dalzell Hunter, India.
Henry Aubrey Husband, Jamaica, B.W.I.

Merwan Soral Irani, Aden.
Samuel Thompson Irwin, Belfast.
George Brownlee Isdale, New Zealand.

Hugh Hunter Jamieson, Australia.
Ah Chit Jap, Straits Settlements.
Francis Evelyn Jardine, Edinburgh.
Calansuria Aratchige Somisara Perera Jayanayake, Ceylon.
Wesley John Jenner, London.
Robert McKenzie Johnston, Edinburgh.
Robert William Johnstone, Edinburgh.
William Llewelyn Jones, Merthyr-Tydfil.

Ratenshah Nariman Kapadia, India.
William Keiller, Texas, U.S.A.
Noel Kemm, Bristol.

William Smith Kerr, Sheffield.
William Wilfrid King, Sheffield.
Patrick Kinmont, Newark-on-Trent.
James Mathieson Kirkness, Blackburn.

Archibald Langwill, London.
John Howard Lechler, China.
John Dickinson Leigh, Sunderland.
Havelock Thomas Lippiatt, Pontefract, Yorks.
George Robert Livingston, Dumfries.
John Stanley Lloyd, Wallasey, Cheshire.
Thomas Edward Lloyd, Abergavenny, Mon.
James Lochhead, Gibraltar.
Charles Damien Lochrane, Derby.
John Louis Lohse, California, U.S.A.
Eric Howard Manley Luke, New Zealand.
Arthur Louis Lynch, Canada.

Alexander MacCarthy-Morrogh, Cork.
William Cuthbert M'Caw, New Zealand.
William Leonard Maccormac, London.
John McCulloch, Canada.
Alexander Morrison McIntosh, Edinburgh.
George Mackay, Edinburgh.
William M'Kay, New Zealand.
Archibald McKendrick, Edinburgh.
Lachlan Martin McKillop, Australia.
Harold Hay Brodie MacLeod, Shrewsbury.
Archibald Cotterell McMaster, Rugby.
James Maconachie, Argyll.
Eric Reginald Delme Maconochie, Maidenhead, Berks.
Antony Ivan Mader, Canada.
Israel Maisels, South Africa.
Sydney Alan Stormer Malkin, Nottingham.
Herbert Frank Marshall, Macclesfield.
Finlay Sinclair Mayne, London.
Walter Mercer, Edinburgh.
Alexander Miles, Edinburgh.
Thomas Mill, New Zealand.
Bernard Langley Mills, Sheffield.
Frederick St George Mivart, London.
John Barré de Winton Molony, London.
Hector MacDonald Monro, London.
Herbert Michael Moran, Australia.
Duncan Metcalfe Morison, Edinburgh.
William John Morton, Australia.
Andrew Watson Munro, Australia.
Henry Temple Mursell, South Africa.

Otto Wilmot Niemeier, Canada.
Henry Clarence Wardleworth Nuttall, Liverpool.

John David O'Donnell, India.
John Stevenson O'Neill, India.
Arthur Gordon Ord, Southsea, Hants.

Keith Shelley Parker, Australia.
James Veitch Paterson, Edinburgh.
John Patrick, Glasgow.
Hans Martinus Perics, Ceylon.
George Reynolds Peterson, Canada.
Oswald Otto Popper, Nottingham.
John Joseph Power, Australia.
Douglas Sherrin Pracy, Atherstone, Warwickshire.
John Millie Pringle, Sheffield.
Samuel Willis Prowse, Canada.
Stephen Horatio Pugh, India.
Edwin Douglas Pullon, New Zealand.
Dodballapur Sivappa Puttanna, India.

Mabel Lida Ramsay, Plymouth.
William Foster Rawson, Bradford.
John Richards, Carmarthen.
Daniel Richmond, Rochdale.
James Wilfrid George Hewat Riddel, Plymouth.
Robert George Riddell, Torquay.
John William Riddoch, Birmingham.
Hugh Jones Roberts, Penygroes, Carnarvonshire.
Hermann Melchior Robertson, Victoria, B.C.
Matthew Edward Robinson, France.
William Moore Skipwith Robinson, Southampton.
Lambert Charles Rogers, Stockport.
James Maxwell Ross, Dumfries.
James Ness MacBean Ross, Surrey.
Zachary Macaulay Hamilton Ross, Sunderland.
Johannes Zacharias Human Rousseau, South Africa.
Sydney Rumboll, Leeds.

Frederick Anastasius Saunders, South Africa.
Athelstan John Henton Saw, Western Australia.
John Alexander Scott, Australia.
Robert Selby, Edinburgh.
Alexander Sharp, Leeds.
Sorabji Pestonji Shroff, India.
Arthur Henry Havens Sinclair, Edinburgh.
Archibald Adam Scot Skirving, Edinburgh.
Phineas Alec Smuts, South Africa.
Frederick Noel Spittel, Ceylon.
Quintin Stewart, West Africa.
William Stewart, Leith.

Sir Harold Jalland Stiles, Gullane.
Gilbert Innes Strachan, Cardiff.
John William Struthers, Edinburgh.
William James Stuart, Edinburgh.
Frederic Herbert Sturdee, Norfolk.
David Campbell Suttie, Glasgow.

David Laurence Tate, Jamaica, B.W.I.
Hugh Neville Adam Taylor, Ebbw Vale, Mon.
Richard Stopford Taylor, Liverpool.
William Macrae Taylor, Edinburgh.
Cecil Henry Terry, Somerset.
William Pelton Tew, Canada.
Arthur Richard Thomas, Dorset.
Rufus Clifford Thomas, Newport, Mon.
Hedley Barry Thomson, Australia.
Bolar Thungamma, India.
Harry Moss Traquair, Edinburgh.
Alfred Croudson Tunstall, Cornwall.
Arthur Logan Turner, Edinburgh.

Charles Howard Usher, Aberdeen.

Alexander Grant Vermont van Someren, Romsey, Hampshire.

Henry Wade, Edinburgh.
Muhammed Abdul Wajid, London.
Walter Oliphant Walker, India.
Sir David Wallace, Edinburgh.
William Richard Spencer Watkins, Manchester.
Alexander Pirie Watson, Edinburgh.
Benjamin Philp Watson, Edinburgh.
Charles Henry James Watson, Surrey.
William Grant Waugh, Sunderland.
Matthew White, Glasgow.
Charles Richard Whittaker, Edinburgh.
George Abeysingha Weera Wickramasuriya, Ceylon.
James Bowman Wilkie, Perth.
David Llewelyn Williams, Cardiff.
Ethel Dorothy Willis, Manchester.
Alexander Johnston Wilson, Airdrie.
Thomas Outterson Wood, Torquay, South Devon.
Walter Quarry Wood, Edinburgh.
Gordon Stewart Woodman, Baghdad.
Alfred Chad Turner Woodward, Bewdley.
Percy Charles Woollatt, Hinckley.
Hiram Bardsley Wyman, Bedworth, Warwickshire.

John Brown Yeoman, Birkenhead.
Alexander Waugh Young, Boxmoor, Herts.
William Young, New Zealand.

CONTENTS

xiii

LIST OF ILLUSTRATIONS

ROYAL COLLEGE OF SURGEONS OF EDINBURGH

CHAPTER I

THE FOUNDATION OF THE ROYAL COLLEGE OF SURGEONS

Introduction—Incorporation of the Barber-Surgeons of Edinburgh—The Seal of Cause—The Incorporated Crafts—Early Members of the Craft of Barber-Surgeons.

Introduction.—During the Middle Ages the practice of what was then called Surgery was shared by two classes of practitioner—the Barbers and the Surgeons. Some kind of distinction was doubtless recognised between the respective spheres of activity of the two grades, but it was so vague and ill-defined that their mutual jealousies and suspicions seem to have kept them in constant conflict.

The origin of the Barber Craft may be traced back to 1092, when the monks were forbidden to wear beards and certain members of the monasteries were set aside and trained for the shaving and bleeding of the monks. Early in the thirteenth century (1210) two ranks were officially recognised in the fraternity—the clerical barber-surgeons or "surgeons of the long robe," and the lay barbers or "surgeons of the short robe," but this differentiation does not seem to have prevented some overlapping in function, for, about a hundred years later Royal decrees were issued forbidding the lay barbers to practise surgery without having been duly examined by their clerical brethren of the long robe. This, however, did not end the matter, for, in 1372, the King of France granted the short-robed barbers the privilege of treating wounds without interference by their long-robed confrères. About the same time (1368) the master-surgeons in England formed themselves into a separate Guild, and, in 1462, "the Mystery of the Barbers of London," whose surgical practice was restricted to blood-letting and healing of wounds, obtained a separate Charter from Edward IV.

Incorporation of the Barber-Surgeons of Edinburgh—The Seal of Cause.—At this time the relations between the barbers and the surgeons in Edinburgh appear to have been less strained than they were in other places. A certified copy extract of the Burgh Records preserved in the archives of the College of Surgeons shows that, on 24th April 1504, the Kirkmaster of the Barber Craft obtained the right to hold divine service at an altar in the Kirk of St Giles, and undertook to provide book and vestments for the altar, and to devote the collections made on Saint Mungo's day for the sustentation and upkeep of the wax lights. The altar was dedicated to Saint Bride; the patron saint of the Craft was Saint Mungo, and Master David Lauder was appointed Chaplain.

There is reason to believe that the surgeons shared with the barbers the privileges and obligations attached to this altar, for, in 1505, when the two bodies jointly presented to the Town Council a "bill and supplicatioun," they pleaded: "itt is weill knawin till all your wisdomes quhow thatt we uphald ane altar situat within your college kirk of Sanct Geill in the honour of God and Sanct Mongow our patrone, and hes no importance [means] to uphald the samyn [same] but [except] oure sober [frugal] oulklie [weekly] penny and upsettis [belongings] qwilk [which] are small in effect till [to] sustene and uphald oure said altar in all necessar thingis convenient thereto . . ."

The object of this petition to the Town Council was that the barbers and surgeons might be enrolled among the Incorporated Crafts of the Burgh and granted a "Seal of Cause" or Charter of Privileges. Their prayer was based on their pious upholding of the altar and on their "gude mynde till do this gude toune all the steid plesour and service that we can or may baith in walking [watching] and wairding [arresting or imprisoning] stenting [bearing tax] and bering all uther portabile chairges within this burgh at all tymes as uther nichtbouris [inhabitants] and craftis dois . . ."

The first request they made was "thatt we micht have yairly chosin amangis us ane Kirkmaister and ourisman to quhome the haill brether of the craftis foirsaid sall obey for thatt yeir."

The Kirkmaster is now styled the President. He is still chosen yearly and receives of right the obedience of all the brethren. On his election, however, he nominates from among the Fellows a Council to assist him in the management of the College affairs.

The petition continues :—

"ITEM—Every maister that is resauit [received] frieman to the said craft sall pay his oulklie [weekly] penny with the preistis meil [tribute] as he sal happin to cum about. And every servand that is feitt [hired] man to the maisteris of the said craft sall pay ilk [every] oulk [week] ane halfpenny to the said alter and reparatioun theirof. And that we haif powar to cheise ane chaiplane till do devyne service daylie at our said alter at all tymes quhen the samyn sall vaik [shall be unoccupied]. And till cheise ane officiar till pas with ws for the ingathering of oure quarter payment and oulklie [weekly] penneis. And to pas befoir ws on Corpus Christj day and the ouatouis [octaves] thairof and all uther generall processionis and gatheringis siclike as utheris craftis hes within this burgh. And that ane of the maisteris of the foirsaid craftis with the chaiplane and officiar of the samyn pas at all tymes neidfull lift and raise the saidis quarter paymentis fra every persoun that aw the samyn. And gif [if] ony [any] disobeyis that we may poynd and distrenyie thairfoir all tymes haifand [having] ane officiar of the toune with ws."

The College no longer enjoys the services of a Chaplain, but an officer still accompanies the President at processions and other gatherings, and the Master of the Craft who collects payments is represented by the Treasurer.

It is further stipulated "That all the maisteris friemen and brether of the said craft reddelie obey and cum to their kirkmaister at all tymes quhen they sall be requyritt thairto be the said officiar for to heir quarter comptis or till avyse for ony thing concernyng the common weill of the said craftis. And quha thatt disobeyis sall pay xxs to the reparatioun of the said alter."

Provision was made in the next clauses to ensure that the

members of the Craft should be efficiently trained to perform the duties expected of them.

"ITEM—Thatt no maner of persoun occupie nor use any poyntis of oure saidis craftis of Surregerie or barbour craft within this burgh bott gif [except—unless] he be first frieman and burges of the samyn and thatt he be worthy and expert in all the poyntis belangand the saidis craftis deligentlie and avysitlie examinit and admittit be the maisteris of the said craft for the honorabill seruyng of oure Soverane Lord his liegis and nychtbouris [inhabitants] of this burgh. And als That everie man that is to be maid frieman and maister amangis ws be examit and previt in thir poyntis following THATT IS TO SAY That he knaw anotamea nature and complexioun of every member In manis bodie. And in lykewayes he knaw all the vaynis of the samyn thatt he may mak flewbothomea in dew tyme. And als thatt he knaw in quhilk member the signe hes domination for the tyme for every man aucht to knaw the nature and substance of every thing thatt he wirkis or ellis he is negligent. And that we may have anis in the yeir ane condampnit man efter he be deid to mak anatomea of quhairthrow we may haif experience. Ilk ane to instruct utheris. And we sall do suffrage for the soule."

"ITEM—That na maisteris of the said craft sall tak ane prenteis or feit man in tyme cuming to use the surregeane craft without he can baith wryte and reid. And the said maister of ony of the saidis craftis that takis anie prenteis sall pay at his entres to the reparatioun of the said alter tuenty schillingis."

Then follows the strange petition :—

" . . . that na persoun man nor woman within this burgh mak nor sell ony aquavitae within the samyn. Except the saidis maisteris brether and friemen of the saidis craftis under the paine of escheit of the samyn but favouris."

The granting of this Seal of Cause by the Town Council on the first of July 1505, formally united the barbers and surgeons and constituted them one of the Crafts of the Burgh. To this union the Royal College of Surgeons of Edinburgh traces its foundation as a corporate body.

The Incorporated Crafts. — When the barber-surgeons were admitted to the Crafts they stood ninth or tenth in order of seniority — the oldest being the Hatmakers, who were incorporated in 1473 or 1474. From early times the Crafts had certain civic rights and, by an Act of Parliament passed in 1469, each Craft then in existence was permitted to take part in the election of the magistrates. The Act says: "Touching the election of aldermen, bailies, and other officers . . . and that each craft shall choose a person of the same craft that shall have voice in the said election of the officers for the time, in likewise year by year." To the Crafts this was a great concession, for before the passing of the Act no one but the Town Council had a voice in the selection of the magistrates, who were chosen by a system of self-election from among the Guildry. This ancient body, whose members alone were eligible for municipal office, was composed almost entirely of merchants, and formed a class quite distinct from the craftsmen, who worked with their hands and were in consequence debarred from election to the magistracy.

One of the first acts of the barber-surgeons after they became an Incorporated Craft was, in concert with certain other Incorporations, to petition the Town Council for a larger share in municipal government. The reply of the magistrates, dated 29th November 1508, appears in the Burgh Records—"The which day the Provost, Bailies and great Council and a part of the Craftsmen of the Town answered the petition presented to them by another part of the said Craftsmen, viz., that six or eight of them might be placed on the daily Council of the Town and that the other part of them might be eligible for the office of Bailie and other offices." To this the Council replied that they could make no alteration or innovation without the consent of the King, and promised to bring the matter before Parliament the next time it assembled. It would appear from this reply that some of the Crafts were already represented on the Council while others were not, but as no alteration seems to have been made, if the question was ever brought before Parliament it would appear to have received an unfavourable reply.

Early Members of the Craft of Barber-Surgeons.—One of the earliest references to a member of the Craft is contained in the Lord High Treasurer's Accounts for the year 1527, where it is recorded that by Act of Parliament, " Our Sovereign Lord granted a yearly fee and pension to his servant George Leithe, his Chirurgeon, for all the days of his life." As George Leithe's

name appears in a list of Deacons of Crafts in the Burgh
Records on 6th August 1539, presumably he was at that
date Deacon of the Barber-Surgeons. He was probably one
of the founders of the Craft.   In 1542, George Leithe,
William Quhite, George Fotheringham and David Robertsoun,
Chirurgeons, received £12 for "passand to the bordouris for
curing of all personis that hapnit to be hurt be the Inglis
menne."   In a Charter or Deed of Bequest, dated 2nd February
1533, and still in the possession of the College, George Leithe
conveys to the Chaplain of the "honest craft of barbers" an
annual payment of thirty shillings, the rental of a property
situated on the north side of the High Street near the Castle
Hill, for the celebration of weekly mass at the altar of Saint
Kentigern[1] in the Kirk of Saint Giles.   The Deacon of the
Barbers is held responsible for the payment of the money to
the Chaplain who, at the beginning of his mass "shall be
bound to exhort the people [to pray] for the souls of the
founders and the souls foresaid and that at the end of the
mass they shall say the Psalm De Profundis [Ps. cxxx] with
sprinkling of holy water on our tomb praying for our souls
and all the souls aforesaid ; and after mass they shall celebrate
Placebo and Dirige [parts of the Office of the Dead] with
nine lessons."

The quaint introduction to this Deed of Bequest may be
quoted :—

"To all who shall see or hear this charter, George Leche, burgess
of the burgh of Edinburgh, and Sir [Dominus] George Litiljohne,
chaplain, wish eternal salvation in Him who is the true salvation of
all : Know ye that we, to the praise and honour of God Almighty
Father, Son and Holy Ghost, and of the most Glorious Virgin Mary,
and of St Kentigern Bishop and Confessor, of St Brigid Virgin, of
the holy martyrs Cosmo and Damian and the ten thousand martyrs
and of all saints male and female, and for the salvation of our souls,
the souls of our fathers and mothers, brothers, sisters, and relations,
for the salvation of the souls of Mariota Dee, spouse of George Leche,
Alexander Cant, Sir William Leche, Canon of Jedburgh, Sir Robert
Stalkar, Chaplain, and Mariora Achesone and of the souls of all those
to whom we have been or are indebted, or to whom by speech set
or otherwise we have in this life done wrong and of all faithful

---

[1] Another name for St Mungo.

departed to whom it may be of advantage, have given granted and by this our present charter confirmed and do give grant and by this our present charter perpetually confirm to God and to the Most Blessed Virgin Mary, to St Kentigern Confessor, to the Blessed Brigid Virgin, to the holy Martyrs Cosmo and Damian and the ten thousand martyrs, and to the said Sir George Litiljohne, Chaplain of the said altar and to his successors, chaplains or secular priests to celebrate [mass] in perpetuity at the said altar of St Kentigern for the good of the said souls," etc.

The William Quhite already referred to as having accompanied Leithe on his expedition to the Borders appears to have been Deacon of the Craft in 1543. His name appears in a list of the deacons who were imprisoned in the Castle as a result of an escapade recorded by Pennicuik in his *History of the Blue Blanket* (1722):—

"During the minority of Queen Mary, a controversy being betwixt the Magistrates of Edinburgh and the Deacons of Crafts for breaking in upon the legal privileges of the Incorporations, which so inflamed the Deacons of Trades with a keen resentment, that in the Tolbooth of Edinburgh where the Courts of Justice then sat, they drew their swords demanding justice; and if they had not been restrained by the King's forces then in the city, whom the Magistrates called to their assistance, they had been killed on the Bench. Being thus relieved, they committed the assassins, as they termed them, prisoners to the Castle where they remained in close confinement till the several Incorporations having met in the absence of their deacons, and concluded to relieve them after the never failing method of displaying the Blue Blanket, which they did and thereby convocated thousands of the King's Lieges in a very few hours."

In 1558, the country being threatened by an invasion of their "auld inemies of Ingland," the Council, merchants and deacons were hastily summoned to take steps for the protection of the City. As a result of their deliberations, Robert Henderson, "Deacon of the Barbers," and seven others were selected to present a petition to the Queen Regent, requesting that certain Nobles might be sent to put the town in a state of defence. To meet the emergency the Deacons of Crafts were desired to notify the number of men they could furnish in case of attack. In all, the Incorporation undertook to supply 717 men, of whom the Barbers are said to have contributed 25, although the following 27 names are registered in the Burgh Records:—

Jhone Wawchthet, and his servand [apprentice]	.	Edward Wawchthet
David Robertsoun	„ .	Thomas Kawpe
Nowye Bruschet	„ .	Thomas Boyes
Archibald Maw	„ .	Jhone Scot
Alexander Percy, and his servand	.	Thomas Blak
Niniane Maw	„ .	Jhone Chalmer
Maister Armle	„ .	William Gray
Maister Babteist	„ .	Jhone Pectarne
Pate Hardye, and his sone	. .	Walter Hardye
Robert Henrysoun, his servandis	. .	{ Andro Wyntoun { Gilbert Prymros

Jhone Weddle.
Patrick Mertene.
Alexander Bruce.
Jhone Libertoun.
James Lindesay.
George Campbell.

Since the refusal of their petition, in 1508, the Crafts took but little part in the town's government, although between the years 1522 and 1524 the names of deacons are occasionally found associated with the Provost and bailies. For some reason they seem about this time to have forfeited their right to vote at the municipal elections, for, in 1559, they supplicated the Queen Regent to have that privilege restored to them. In this they were successful, and again for some years deacons sat in the Council.

In 1582 a dispute arose of a more serious nature than usual, in which Gilbert Primrose, Deacon of the Surgeons, took a leading part.

The deacons, it seems, objected to the City Assessors, or Assistant Judges in the Bailie Court, voting in the election of the magistrates which, it was alleged, they had no power to do under the Act of Parliament of King James III. The magistrates, on the other hand, declared that the Assessors (who were their friends) had a right to vote as they had done for many years, and that, as the question had been decided long before, the Council had no power to go back upon the decision.

On the day fixed for the election a large crowd, probably composed of craftsmen in sympathy with the deacons, assembled outside the Courthouse and prevented the Assessors from entering the building. When this became known to the bailies, they elected from among themselves a number equal to that of the absent Assessors, to act in their places. To this the deacons objected, and Gilbert Primrose, who spoke for them, declared they would recognise no officials elected by such means. This led to a heated debate, in the course of which Gilbert Primrose was accused by the bailies of opening the Council-house door and bidding the people to enter, so that a large number gained admittance and a serious tumult ensued. In answer to the charge Primrose replied "that he opened the door to gang awa and did na thing contraire the Kingis Maiesteis lawes." The magistrates were then elected, the deacons still refusing to vote. As the newly elected bailies were proceeding to the Tolbooth to perform the usual "fensing" they were set upon by the mob, who handled them so roughly that they had to run for their lives.

The Privy Council then intervened, and at last the question of the status of the Crafts in municipal affairs was settled by arbitration, the King himself acting as umpire. Under the new arrangement, known as the Decreit-Arbitral or Set of the City, it was settled that the magistrates were to be chosen only from among the merchants. Six deacons and two craftsmen were to have seats on the Council, and all the Deacons of Crafts were to have a vote in the election of the magistrates.

The Crafts, now fourteen in number, took order of precedence as follows: Surgeons, Goldsmiths, Skinners, Furriers, Hammermen, Wrights, Masons, Tailors, Baxters, Fleshers, Cordiners, Websters, Waulkers, and Bonnetmakers. Their place of meeting was the Magdalen Chapel in the Cowgate, which belonged to the Hammermen. Here they assembled at intervals for the transaction of business and for the discussion of questions relating to the rights and privileges of the Trades in general. They appear to have agreed among themselves to a great extent, and to have been able to offer a stout resistance to the sometimes tyrannical despotism of the merchants. From among their number the deacons elected one to be their Deacon Convener for the year. This office was held in high respect, and to the Deacon Convener's care was entrusted the custody of the Tradesmen's Banner—the famous Blue Blanket, which was kept at the headquarters of the Crafts, the Magdalen Chapel. Thus the year 1582 found the Crafts prospering, and particularly the surgeons, who had been advanced to the head of the Trades, a prominence to which they were not entitled by seniority, but which was granted them either on account of the anomaly of their position in being included among the City Crafts, or more probably by the influence of their deacon of the time, Gilbert Primrose.

CHAPTER II

EARLY RECORDS OF THE CRAFT

The Plague—The " Letter of Exemption "—Offences against the Craft—
Early Records of Affairs of the Incorporation—The First Minutes of
the College—Apprentices—Gilbert Prymross—The Trained Bands—
Domestic Quarrels—The "Act of Ranking"—Admission to the Craft—
The "Cure of Patients"—The Mortcloth—Sabbath Observance—
Signing the Covenant.

THE Burgh of Edinburgh, within which the members of the
barber-surgeons were privileged to exercise their calling, was
in the end of the sixteenth century a comparatively restricted
area occupying the ridge of the hill which ascends from Holyrood to the Castle.   According to Hugo Arnot "the ridge
of this hill forms a continued and very magnificent street.   From
its sides lanes and alleys, which are there called *wynds* and
closes, extend like slanting ribs; so that, upon the whole,
it bears a striking resemblance to a turtle, of which the Castle
is the head, the High Street the ridge of the back, the wynds
and closes the shelving sides, and the Palace of Holyrood-house
the tail."   The town was about a mile in length, and half a
mile in breadth, and the greater part of it was walled as a
protection against the incursions of the English.   "From
confinement of space . . . . the houses were piled to an
enormous height, some of them amounting to twelve stories.
These were denominated *lands*.   The access to the separate
lodgings in these huge piles was by a common stair, exposed
to every inconvenience arising from filth, steepness, darkness,
and danger from fire" (Arnot).

The Plague. — Such conditions were not favourable to
health, and during the century the town was visited from
time to time by a contagious form of disease spoken of
as the plague.   The magistrates found it necessary to take

active steps to suppress it, some of which were more rigorous than effective. At one time certain of the merchants—particularly those who dealt in wool, hides, cloths, and skins—were ordered to close their shops, all windows and doors being closed and not opened without a reasonable cause.

Another order, more likely to be attended with good results, was that ordaining that "All such infected persons as God relieves them of pestilence and gives them heal, that they converse not nor haunt not with whole folks for the space of forty days thereafter, without they have a white wand in their hand, or a white cloth sewed upon their breast in token of their sickness, if they come furth, that other clean folks may eschew them, under the pain of death."

The punishment for concealing the disease was most severe, generally branding on the cheek in the case of women, or on any part of the body in the case of men, along with banishment; but an instance is recorded in the year 1530, when a man, for not revealing the sickness of his wife and for attending a service in St Giles, she being *in extremis*, was ordered to be hanged the same day in front of his own door. In the carrying out of the sentence, however, the rope broke and the gibbet collapsed, whereupon, "being a puir man with small bairns and for pite of him" he was allowed to escape with banishment for life. For a like offence a woman was condemned to be drowned in the "quarry hole," a lonely spot at the east end of the Calton Hill.

With the return of the plague in the summer months of 1585, renewed efforts were made to stamp it out. The towns-people were forbidden to lodge strangers in their houses even for a single night; and "dustefute" (the hangman) was ordered to kill all swine, cats, and dogs wherever he might see them.

To James Henderson, who became Deacon of the Surgeons in 1587, was entrusted by the Town Council the duty of visiting "all persons who shall be infected with the sickness of pestilence and give true judgement to the Magistrates at all times and siclike to visit all hospitals in the burgh and the poor who shall happen to be sick or sair, lame or hurt . . . . for which he shall receive a yearly stipend of twenty pounds."

It may therefore be claimed that this James Henderson was the first to hold the office of Medical Officer of Health in Edinburgh. These obligations were performed by him with such satisfaction to the Council that they excused him from payment of any taxes or contributions levied on the inhabitants of the Burgh during his life. He himself contracted the disease and recovered; but his wife, who had caught the infection from him, died. Among the papers of the College is a receipt from Henderson for twenty pounds, borrowed by him from the Incorporation in 1593, which he promises to repay "without guile or fraud."

The "Letter of Exemption." — Plague and pestilence, however, were not the only cares of the surgeon, his attention being called in another and not less important direction. It had now come to be recognised that the art of warfare could be carried on more effectively with medical aid. Hitherto the surgeon had been present on the field of battle only as a combatant, no special duty being assigned to him in virtue of his professional skill, and the care of the sick and wounded had been pretty much left to chance. It was no longer to be so; a higher claim was made upon the services of the surgeon and soon it became the rule rather than the exception for armies to take the field with a full complement of surgeons. In 1542, army surgeons are first mentioned, and from that time may be traced the foundation of that splendidly organised Medical Unit in the Field with which we are now familiar.

A Charter granted under the Privy Seal to the Incorporation in 1567, to a great extent confirms the advance in the application of their science just mentioned, and confers additional privileges upon them, conditionally that they accompany the army when required to do so. Executed by Queen Mary but four days before her ill-fated marriage with Bothwell, this Charter, of perfect caligraphy, bears date 11th May 1567, and shows that in a comparatively short space of time the surgeon, by diligent application to his craft, had become almost indispensable to the army as well as to the citizen. This "Letter of Exemption," as it is generally called, refers only to chirurgeons, who are therefore no longer required, runs the deed, "to bear armour nor pass in battle in our hosts, raids, gatherings, assembles, weaponshawings, or wars to be made by us or our successors . . . by land and sea within this our said realms or without the same; and also from all compearance and passing upon any inquests or assizes on actions criminal or civil . . . Provided always that they be present with our armies ready to do their cure and duty to all such persons as shall have mister [want] thereof."

The surgeons welcomed this new departure and recognised in their military connection a source from which much practical knowledge might be obtained. At least one of them, who was selected for service against the English in 1558, and who became deacon a few years afterwards, benefited in no ordinary degree by his experience, as may be inferred from this quaint abstract from the Burgh Records: "The Provost, Bailies, Council, and Deacons upon consideration of the great labour and expense made by Robert Henderson, Chirurgeon, at the command of them on divers persons hurt within this town and in special upon a dead woman raised forth of the grave after she had been lying two days in the same alleged to have been wyrreit [strangled]; curing and mending of the two false noteries whose hands were stricken off; dressing and mending of a man and a woman stricken through the body with a sword by the Frenchman, To deliver to the same Robert the sum of twenty merks."

Offences against the Craft. — Various documents in possession of the College show that offenders were frequently dealt with for usurping the rights of the Craft both in practising surgery without a licence, and for making and selling aquavitæ. They were mostly disposed of in the Bailie Court under the penalty of a fine, but occasionally they ended in the Court of Session. In the year 1578, while Alexander Bruce was Deacon of the Barbers, a serious case was disposed of. A certain Duncan Hunter, Laird of Ballagane, "a pretended chirurgeon," was found guilty of having employed "a sword stepper" named James Hunter to apply "emplasteris and sawis [salves] to divers persons in this burgh," and for this offence James was fined forty shillings, and Duncan was forbidden to exercise any surgery or barbercraft within the burgh under a penalty of ten pounds Scots.

For unlawfully making and selling aquavitæ many convictions were obtained against women as well as against men; the usual penalties inflicted were a pecuniary fine and the escheating of the utensils employed in the making of the aquavitæ.

Early Records of the Affairs of the Incorporation.— Although the barber-surgeons were incorporated in 1505, no official record of their business appears to have been kept until the year 1581. Prior to the year 1556, the Burgh Records are our main source of information, but from that date onwards various documents in the possession of the College throw interesting side-lights on the manners and customs of the times and of the men who conducted the affairs of the Craft.

In the earliest of these documents, dated 15th February 1556, James Maxwell "dwelland in Rouen" acknowledges to have received from " Alex. Bruce dekeyne of ye barbours ye sowme of £4, 3s. 4d. for yair partt of ye stentt last gaderite in name and behalf of Gavin Commendatour of Kyllwyning and ye said James Maxwell for ye downe getying of 16 denniers payit be ye scott merchand in the Dukye of Normandie in France."

Another writ of the same description, dated November 1565, contains an account of a meeting of the Town Council and deacons, at which arrangements were made for repayment of 10,000 merks, lent by the merchants, craftsmen and citizens to the King and Queen to put down an insurrection raised by the Earl of Murray in the West. Among the names of those present appears that of John Chalmer, Deacon of the Barbers.

From these sources we learn that Alexander Bruce was Deacon of the Craft in 1556, and John Chalmer in 1565.

A receipt from Bailie John Sym records his having received from the barbers the sum of £43, 13s. 4d. as the taxation " and lent monye to ye King and Queneis and for ye superioritie of Leithe."

The Minutes of the Surgeons' Meetings.—From the year 1581 the proceedings of the barber-surgeons have been continuously recorded in the Minutes of their meetings, and from these more detailed information regarding their affairs is available. The earliest Minute, dated 2nd February

1581, contains the names of the members of the Craft at that time.

The Nameis of ye Masteris.

Gilbert Primross, deckin	Patrick Martine
Noyer Brussate	Hendrie Blyth
Robert Henderson	Jhon Lowsone
Alexander Bruce	Hendrie Lumsdene
James Lindsay	Michall Bassetyne
Jhon Woddal	Alexander Fiddas
James Craig	Jhon Libbertoun
Alexander Tweedie	Jacobe Brun

From subsequent Minutes it appears that the office-bearers consisted of the deacon, four masters, who formed a Council, two keepers of the keys of the "silver box" and a keeper of the key of the "kyst." The junior member performed the duties of officer, and a clerk was appointed, at a yearly salary of forty shillings.

The Incorporation met four times in a year, usually at the deacon's house or in his "yaird," but it is also recorded that from time to time it met for the transaction of business, for the auditing of accounts, and even for the holding of examinations, in the "auld Kirk," in the "new Kirk," and in the "ile" of Saint Giles.

The system adopted for the management of the financial affairs of the Incorporation was simple and in keeping with the times. The funds, consisting of coins of various denominations, were kept in a box on which were two separate locks, each requiring a different key. This box was placed inside a larger box with a single lock, and deposited for safe keeping in the deacon's house. On one occasion, in 1592, the funds in the box amounted to "six new rose nobilis, twa auld rose nobilis, four four-pound pieces, ane fyve-pound piece and ane crown of the sone, two Scottis testamis, ane Inglis testem and ane half merk piece."

With the exception of small loans, no investments appear to have been made, but an account was kept of all intromissions. At one time the monetary transactions were left pretty much to the discretion of the deacon, subject, as is apparent from the following abstract, to the approval of the members: "The Masters of the Chirurgians hes dischargit [prohibited] their dekin whatsoever for the time to lend ony money to ony personis whatsoever without all their consentis and assentis had thereto. Nevertheless if it sall happin thame to haif ado ony needful business ordanis thair dekin to disburs ony money necessor until the haill masteris be convenit who sall allow hes ressonable desbursing and sall pay to him the sum again."

Although the keys of the cash-box were in charge of the office-bearers the deacon seems to have been held responsible for its safe keeping, at least this is the inference drawn from a Minute of 21st October 1596, which shows that the funds had been stolen from the deacon's house. "The qlk day John Nasmyth dekin in the year preceding payed and delivered to the craft the sum of £45, 6s. 8d., which was theftuously stollen away from him furth of his cellar, the craft's kist and box being broken by the wiked person. Of the which sum the present deacon and masters discharge the said John Nasmyth of all his intromissions whatsoever preceding the date hereof for now and ever. Providing always that if the said John can get wit who has stollen the said money furth of the box he shall have . . . thereto as his own proper goods, with this addition, that if the like occur again in any other personis hands, that the sum whatsoever that shall happen to be taken away shall be rendered again as the said John rendered and payed again the foresaid £45, 6s. 8d."

Apprentices.—To qualify for examination, the aspirant to the practice of surgery at the end of the sixteenth century had to be apprenticed to a master-surgeon for six years, during which time he lived in his master's house. On being apprenticed he paid twenty shillings to the Incorporation for "his gudes" and two shillings clerk's fees. At the expiry of his apprenticeship he became an assistant or "servand"; or qualified as a master at once by examination and payment of a sum decided upon by the Calling. He had also to prove himself to be a burgess of the City.

It was soon discovered, however, that apprentices out of their time and before passing their examination, frequently practised on their own account, thereby usurping the privileges of the master-surgeon, and in this way often bringing the

B

profession into disrepute. A law was passed dealing with these offenders, who, in addition to other punishment, were forbidden the right of examination for one year after the offence.

The most important question that occupied the attention of the Calling about this time was one that affected the succession of freemen's children to the Craft privileges of their father. To this subject the surgeons' books contain many references. A quotation from one or two will explain the situation clearly: "The Deacon and Brethren having respect that Mark Libberton is a freeman's second son howbeit that no freemans' sons of the Craft have liberties through their father but the eldest son only, yet we nevertheless moved by favour and pity towards the said Mark admit him to be a master and freeman of the barber craft only . . . and ordaine the said Mark not to have any signs of chirurgie in his bught nor house oppenly nor privately such as piggis, buistis or chirurgiane case or box pertaining to the chirurgeon."

That the eldest son alone should have a right of entry to his father's craft seemed to the Incorporation an injustice. The steps taken to remedy this and to extend the privilege to all of the sons and, under conditions, to the husbands of the daughters of freemen, are set forth in a Minute of 26th September 1591, and in effect is, that all the sons and daughters of the freemen of the Craft shall enjoy the privileges of their fathers, providing the former are found qualified by examination, but in case any of the latter should stray from the path of virtue, neither she nor the man that marries her shall have any privilege or right by her father although he be a freeman of the Craft and a burgess of the City. In conclusion, the deacon and brethers undertook to observe and keep this Act inviolate as a "good and godly order and law amongst them according to the use of other crafts of the burgh." The object of the Act will be better understood when it is remembered that apprentices lived in their masters' houses as members of the family and that many inducements were held out to them to become their masters' sons-in-law.

From other entries it appears that a surgeon's widow, providing she employed a "servand," i.e., one who had served his apprenticeship, was permitted to carry on her husband's barbering business after his death. As an instance of this it is recorded that a certain "William Wood servand to umquhile John Lowson, chirurgeon, freeman and burgess of this burgh, entered as Servand with Bessie Lundie his Mother-in-law and agreed to live with her in household and in one booth during her lifetime, so that there would be no necessity for them to keep two booths hereafter neither of the chirurgeon nor barber crafts ... but it shall not be lessom to the said William to use any further liberty but the barber craft only."

Gilbert Prymross.—Gilbert Prymross was one of the most prominent of the earlier members of the barber-surgeons. He was born about 1535, of a Perthshire family, the present representative of which is the Earl of Rosebery. The date of his admission to the Craft is not known, but he was an apprentice to Robert Henrysoun in 1558, and was one of those who joined a corps then raised "for the defence of the toune" against "our auld inemyes of Ingland." He was thrice elected deacon, in 1576, 1581, and 1602. He was surgeon to King James VI., and Dr Peter Lowe, the founder of the Royal Faculty of Physicians and Surgeons of Glasgow, dedicated his treatise on Chirurgery to him and to James Harvie, another member of the Craft who had been Prymross' apprentice.

The Minute recording the election of Prymross as deacon for the third time, in 1602, is signed by thirteen masters (including himself) who promised by the faith of their body and under the bane of perjury and defamation, never to violate any points of the Seal of Cause, but to maintain it inviolable, and to obey the deacon in all things during his time. Prymross was punctilious in carrying out the laws of the Craft. At the first meeting after his election all the absentees were fined; the practice of fining members for absence at meetings had been in abeyance from the time of his previous tenure of the deaconship in 1581. It was during his second period of office that Minutes of the meetings were regularly kept, and during his third period many new laws calculated to promote the welfare of the Craft and to raise its dignity were passed. A general increase in the fees of entrants was made. A surgeon had to pay at his admission sixty pounds

Scots, and a barber forty pounds Scots. The latter was also required to certify in the Town books that he would not use any point of surgery under a penalty of twenty pounds. An apprentice had now to pay at his "inbooking" forty shillings instead of twenty shillings, and three shillings and three pence each to the clerk and to the officer. Another reform ordained that every master and every freeman of the Craft should pay a quarterly subscription of six shillings and eight pence, instead of the weekly penny "which was wont to be payed of auld for supporting of the persons of the Craft that shall happen to decay."

Prymross died at Westminster, on the 8th of April 1615, and was buried in the old Greyfriars. The spot is marked by a monument bearing a Latin inscription which may be translated: "To Gilbert Primrose, Chief Surgeon to James and Anne, King and Queen of Great Britain, France, and Ireland, his heirs erected this monument. He lived happily 80 years. To the end of his life he was chief Surgeon to the King, and died, adorned with Testimonials of Public sorrow from Prince and People, in the year of our Lord 1615, the 8th day of April."

In the Museum of the College there is an interesting relic of Prymross. It is labelled "A replica of the Mortar used by Gilbert Primrose, an ancestor of the Earl of Rosebery and a Deacon of the Chirurgeon-Barbers in 1581." This was presented to the College by Lord Rosebery on the occasion of a banquet given to commemorate the opening of the new hall in December 1909. His Lordship, in proposing the health of the College, thus referred to his forbear Gilbert Primrose, "What I have in my hand at this moment, for I brought it for that purpose to-night, was the Mortar which he employed in compounding the gruesome drugs which he administered to the unfortunate population. I can only surmise, as I owe the possession of this Mortar to the authorities of the Town Museum of Hawick—for which I owe them a life-long obligation—that Gilbert Primrose, in the exercise of his volunteering proclivities or duties, must have lost his Mortar on the Border, in action against our old enemies the English. We all remember the old saying, '*relicta non bene parmula*.' I know not whether '*parmula*' may be stretched to include that vessel. If it can, I strongly surmise that that is the way in which that gallipot fell into the possession of the hereditary enemies of our race. So it passed into the Borders at Hawick."

The Trained Bands.—Although Queen Mary's Charter of 1569 exempted the surgeons from bearing arms in battle, an account in their books in 1595 recording an outlay of ten pounds "for powder on the Muster day," indicates they were still liable to some kind of military service. This may be due to the citizens of Edinburgh, in 1626, having been formed into companies for the defence of the town in case of emergency. More direct proof of their attendance at military drill may be found in another Minute which forbids any of their number to leave the ranks to attend a patient unless he be sent for.

In 1627, the " City Youths " were formed into two companies, one composed of merchants, the other of craftsmen. The former were to march in front of the City Trained Band, the latter in its rear. They were to be ready to turn out at all times of the day or night at the sound of the drum. In 1631, it was ordained that all the servants of the company that carry muskets shall each have a pound of powder at the expense of the Craft.

That the surgeons considered compulsory attendance at drill an injustice to themselves is quite conceivable, and little surprise will be felt when, on one of their number being appointed to a command in the Trained Band, he protested, alleging exemption under their old Charter of 1567. This led to the following communication (still in the possession of the College) being sent by the Lord Provost, Sir Alexander Ramsay, to " Captain Mickle of the Trades Youths."

"The Chirurgeons pretending exemption from Weapon-shawings upon some old rights and notwithstanding they are poynded for not coming to the drilling—Therefor until they be heard and that the Council's mind thereupon be known — These are to desire you restore their poinds at sight thereof."

The matter on coming before the Council was remitted to the Deacon-Convener and the whole of the Crafts, who, having met in the Magdalen Chapel, declared "All in one voice concerning the Chirurgeons that their gifts and Acts of Council to be Just and Right and that both Masters, Servands and

Apprentices are freed from any duty in exercising in Warfare."

Domestic Quarrels.—At this period the Craft had no little difficulty in preserving law and order among themselves in domestic affairs. Peace and harmony were sometimes absent from their meetings, and the monotony of decorum was occasionally broken by acts of misbehaviour. Laws were passed to minimise this evil, advice was given, fines were inflicted, and more serious punishment threatened, but a few refractory spirits and ungovernable tempers caused many acts of insubordination at the Craft's conventions. The Minutes dealing with these incidents are usually set in terms that leave an unmistakable impression of their seriousness. In one of these, dated 1595, the deacon and masters request none of the brethren to speak any " proude words " in time coming in their presence when they be " speirt at in their voittings " or in giving their opinions in their affairs, but shall permit the deacon to speak in all their common affairs concerning the Craft. They are also commanded " not to injure others hereafter in word or deed at their common conventions and assemblies, but to keep moderate silence and modesty in words and in countenance or deeds." Another Minute of a later date ordains that none of the Craft shall utter or speak any slanderous words against others concerning their calling, to the discredit of their brethren in " impairing their fame or otherways." Again, in the year 1668, a lengthy Minute describes more fully the measures taken to prevent disputes and contentions arising in the debates. In introducing the subject, which is said to be " for the better ordering of the behaviour of the members of the Incorporation ane towards ane other and for the avoiding of animosities and confusings amongst them," it is ordained that " none shall give their judgement or vote in any business until they be speirred at by the deacon and that every man speak discreetly and that to the deacon, under the pane of four shillings scots in case of failyie." Also that none in any manner of way disturb or interrupt others while they are speaking, under a like penalty. And " siclyke that nane profane the name of God by swearing, cursing and banning under the pane of six shillings scots, and further, that no one rise out of their places appointed

by the Act of Ranking, to the disturbance of the meeting."
In conclusion, an earnest appeal is made for peace and unity,
and that none shall speak contemptuously or distractfully
against the ancient Rights and Liberties or Standing Acts
of the Incorporation, but shall carry themselves "ane towards
ane other in all occasions civillie and discreetlie, as become
men of such ane civill profession."

A few years later, as evincing an unmistakable desire for
further social reform, the Calling, "taking into consideration
how indecent and unbecoming it is to them as grave and
sober persons to be drinking and smoking tobacco at the
times of the general meetings at the Convening-house to the
annoyance of one another and hindrance to the affairs of
the Calling," the same were prohibited under a penalty of
half-a-crown.

If the masters of the Craft at times neglected the duties
of their own station, it is not surprising that their apprentices
did the same. This they did to such an alarming extent that
on account of their misconduct to their masters, not only in
"evil thoughts" but also by "way of deed," it was ordered
that none of the "Servands or prentices present and to come
shall use or wear any dagger, quhanzie or knife (except ane
knife to cut their meat, wanting the point) under the pane
of loss of their freedom and liberties of the Craft and all
other privileges they might enjoy through their masters."

At another time three apprentices were summoned before
the Calling for stealing and pledging a cloak belonging to
the deacon's servant and "drinking thereupon, to the great
offence of God and scandell of the Incorporation and
speciallie to the boy to whom the same was done." They
were ordered to crave the Calling's pardon in an humble
manner "for ye hie and notorious offence" and never to do
the like again.

Pecuniary fines for simple misdemeanours, loss of the
freedom of the Craft or imprisonment in the Tolbooth for
more serious misdeeds, were the customary penalties inflicted
by the Calling upon transgressors against their laws, but, in
1585, a sentence of an unusual character was passed upon one
of their members for an offence (not described) against the
Incorporation. Not only had he to humble himself to the

deacon and brethren, but he had also to ask their forgiveness upon his knees.

Five pounds was a fine once paid by a member for uttering " unrelevant speeches " against the deacon, deforcing the officer and leaving the meeting without permission.   Incarceration in the Tolbooth was the fate of another member of the Craft for " injurious and contumelious speeches " uttered by him against the deacon.   He was liberated by the magistrates, however, on promising to give satisfaction to the Calling.   But when brought before them, and on being removed to an outer room, he most " contemptuously " before the deacon and brethren could resolve upon his sentence, pushed his way out of the Convening-house " whereat ye haill brethren wer heartilie offended and ordained him to be censured therefor."   An apprentice was also committed to prison for abusing his master.   He was sentenced to remain there, " aye and until he gave satisfaction to his master," which he did—and was forgiven.

A more serious affair was that of Francis Easton, servant to the deacon, who was lodged in the Tolbooth for having " beaten and stricken the deacon's wife, his children, and servant, and for having offered to put violent hands on the deacon himself."   He was not to be taken into service again under a penalty of £100. Perhaps, however, the most interesting case is that of Robert Kennedy who went to prison for his misbehaviour to Thomas Kincaid, his master.   It is thus recorded in the Minutes : " The whole Calling being convened in the Guidman of the Tolbooth house, the above Robert is to acknowledge his offence in presence of the whole calling and also to be fined £50, which the Boxmaster is to extract from him for the Calling's use, and also the forsaid Robert's acknowledgement of his offence which relates to Thomas Kincaid to be thus—That he is sorry that he should have expressed himself so disgracefullie to him by answering that he was 'ane freer Chirurgeon than Thomas Kincaid and as guid a man as he or any Kincaid of his kin' which are known to be untruthes, and he subscribe the same act himself under his hand by the next meeting, otherwise to return to prison again."   [Robert's signature follows the Act.]

The " Act of Ranking."—The Act of Ranking previously mentioned, engaged the attention of the Calling for some considerable time, and was the subject of much deliberation.

Although somewhat lengthy, it is full of information, establishing as it does an order of precedence from the deacon to the last admitted member. It became law in 1667, and rules that the deacon for the time shall have the principal place in all meetings . . . and next him the old deacons are to take their places . . . everyone according to the priority of time of his deaconship. " But so that if any of them ane or mair have been Deacon-Conveners they ought to take place and vote before the other old deacons that have not been in that office, and amongst themselves according to the priority of their Deacon-Convenership, reserving always out of peculiar respect and favour to Alexander Penycuik of Newhall (and to him alone) his place to sit and vote next the present deacon for the time, he being both the eldest master and the eldest deacon of the Incorporation now of a very long time. And it is hereby declared that all the old deacons by virtue of their being deacons, without any further choice are masters and councellors to the present deacon in all matters of the Incorporation." The Boxmaster is placed next to the old deacons, and the remaining brethren are to sit and vote according to the date of their admission.

Relating to this Act, which appears to have been of great importance at the time, there are in the College archives three letters or the proxy-votes of three of its most distinguished members of that period—Alexander Penycuik of Newhall, Christopher Irvine of Bonshaw, and James Borthwick of Stow.

The proxy of Christopher Irvine deals with the question in detail. Addressed to the " Right Hon. the Deacon of the Chirurgeons of Edinburgh," it runs :—

" Whereas I am desired by the Deacon with severall of the masters that I might, according to an act of the Calling leave my vote in writting concerning the placing of the Boxmaster at the public and private meetings, especially seeing I am concerned as well as others in a younger master taking my place before me—I do declare that I think in my conscience that the Boxmaster, as an honorary employ-ment for the weill of the Calling, ought to have place next the old deacons, and seeing he hath no other reward for his pains, I think this is the least favour we can afford him for his service and travill according to the laudible constitution and customes of all well ordered societies. Neither do I hold myself wronged when a younger master chosen to that place and office taketh place before me, but rather thinketh it my duty for the good and honour of the Calling to urge him in what we lyeth and advance him thereto, and this I leaveth for my vote that any man chosen to that office should have place next the old deacons.   Written and subscribed by my own hand at Edinburgh this 3rd day of October 1667."

The Act of Ranking which was read at the annual election of office-bearers, was rescinded in 1713 because of the frequent disputes and animosities it had occasioned both in their private and public meetings.   It was then arranged that the Deacon should be called first on the roll, then the Treasurer, and the other members according to the date of their admission, without respect to any of them having held office as Deacons, Conveners, or Treasurers.

Irvine seems to have been responsible for the revival of an old Act which aimed at a higher educational standard in the apprentice.   Himself a scholar and distinguished philologist, the educational defects of the apprentice would no doubt appear more serious to him than to others.   In 1643, some years before Christopher Irvine became identified with the Incorporation, attention was called to the prejudice it received at the hands of apprentices who were " not literate and unrudly " and who had not learned their " four parts of grammer."

An Act was then passed that all apprentices should be examined in this subject by a committee before indentures were signed between them and their masters, but as no pressure seems to have been put upon apprentices to conform to this law, it had probably been neglected.   In 1661, at the instance of Irvine, it was again enforced, and in the year mentioned an apprentice was booked for five years upon this proviso, viz., that because he had got no further in his learning than the three parts of grammar, he was not to be discharged from his apprenticeship until he satisfied the examiners of his proficiency. His master, in the meantime, undertook to keep him to his lessons under a penalty of £30.   A further advance was almost immediately made by booking an apprentice conditionally that he learnt his grammar complete and gave satisfaction to the clerk by speaking "congruous latin and interpreting of an outpour," otherwise his indentures were to be cancelled.   Like Pennycuik and Borthwick, Irvine had travelled abroad and had seen much service in the field. He was with Monk's army in Scotland, and afterwards became surgeon to the Horse-Guards. In 1681, in consideration of his having received all the " Degrees of the Schools" that give ornament and authority in the professions of medicine and surgery, and of his various army commissions, he applied to the Privy Council that they would be pleased not to suffer him by any new gift or patent " to be stated under the partial humours or affronts of the new Incorporation or College of Physicians, composed of men altogether his juniors (save Dr Hay) in the studies of philosophie and practice of physick." This was granted and later on confirmed by an Act of Parliament. The date of Irvine's death is not known. The surgeons' books, however, show his last subscription to have been paid on 9th May 1693. On 19th June 1693 he is referred to therein as the " umquhile [deceased] Dr Irvine." He was married to a daughter of the Laird of Potterrow.

Some particulars may be gathered regarding Alexander Pennycuik from the Surgeons' Records and also from the Acts of Parliament of 1663. According to the former, Pennycuik, who is described as " Chirurgeon to his Excellensie," was admitted freeman and master of the Surgeons and Barbers in November 1640 in consideration of his " literature and qualifications," for the love they bore towards him, and on payment of 200 pounds Scots. Previous to this he had seen service with General Bannier in the Thirty Years' War. Between 1642-48, he was employed as Surgeon-General with the Scots forces in Ireland, and in the latter year saw service with Major-General George Monro in Scotland. In 1650, he took charge of the sick and wounded left behind in Stirling Castle. During the whole of this time he only received for his services the sum of £165. In 1663, he petitioned Parliament for the balance due to him, viz., £3668 stg., and further declared that he had sustained great loss by his loyalty to the King in respect that his house in the country, his lands, corn, and cattle had been plundered and destroyed by the English usurpers to the amount of £166 stg., and that he had been put to great expense in relieving his " mates and servands" after the unhappy affairs at Preston and Worcester. He was born in 1605 and lived to a great age.

Admission to the Craft.—Although the usual way of obtaining the freedom of the Craft was by examination, this ordeal was occasionally dispensed with in cases where the candidate had sufficient influence or was possessed of exceptional qualifications. The reasons advanced for granting this favour are many and varied, and in most cases seem justifiable. As they are given in the Minutes, a few examples will enable the reader to judge for himself.

In 1612, James Harvey, Surgeon to Her Majesty, was admitted surgeon—" In respect that he is upon the point of his journey to pass to Her Majesty, and in consideration of the good way in which he has already served Her Majesty."

John Pringel was admitted free surgeon, in 1623, in consequence of his services in France and in Flanders, where by his pains and travels he had become learned and expert in the art of Chirurgie, and for his having served as " General Chirurgion to Colonel Brog," and also at the earnest request of " ane nobill and potent Lorde, Thomas, Earl of Melrose."

The Craft, in 1649, admitted Andrew Brown without examination—" because of his known abilities and of his constant adhering to the cause of God in the midst of so many trials and temptations within the Kingdom of Ireland and transporting of himself and his wife and family to this Kingdom from thense."

John Scott was admitted barber at the earnest request of " the Right Hon. my Lord Chancellor, my Lord President and of my Lord of Register, but the like request is not to be granted again in the future."

An amusing case was that of John Dickson, apprentice to Archibald Hay, Surgeon to His Majesty, who applied for admission to the Craft by favour. To this the Craft assented, " they having a respect for him, not only for his master's cause but also for his own," providing he would pay the usual fees " which he was willing to do desiring he might go to his brother, to bring the same, and [the Craft] having stayed for his again coming with the performance of his promise, he did send his brother's man with this commission 'that he was sent to the deacon and masters from the said John [to say] that he would not give tuppens for any privilege they could afford him' and refused to come back again himself to the company."

As instances of failing to pass the examination are reported, it seems to have been the custom of the Craft at this time to record the results of all examinations, whether favourable to the candidate or not. Conspicuous in the list of failures is the name of Andrew Scott, who after examination was found "not as yet in qualification sufficient to be Chirurgeon to the King's Majesty."

Another case was that of a barber who wished to become a surgeon, but after three days' trial he was suspended "till his further qualifications and abilities in the art."

The "Cure of Patients."—Of the sources from which the Calling derived an income, one at least, on account of its doubtful popularity, is deserving of special mention. In 1614, an impoverished exchequer induced the Craft to introduce a tax which varied according to the individual skill and ability of the members, and resulted in many unequal contributions. Designated the "Cure of Patients," the Act ordained that whenever a surgeon or barber received upwards of ten pounds for the curing of a patient, he should pay ten shillings to the funds of the Calling. The sum realised in this manner in one year amounted to £23, 10s. Of nine members that contributed one alone paid £9, 10s. This Act remained in force until 1645, when on account of its abuse and neglect it was abrogated in favour of another which arranged for a regular quarterly payment of thirty shillings by the surgeons, and thirteen shillings and fourpence by the barbers—unless the latter "be reduced to that state that they are unable in means" to do so.

On reference to a quarterly account in the year following the passing of this new Act, eighteen members seemed to have composed the total number of the Craft, six of whom were surgeons, five surgeons and barbers, and seven were barbers alone. Twenty years later these numbers had increased to twelve, nine, and fifteen respectively.

The Mortcloth.—Another way of helping the funds to a small extent was by the fees paid for the loan of the mortcloth or funeral pall, which was used at interments for covering the coffin. This old custom amongst the Crafts is first mentioned in the surgeons' books in 1588, when at a meeting of the Incorporation it was agreed that a "mortclaith should be made of such fashion as shall be thought good by the deacon to devise." This one is always referred to as the "mortclaith with ye airmes," presumably on account of the armorial bearings worked upon it. After doing duty for twenty-six years it was discarded in favour of another made of velvet. The new one, according to the accounts, cost one hundred and seventy-five pounds two shillings, and was paid for partly out of the Incorporation's funds and partly by subscription of the members, who had a free right to its use. If any of the brethren, however, failed to subscribe it was ordained that neither their "wives nor their bairnes" were to have the use of it at their funeral. Its use was not apparently restricted to the members of the Craft, as upon one occasion twelve pounds Scots was paid for its loan; at another time six pounds, while the "gude wife of Bukkie" got the use of it for ten merks.

By an Act of 1636, all absentees from the funeral of a deceased brother were liable to a fine of twelve shillings Scots, and this, so runs the Act, "because some of the companie preferred their own commodities to the charitable point of appearing themselves to the convoying of the corpse of the deceased to the grave or buriall."

Sabbath Observance.—In 1647, the passing of a no less worthy and important Act, testifies to their intimacy with the instincts of charity, and proves the surgeons of Edinburgh to have established a regular system of extending free advice to poor people more than 250 years ago. In that year, after fixing their meeting day to be the first Monday in February, May, August, and November, they also arranged to "give advice to all poor diseased persons that requires their counsel" on the first Monday in each month at two o'clock in the afternoon. It was found, however, that Monday was an unsuitable day for the purpose, because the brethren required to be warned of the meeting the day previous. But this day being Sunday, the Calling said that the Sabbath day ought not to be used for such a civil purpose, it being the Lord's day, and only proper for Divine Service. If such was then the view of the Calling, it had undergone considerable change since 1630, for at that date they took one of their number by the ears for complaining to the Kirk and Council that the barbers exercised their craft on the Sabbath day. Upon being told plainly that he had no right to interfere with the liberties of the barbers, who were doing nothing unlawful, he replied, " Who would, who would not, he would have their liberties restrained."

Five years later, in 1635, the surgeons passed an Act making it unlawful for the barbers to cow, clip, shave, or wash any person on the Sabbath day which they now said was " contrary to God's law and debauching of servants." In course of time, this law was so flagrantly transgressed that the Incorporation, in 1666, decided to make an example of anyone found breaking it. They therefore appointed two masters who exercised trimming to visit the shops of the barbers and see that no contravention of the Act of the Sabbath day, which is " so dishonourable to God and prejudicial to the Craft," took place, and also to see that none but qualified servants were employed and that their instruments, dressing cloths, combs, razors, and pincers were clean and neat. The deacon had the nomination of the visitors, as they were to be called, and he along with the Boxmaster was to commence the practice.

The visitors were not long in making a capture, and the victim was not only a Sabbath-breaker, but an unfreeman barber whom they caught red-handed. He was consigned to the Tolbooth, and in the following plaintive letter prayed for his release:—

" RIGHT WORTHIE,

That whereas out of guid will and freely I was cutting the hair off ane gentleman's head, ane of the College of Justice who is my agent and dois my whole business for me and all other my affairs for trulie I did not raze ane hair of his face, and now Sir your Corporation has caused incarcerate me here into this Tolbooth, and I being but ane puir man and my puir daughter has been lying sick of ane hot fever and is not well recovered nor convalescent and I have non to wait on her and give her ane drink and to stay in the house with her at night she not daring to lie alone being but a child. Therefor Sir I humbly entreat you for Gods cause to liberate me from this prison house and to cause set me free and I shall meddle no more with your trade hereafter but shall take me to some other calling for I am both scarce of money and my natural affection towards my child putts me to it. And therefor Gods cause Sir do not slight nor delay me in this my petition and your answer here of most humbly I beg.

WILLIAM PAUL."

Nor did the unfreeman surgeon escape the vigilance of the visitors, who upon another occasion accused a certain George Bell of breaking their statutes, especially in "laying a shearcloth about the laird of Fedderat." George confessed to the making of the shearcloth, bringing it to the house and to the embalming of the corpse. On promising never to do the like again he was discharged.

Among the papers belonging to the College and apparently the only one of its kind, is a receipt from "Margaret Craw, spouse to Robert Cuthbertson, drummer in Edinburgh," acknowledging to have received from the Boxmaster of the surgeons "ane stoope, ane basin, ane razor, and ane comb." At an earlier date (1588) a Minute records that Gilbert Primrose was requested to return a "kettle" and umquhile Alex. Bruce's wife to return a "basin and ane chauser."

This seems to point to the fact that the utensils of the Craft were at this time owned by the Incorporation, the stoup being accounted for perhaps for the measuring of aquavitæ. Some stoups seem to have had a chequered career. One is mentioned as "lying in pledge for 18 shillings," and another, which belonged to the Craft and was endearingly termed the "auld tyn stoupe," is reported to have been "taken out of the kist and sold for 48 shillings."

All the valuables belonging to the Craft were apparently kept in the kist, which on the election of a new deacon was opened and an inventory of its contents taken. On one occasion when this was done, it was found to contain "the old and new books, the box, two pensellis, the velvet mortcloth, the cloth mortcloth with the arms, two buistes with certain writts and twa leather pokes with some writts and a Seal of Cause." The locks were then put on again and the key handed to the keeper.

The Covenant.—The fact that the surgeons signed the Covenant must not be left unrecorded. This they did on 25th August 1638, and also ordained "their haill prenteisses and servands to subscryve the same als weill as themselfis, and that there sall be in no tyme coming any freeman admittit, either chirurgeon or barbour, nor any buike prenteisses or servands, but sic as shall subscryve the covenant."

CHAPTER III

THE BARBERS AND THE APOTHECARIES

The Simple Barbers—The Surgeon-Apothecaries—Preist, the
Canongate Barber—The Case of David Pringle.

The Simple Barbers.—Although the terms of the Seal of Cause
are not so definite that a misconception of their meaning is
impossible, it seems fairly clear that at the time of its foundation
the Incorporation consisted of two Crafts—the Surgeons and
the Barbers—and that although the barbers had practised
the art of surgery to some extent previous to their union with
the surgeons, they were then forbidden to exercise any part
of that craft until they had become expert and had passed an
examination in anatomy. From this it would seem that all
members of the barber craft were at that time not only
eligible to become surgeons, but were expected sooner or
later to do so, and that their entry into the barber craft was
only preliminary to their becoming qualified as surgeons. In
1588, however, another class of barbers was established, who,
unlike those just referred to, were to remain permanently as
such. They were permitted only to cut hair and shave, very
much as the barber of the present day does, and to distinguish
them from the others, they were called "simple barbers." The
Act under which they were instituted says: "That all and
whatsoever person that shall happen to be made master and
freeman among them in time coming that is not able and
expert to abide and have a sufficient trial and examination
of his qualifications, science, and erudition of the art of
chirurgie, shall have no further liberty and privilege but to clip,
cow, shave and wash, and make aquavite only without any
further liberty to use and exercise any part of the art of
chirurgie." The fact of their being admitted without payment
of any entrance fee may be the explanation of the decision

C

which the Incorporation arrived at soon afterwards that no chirurgeon or barber should be admitted hereafter "but honest men who are able of their own substance and geir to pay for their admission," and that in future each chirurgeon should pay at his entry threescore pounds Scots and each barber forty pounds Scots.

The Act of 1588 remained in force for twenty-eight years, during which period it was taken advantage of by eight persons only. That part of it which referred to the admission of simple barbers was revoked in 1616, and the entrance fee of the chirurgeons was raised to one hundred pounds Scots. During this time, however, apprentices, sons and sons-in-law of freemen were also admitted to the barber craft, but without prejudice to their being admitted surgeons whenever they should be able to pass the necessary examination. These must not be confused with the simple barber who had no qualification whatever to aspire to that privilege.

In these circumstances we approach the decade ending with the year 1650, a most critical and important one in the life of the Incorporation. For some time past the Craft had experienced the greatest difficulty in maintaining its strength. Since 1640, its numbers at any one time had never exceeded eleven, and as all the barbers had then succeeded in becoming surgeons, some means had to be found to prevent the Incorporation from disappearing altogether. The regulations were consequently relaxed, and two apothecaries—James Borthwick and Thomas Kincaid—were admitted surgeons, although neither of them had served an apprenticeship to a surgeon in the City of Edinburgh. In spite of this "through ye decease of certain masters in ye common visitation" their number in 1647 had fallen as low as eight, and as this was considered too few for the transaction of business some apprentices were again admitted to the barber craft preliminary to their becoming surgeons, which they all did within a few years.

Having now increased their number to sixteen, the Incorporation decided that no more barbers should be admitted freemen until they were fully qualified in surgery, and passed an Act to that effect in the following terms :—

"Considering the differences and debates that either hath been or may be hereafter anent the admission of any free Chirurgeon in or among them and also for clearing their Seal of Cause and to avoid all such in time coming they have statuted and ordained that no man hereafter whatsoever, shall be admitted freeman Chirurgeon in and among them except he be the lawful son of a free Chirurgeon or have served a free Chirurgeon as an apprentice five years complete according to the order and custom or them that have married a free Chirurgeon's lawful daughter she being a virgin, and this to be without prejudice unto the Deacon Masters and Brethren forsaid when they find their number small which is hereby declared to be the number of ten, that then and in that case it shall be leisome and lawful to the Deacon Masters and Brethren forsaid when the said number of ten is not complete to admit of any other whom they shall think expedient for making up the said number, and this number to be without prejudice to freemens' sons, apprentices, men marrying freemens' daughters as said is, to come in freemen Chirurgeons in and among them after they having been admitted tried and found sufficiently qualified by the Deacon, Masters and Brethren of the said art, according to the said Act of Tryall of Intrants made thereanent which act is hereby declared to be extended to these likewise those that shall be admitted upon necessity in the case forsaid. And also taking to consideration the great prejudice and manifest aspersions the body of Chirurgeons hath sustained by admitting of freemen barbers not being qualified Chirurgeons. Therefore the Deacon Masters and Brethren do hereby statute and ordain that at no time hereafter any barbers shall be admitted in time coming except he be tried and found sufficiently qualified in Surgery as said is, and also statute and ordain that hereafter everyone that shall be a freeman Surgeon shall pay no less to the box than prentices, only the eldest son of any freeman being excepted and those that are admitted upon necessity which law is the will of the Deacon and Masters notwithstanding of any act or acts made heretofore in the contrair especially an act made in anno 1602 and in anno 1616 anent the admission of freemen Chirurgeons which is hereby declared to have been dispensed with but now absolutely abrogate annulled and recinded and shall stand in no force nor effect in all time coming."

At the time of passing this Act, viz. 1648, the Incorporation was composed of sixteen members, namely six surgeons, four barber-surgeons and six members of the barber craft still pursuing their studies in order to qualify themselves for the rank of surgeon. This distinction we are able to trace by the

quarterly payments recorded in the Minute Book of that
period, which were thirty shillings, forty-three shillings and
four pence and thirteen shillings and four pence respectively.

The Surgeon-Apothecaries.—Such was the state of affairs
in the barber world in Edinburgh until 1657, when the character
of the Incorporation gradually underwent an important change.
Owing to the efforts of the two apothecaries, James Borthwick
and Thomas Kincaid, previously mentioned, pharmacy was now
taught along with the art of surgery, and as these combined
pursuits proved more attractive to apprentices than surgery
and barbering, the latter craft fell into decay, not through
any act or statute of the Incorporation, but simply through
its lack of popularity. Borthwick and Kincaid are said to
have accompanied the Scottish army which invaded England
"as Mates to the Surgeons," and on the termination of the
war returned to Edinburgh and resumed the employment of
apothecaries, to which trade they had been apprenticed, but
finding favour with the surgeons they were received into
their Incorporation with the result that from this time may
be traced the passing of the surgeon-barber and the advent
of the surgeon-apothecary.

It will be understood that for many years the exclusive
right enjoyed by the barbers and surgeons of exercising their
trades, was limited to the ancient bounds of the City, and did
not extend to the outlying districts or suburbs, as they were
called, of Leith, the Canongate and Portsburgh, which had
trading arrangements of their own. In 1636, however, when
the superiorities of the Canongate fell into the hands of the
City, considerable friction arose amongst the various crafts
which were now to be linked up with those of Edinburgh. The
barbers of the Canongate, who had hitherto been free traders,
showed great reluctance to come under the jurisdiction of
the surgeons and barbers of Edinburgh, and to be compelled
to subscribe to the funds of a Society from which they would
reap but little benefit in return. It is to the credit of the
surgeons that they allowed some years to elapse before
attempting to exercise their authority. Although the Town
Council, in 1641, had passed an Act "that in the matter of
Chirurgie the inhabitants of the suburbs should be provided
with skillful and honest men and not left to the arbitrament

and impostor of women and ignorants," it was not until May 1649, after some encroachment had been made upon their privileges, that the surgeons induced the magistrates to order the bailies of the newly acquired district to take in the basins and signs of the unfreemen barbers within their burgh until they should come in and subject themselves to the orders of the surgeons of Edinburgh. To this Act the authorities of the Canongate paid so little attention that, a month later, one of the Edinburgh magistrates was sent down to the Canongate along with the Deacon of the Surgeons to see the order carried out.

This seems to have had but little effect, for, in the following July, the bailies of the Canongate were summoned to appear before the Lord Provost and Council of Edinburgh, and they promised "to give concurrence and assistance to the Deacon of the Chirurgeons against the unfreemen within their bounds at any time he pleased to require or desire them to that effect." This brought matters to a crisis, and eventually the barbers themselves were arraigned before the Court at Edinburgh, when they protested that neither the magistrates nor the surgeons were ever authorised by any right flowing from the barony of Broughton, to assume a control over them in exercising their craft within the Regality; that they were never erected into a company nor subject to a deacon; but that they, their authors and predecessors, had pursued their trade in the past at their own hand only, without permission or warrant from anyone. On the magistrates declaring, however, that barbering within the Canongate could no longer be carried on without a licence, a certain Robert Preist and five other barbers submitted themselves and expressed their willingness to comply with the magistrates' decision. They were then appointed by the surgeons to be free barbers within the bounds of the Canongate only, where they were to have full power to follow the barber craft; the surgeons on their part undertaking to protect them against all others not so admitted. They also took the oath to obey all the Acts of the Incorporation, to pay a quarterly subscription of thirteen shillings and four pence for themselves, and four pounds, and forty shillings respectively, for the booking of servants and apprentices.

Preist, the Canongate Barber.—A dispute which arose

about this time between the Craft and Preist, the Canongate barber already mentioned, throws an interesting light on the conditions in the City when it was under the power of Oliver Cromwell. In fact it was no less important a person than Cromwell's "honest" lieutenant, George Monk—afterwards created Duke of Albemarle for his services at the Restoration— who finally settled the question.

When the City was occupied, in 1651, by the English troops, Preist appears to have made so many influential friends amongst them, that in spite of his oath to dwell and pursue his avocation within his own burgh, he took a shop within the City Walls, and there for a time successfully plied his calling in defiance of the magistrates and of the surgeons. As this privilege was more than the Incorporation had power to grant even to their own sons or apprentices until they were admitted surgeons, the Craft was seriously concerned.

Incensed at Preist's presumption, and envious, no doubt, of the good trade he was driving, the freemen barbers of the Town complained of his presence amongst them and petitioned the surgeons to have him at once removed. Two of their number, they declared, were already ruined since Preist's encroachment, and unless he was speedily suppressed, they were afraid that more of their brethren would be brought to poverty and so become a burden to the Society and to the place they lived in. "Therefore our humble desire and request is to you," concluded the petition, "as ye will be answerable to God and prevent the fearfull cases of many families, widows and orphans within your Incorporation, be faithful in the trust put upon you by us and so much the more because of the oath of God lying upon you that ye leivens lawfull means for maintening of us in our lawfull rights and privileges, which we are confident will bring much peace to you in the day of your accompts, encouragement to all your successors, and comfort to us who are groaning under the present oppression."

Preist was now cited to appear before the surgeons for transgressing their Acts and for violating his oath. The meeting took place on 4th October 1651, when, in reply to the Deacon as to why he had broken his word not to trim nor to put out signs nor basins within the burgh, but in the Canongate only, Preist said he would not observe that oath nor obey that

Act, but that he would work within the burgh of Edinburgh according to the liberty and warrant granted to him by the Captain of the Castle, and in a disdainful manner said, "goe ye ask of him by what liberty I work," and immediately he turned his back rudely saying, "do what ye will ye will not mend yourselves," and went out of doors. The surgeons then applied to the magistrates to have Preist sent back to the Canongate, but a letter dated August 1652 shows that although he was then under orders to quit the Town, he had not complied with them.

The letter is addressed to "Our loving friends the Deacon and rest of the trade of Barber Chirurgeons within the Citte of Edinburgh," and bears the signatures of the four English gentlemen who had been recently appointed Judges or Commissioners for the Administration of Justice in Scotland. It briefly states "whereas Robert Preist barber inhabitant in the Citte of Edinburgh, being not free thereof, is ordered to remove out of the same, but we being informed that between terms, houses, at least any convenient, are not to be taken, and he being willing to remove at the end of the term, and in the meantime not to hang out his basins, we therefore desire that this, his reasonable request, may be afforded, and we shall take it as a courtesy. And so rest, Your friends, George Smyth, A. Owen, T. March, Edward Mosely."

Unwilling to break into open dispute, and possibly influenced in some degree by the quality of the writers, the surgeons exercised their discretionary powers by not insisting upon Preist's removal so long as he refrained from exhibiting the symbols of his trade.

Robert Lilburne, Commander of the English troops in Scotland, better known perhaps as one of the Regicides, wrote a letter to the Lord Provost, containing a proposal that his Lordship should permit Preist to continue his business in Edinburgh, in spite of the surgeons and of their jurisdiction over the barbers. The letter was written on 30th March 1653, at Dalkeith, where the English had established their Head-quarters, and runs as follows:—

"My Lord,

"This bearer, Master Preist having (so I am informed) for about these ten years past followed the profession of a barber in Scotland

and behaved himself civillie and inoffensivlie, and having for about
a year and a half past, lived in Edinburgh, and being now threatened
to be debarred from the exercise of his profession there. I am
desirous of recommending him unto you, that you will give order
that he may be permitted to exercise his calling for the trimming
of the English Officers and others in Edinburgh, which I conceive
you may do without infringement of the liberty of any Companie
in the Cittie (he not at all meddling with Chyrurgerie) and thereby
you will show ane act of civillitie to the officers, and I shall be
readdie upon all occasions to answer your respect to them and
him therein."

With the Commander of the Forces, the English Judges
and the Captain of the Castle, all actively interesting themselves
on Preist's behalf, it is not surprising that the Incorporation
was somewhat anxious as to its position, besides being deliberate
and cautious in its actions. A letter from a well-wisher of the
Craft holding a position of public trust, in reply to one he had
received from the deacon and brethren of the Incorporation,
shows them to have been cautious. While giving good advice he
reminds them that in such affairs, they alone were not sufferers,
but the whole nation along with them. In referring to that
" contemptible fellow Preist " he considered it strange how a
man could offer to pity him in so unjust a thing. As for the
Officers of the Army, he continues : " I know not what they may
not do if they pity him, and as for his power with the Judges of
Parliament, which is most to be feared by you, I am confident,
as yet, there is no such thing passed here in Parliament, neither
do I think they would stoop so low as to take notice of such
things, for sure I am, that such things will not be honoured by
the Authorities wherein I hope we shall not be wanting to
obviate or represent as occasion offereth. In the meantime," the
letter concludes, " be not discouraged but maintain your liberties
with prudence and confidence against your present disturber,
and all such snarling corries of whom be not afraid but assert
your liberty for I find not nor fear not no danger in so doing."
The letter bears the signature of John Mylne, who besides
being Master Mason to the late King was much given to
politics. He several times represented the City of Edinburgh
in Parliament, and at the time in question was in London upon
Parliamentary business.

This letter seems to have encouraged the Incorporation, and to have inspired them with so much confidence that they immediately intimated to Preist, with all legal formality, that unless he removed out of the Town by Whitsunday 1653, they would declare him " infamous " and debar him from the benefits of his liberty " in all tyme coming."

But Whitsunday passed, and the new year dawned, and still Preist continued his work in the City.   The march of events at this time is difficult to follow, but apparently recent changes had lost to Preist his most valued friends.   Two of the Judges had already been recalled, and the spring of 1654 found Lilburne superseded by Monk, whose courtesy and urbanity made him many friends in the Scottish Capital.   Now was the opportunity for the surgeons to seek justice.   This they did, and they obtained it.

A later letter on the subject reveals that on the representation of the surgeons, Monk ordered a Commission to assemble, to inquire thoroughly into the case and to report the result to him.   Finally, in September, Monk wrote from Dalkeith— " Upon the report of the Referees within mentioned, it having been made appear that one, Robert Preist, gave his oath without compulsion and therefore ought to fulfill the same. I do therefore thinke fitt and order that the said one Preist dos remove out of Edinburgh within three weeks after the date hereof, and live conform to his oath."—Signed George Monck.

The Incorporation, having at last gained their end, generously restored to Preist his forfeited privileges, though it refused a request that he might remain unmoved until Whitsunday 1655.   Thanks to Monk, Preist was relegated back to the Canongate and does not seem to have again troubled the Calling.

Thus ends an episode which, besides bringing the Craft into opposition with many persons whose emnity at such a critical period it was perilous to incur, caused them much trouble and a considerable amount of expense, as is shown by the Surgeons' accounts.   Between 1st September and 13th December 1654, it cost the Calling 159 pounds Scots.   The details of another sixty pounds Scots which were spent in one week in the preceding year includes items which are both instructive and entertaining, although the shadow of ambiguity rests upon them.

> 4th April, 1653. Spent in Thomas Mesent's house upon ane Friday at night in relation to Robert Preist's business £03 03 00
>
> Upon the Saturday thereafter in the morning before going to Dalkeith £02 02 00
>
> For our Dalkeith voyage for seven horses . . £12 00 00
>
> For our dinner £18 02 00
>
> At our return at Robert M'Kean's house . . £05 07 00
>
> Upon the Friday morning with Robert Anderson . £00 15 00
>
> Given to Anna Kerr £06 00 00
>
> More for thanking some particular persons . . £08 12 00
>
> At a consultation with the Judge Advocate . . £17 05 00

Whatever may be the correct interpretation of these entries, there exists in the College archives a scrap of paper, penned in a careless way, and signed by ten members of the Craft, which may serve to dispel any suspicions they may arouse.

"We undersubscryband for the weill and profite of ourselves Our awin credit and ye respect of our profession and for uther good considerations moving us Be the tenour heirof of our awin proper motive Bands and obleiss Us ilk ane for our awin parts. That we shall nowayes hant nor be fund in Tavern or Taverne house within ye burgh of Edinburgh fra ye dait of thir presents To ye xxx day of August 1622 yeirs. Except allanerlie [only] at dinner and supper Under the pane of payment to our box of ye sowme of fyve punds totius quotius for ye weill of ye craft. Anent is our hand at Edinburgh the 30th day of August 1621."

We do not know what particular motive the barber-surgeons had in uniting themselves in such a laudable purpose, but it is probable that in a small city such as Edinburgh then was, their example would do more towards the improvement of social life than had been effected by the then recent legislation of the Scottish Parliament.

The Case of David Pringle.—Another illustration of the troubles which frequently arose from Corporation privileges, was the case of David Pringle in 1670. Pringle, it appears, entered the Calling in 1660, and in 1668 became Treasurer. Both his father and grandfather were surgeons before him, the latter having been deacon in 1612. At the time in question

Pringle held the appointment of Apothecary and Surgeon-Barber to the Heriot Hospital. The first of June being anniversary day, the magistrates were expected at the Hospital at nine o'clock to attend the sermon usually preached on that solemn occasion. About seven o'clock on the morning in question, when all his servants were out on business, Pringle was suddenly called upon to cut the hair of the boys in the Hospital —about sixty in number—so that they might appear in better order before the magistrates. Being pressed for time, he sent his boy for the first barber he could find to help him. Unfortunately, this happened to be a certain William Wood, a barber licensed to practise in Portsburgh only, and who therefore had no right to work within the Town.

On this coming to the knowledge of the deacon a meeting of the Incorporation was at once convened, and Pringle was asked if he had employed an unfreeman to work in the Hospital. He acknowledged his fault, explained the circumstances under which it had been committed and promised to be more careful in the future.

This should have ended the matter, but, according to Pringle's account, the deacon had some malice against Wood and therefore urged upon the Calling the necessity of punishing him by imprisonment. Wood was lodged in the Tolbooth after a severe struggle with three city officers, who had to carry him there, and on Pringle interposing on his behalf, the Calling ordered Pringle also to be incarcerated. Pringle declared that for this purpose officers were stationed at the foot and at the head of the close to watch and catch him. Eventually he was arrested and brought before the magistrates on a bill presented by the Incorporation. The introduction to the charges brought against him is interesting.

"The Incorporation of Surgeons," it says, "being anciently the chieftest and first trade of Edinburgh and erected into an Incorporation by King James IV. in Anno 1505 and by their care and diligence in enacting good and profitable acts and orders among themselves, they are become in a flourishing condition and so useful to the whole nation, as that their numerous patients at the fight at Gogarstone, the insall at Musselburgh, at Dunbar, Inverkeithing, Worcester and the late rebellion in the West, whom they served gratis, may be sufficient witness. Amongst the acts and statutes of the Calling, there is one which has been greatly conducible for its good, viz. :—that no freeman shall employ any person but either Prentice or Servants Domestics whose names are to be recorded in the books of the Calling, which has been unquestionably and unviolably observed by all the members of the Craft as being fully convinced of its expedience and usefulness and has been amongst many others a good means of the Incorporation to the present perfection which, without boasting, may be compared for the speculative and practical part of Surgery to any of the three kingdoms, until of late the same act was transgressed and broken by David Pringle in manner underwritten."

A long list of charges was then made out against him, the most serious of which—besides the offence named—seems to have been that of protecting the man whom he had employed or, in the surgeon's own words, in trying to get Wood released "over the Calling's bellie," and in threatening to pursue the deacon if he persisted in pursuing Wood. Pringle also endeavoured to shield himself by asserting that Heriot's Hospital was not a part of the burgh, a declaration which caused the magistrates to become defenders in the suit in so far as the interests of the City were concerned.

In conclusion, the Incorporation declared that even the Writers to the Signet debar their respective members from the exercise of their calling for far less serious faults, and that this was not Pringle's first deed of turbulence against the Calling, for within the past year he, having been Boxmaster, had refused to make a statement of his accounts until threatened with imprisonment, "besides other haughty ways," such as jostling the Clerk who was chosen by the plurality of the Calling because his vote was against him, "backed with outragious speeches to him."

Pringle, however, was not content to be tried by the magistrates, and on applying to the Privy Council for redress, the Earl of Argyle, the Earl of Linlithgow, and the Lord President were selected to hear the case and give judgment. In the end he acknowledged his error and gave a written apology to the surgeons, who in turn restored to him all the privileges of the Calling.

Not without interest is a copy of Pringle's contract with the Hospital, procured no doubt by the Calling for the purpose of carrying on the litigation. Dated 8th April 1662, it relates that

Pringle was appointed Apothecary and Chirurgeon-Barber to Heriot's Hospital as the nearest relation to the founder, and that *ad vitam aut culpam*. His salary was to be fixed by the Auditors of the Hospital, with the advice of James Borthwick and Thomas Kincaid. He was to have care of all the sick in the Hospital and to receive extra payment for all drugs administered either in surgical or internal diseases. All his other duties, such as cutting and polling the heads of the scholars, external applications to surgical diseases and operations, were to be included in the yearly salary to be appointed to him.

Pringle's differences with the Craft were soon forgotten. He became deacon in 1684 and in the following year accompanied the Lord Provost to the army, where he performed the duties of Surgeon to the Edinburgh Regiment—probably in connection with Argyle's fatal attempt to overthrow the monarchy.

CHAPTER IV

THE MEETING PLACES OF THE SURGEONS

Dickson's Close (1647)—Kirkheuch (1650)—Curryhill: Surgeons' Square
(1656)—The New Hall and Anatomical Theatre (1697)—The "Bagnio"
—Proposal to sell the Hall—The New Hall at Nicolson Street (1832)
—Meeting Places of the Council.

PRIOR to the year 1647 the Incorporation had no regular
place of assembly. It had apparently been the custom to
hold their meetings for the transaction of business as well
as for the periodical lessons in anatomy in the deacon's
private house, an arrangement that from various points of
view was highly inconvenient. At a meeting held on the
14th June 1647, it was resolved to secure a meeting house of
their own, and it was remitted to David Kennedy and James
Borthwick to rent a house temporarily at a reasonable rate
"as if it were for themselves."

Dickson's Close.—The following month they reported that
they had taken "three rowmes of ane tenement of land in
Diksone Close for payment of fourtie poundis zeirlie," whereupon they were further empowered to provide a table, a table-
cloth and some forms. The accounts show that these were
duly supplied at the following cost:—

For a board and two forms—given to John Scott, wright	£20	0	0
For drinking money to his men, together with the workmen carrying thereof . . .	2	15	0
For a green table-cloth	30	0	0
For covering and dressing the forms . .	13	6	0
For half a dozen of chares	36	0	0
For carrying the skeleton to the Convening House	0	6	0
For two loads of coal	1	10	0

The Craft met in their Convening house for the first time
on the 20th August 1647. Two years later they rented a

front room in the house of one of their own members, presumably as a business place, as a donation was soon afterwards
made for the " furnishing of an office."

Kirkheuch.—After staying three years in Dickson's Close,
the Calling, in the spring of 1650, removed to new premises
at the "foot of the Kirkheuch," within a stone's throw of the
Old Kirk of St Giles. The house, however, does not appear
to have been to their liking for they tried to vacate it at the
end of six months, but the landlord would not agree and
refused to allow them to remove their goods. The particulars
of the dispute are contained in a Minute of 4th March 1651,
which says "that Thomas Carter, one of their members, was
sent to see what of the Calling's goods being in the Convening
House, in Robert Hardie's lands at the foot of the Kirkheuch,
were extant, to the fore, unplundered or away taken by the
English soldiers." He was also required to give over the
house and make payment of the last half-year's rent. It
appears that the house had already been given up by John
Bissit when the first half-year's rent was paid, but the landlord,
after receiving the rent, amounting to fifty merks, had refused
to allow any of the Calling's goods to be removed, although he
had " chalked the doors " (a sign of the premises being to let)
before the term of Whitsunday last. He had also the key in
his possession and had made use of the house since the term
" when the English soldiers left their quarterings and marched
towards Stirling." Thomas Carter and John Bissit, who acted
for the Craft, desired that their diligence might " be inset in
the books " to which we owe the record of the incident.

The receipt given by Robert Hardie is still possessed by
the surgeons. The total amount for rent and et ceteras, came
to £41, 10s. 8d., but Hardie seems to have been satisfied with
£20 in complete payment of his claim.

During the years 1654-1655, the Craft found accommodation
for their meetings first in "two front rooms in John Scott's
house," and then in a "chamber" belonging to Thomas Kincaid,
both of whom were members of the Craft.

This frequent change of quarters must have had a serious
effect upon the social position of the Incorporation, besides
being a source of inconvenience to its members.

Surgeons' Square.—It had long been the desire of the

Incorporation to establish themselves in a Hall of their own and when, in 1656, a favourable opportunity presented itself of securing a suitable site in a desirable neighbourhood they seized it.   The site, which later came to be known as Surgeons' Square, was that occupied by Curryhill house and yards, formerly the property of Sir James Skene, later of the Town Council, by whom it was sold to the surgeons.

As described in the Deed of Transfer, which is still in possession of the College, it lay "between the yard of umquhile Andrew Henrysoun upon the west, the town wall of the burgh (reserving always the space of sixteen foot in time of war for the defence of the burgh) upon the east and south, the auld dyke and fosse of the said yard and Kirkyard of the Brethren of the Blackfriars of the burgh of Edinburgh, now called the High School Yards, upon the north parts upon the one side and other, with full entry through the High School Yards as the same was possessed by Mr Samuel Jonstoun who resigns his right of the property thereof in the hands of the Town Council."

The price paid for the property was 3000 merks, and the Incorporation had also to pay the Town Council a feu-duty of ten merks.

The house thus purchased by the surgeons seems to have been built at the instance of the Council in pursuance of a bequest made to them for that purpose.   According to an Act of Council of 17th December 1639, it appears that Mr Bartholomew Somervell, portioner of Saughton Hall, "being desirous of the means bestowed upon him by God Almighty to dispose ane part theirof to some pious use after him" made over to the Town Council the sum of 26,000 merks, of which 20,000 were for the endowment of a Professor of Divinity and 6000 for building him a house, "the said house to bear the ensign, name and arms of the said Mr Bartholomew, in his remembrance."

Soon after they took possession of their new quarters the surgeons set about extensive alterations and additions.   In the course of a few years they built two new walls and heightened an old one, laid out a garden at an expense of £200, built a gardener's house, and appointed a gardener who was to furnish the garden with all kinds of "medicinal herbs and flowers that can be had anywhere."   He received no fee for his services, but

THE "TENEMENT" IN DICKSON'S CLOSE.

The stair and walls are still standing, though the overhanging
timber front has been removed.

Sketch by James Drummond, R.S.A., in 1850.

S.W. CORNER OF SURGEONS' SQUARE IN 1829.

Showing from left, Surgeons' Hall, Gordon's Class Room, Royal Medical
Society's Hall, and Knox's (formerly Barclay's) Class Room. From *Old and
New Edinburgh*. *(Blocks lent by Dr J. D. Comrie.)*

[*To face page* 48.

was allowed to live in the house rent free during the Calling's pleasure.

While the gardener's house was being erected, some building material disappeared, and a small committee was appointed to visit the garden and to report how much timber they found there for building the house. Their report was that "there is much amissing," but they could not say how much until the building of the house was completed. The solution of the mystery may be traced through the entry that the Treasurer was instructed to "see that Walter Trimble (one of their number) provide sufficient dailles [posts] for finishing of the gardener's house in place of those which he made use of belonging to the Calling for his own house."

The Curryhill house does not appear to have proved suitable for the purposes of the Craft, and the question arose of erecting another building.

A meeting was called on 18th May 1669, when, in response to the deacon's inquiry as to "what they would do anent the building of their Convening House," each member present agreed to give or to lend a hundred pounds. It was further arranged to convene the absent members and to ask them to do the same, so that the house might be put up at once after so long delay. Those who gave their money were to have their names put up in the house, but those who only lent their money were not to have their names put up, but their money restored without interest, when the Calling could conveniently do so.

It would appear from the records that for some time previous to the purchase of the Curryhill site the financial position of the Craft had improved, and that considerable sums of money passed through their hands. We find, for instance, mention made of an obligation of "Kylspindies" for 2000 merks and another for £100; later the Treasurer reported having renewed "the laird of Niddries bond" for 5000 merks, and having "received twa cautioners, viz., the laird of Edmiston and his brother William Wachope." But the heavy calls made upon it for the purchase of Curryhill and the subsequent payment of £500 for masons' work to Mr Mylln (whose accounts are still intact and pinned together as they were 260 years ago) had probably exhausted their ready money, so that they were unable to build the house without recourse to a collection

D

among themselves. The available funds had been further drained to the extent of £1466 expended upon "consultations with advocates and their men in relation with the Physicians' Business and for building material for the house."

In spite of all their efforts the Calling found themselves unable, in 1669, to proceed with the building of the Hall. They appear to have continued to hold their meetings in the Curryhill house, in spite of its limited accommodation and its dilapidated condition. In 1676, it was found necessary to take it down "where it was faulty and likely to fall" and to take the slates off the roof for preservation, and ten years later the roof was reported to be "neither wind tight nor water tight." Nevertheless the Calling does not seem to have hesitated to entertain certain proposals made by the Presbyterian inhabitants of the College and Tron Kirk parishes, for the letting of the house to them as a place for the celebration of divine worship. These proposals are set forth in the form of a petition which states that "as the King's Most Excellent Majesty by his several declarations has been graciously pleased to allow unto them [the Presbyterians] full liberty to meet and serve God after their own way and manner, be it in private houses, chapels, or places purposely built for that use upon conditions therein expressed . . . and finding that that old decayed house belonging to the Calling, that is now ruinous, would be a fit and convenient place for them (if the same were rebuilt) to hold divine service if the Calling would let them have it on reasonable terms." This the Calling agreed to do.

While their Convening house was occupied by the Presbyterians the surgeons met in their "ordinary house," which seems to imply that there were two buildings on the High School Yards site—one the Curryhill house, and the other a house which the Town Council had built for the use of the Professor of Divinity in the College of Edinburgh. The old house, however, still remained in the hands of the Calling, for, in 1694, they ordered a new roof to be put upon it, and in 1707 it was divided into three rooms for the better accommodation of the officer.

The New Hall and Anatomical Theatre. — In 1696, circumstances arose which impelled the surgeons to proceed with the building of a Convening house and Hall suitable to their standing. On a petition by the Incorporation the Town

Council granted them an additional supply of anatomical material—"the bodies of fundlings who dye betwixt the tyme that they are weaned and thir being put to schools or trades . . . but on the express condition that the petitioners shall befor the terme of Michallmas 1697 years, build, repaire, and have in readiness, ane anatomicale theatre where they shall once a year (a subject offering) have ane public anatomicale dissection, as much as can be showen upon one body, and if the failzie thir presents to be void and null."

At a meeting of the Incorporation held on 2nd June 1696 it was unanimously decided to proceed with a building, and a committee was appointed to carry the matter through.

As there was no time to lose, the building committee at once set to work, and on their instructions Mr James Smith, architect, drew up a plan of a house, and received "a guinea and a glass of wine for his trouble." He offered to build and finish it, with the exception of the glass work and furnishing of the "Great Hall," for the sum of £500 stg. The offer having been accepted and all necessary arrangements made, the foundation stone was laid in August 1696, the Boxmaster having first "cast in a guinea under the foundation stone in conformation to the ordinary custom used in such cases." The guinea, it was added, was to be allowed in his accounts.

In February 1697, the committee reported that the roof was expected to be put on by Whitsunday, when some part of the house might be ready for occupation, and if the Calling thought fit the laboratory could then be let to anyone of their number who would give the most rent for it. Instructions were given that the "arched windows" were to be made "chess windows with French glass," and a suggestion was made that one of the workmen, who was well known to be very skilful and could work well in carving of timber, should cut a "chimney piece and a door piece for the great hall." Five hundred merks were paid to John Wardrop for lathing and plastering the "Great Hall," for making a large oval table and for putting a revell or archway to the stairs leading to the Hall. So pleased indeed were the surgeons with the work done by John Wardrop, that they gave as a gratuity to his wife £5 stg.

The laboratory, which consisted of three rooms in the under basement of the house and towards the west end of it, was eventually leased to Alexander Monteith, who happened to be deacon at the time, for a period of two years at £50 per annum. According to his agreement with the Calling he was to allow "Intrant Apothecaries" the use of it during their trials, and also to build his own furnaces, the cost of which would be refunded on his vacating the premises. Among the items of this account, which amounted to £136, 12s. 0d., £31 appear to have been paid for 3100 bricks, £20 for four hundred "gally-pigs," and £5 for a "great hot pot." In 1697, Monteith took possession of the laboratory.

The new Surgeons' Hall was ready by Michaelmas 1697, as stipulated. It does not appear to have been erected on the site of the old Curryhill house, as the Minutes show that, in 1707, that building was divided into three rooms for the better accommodation of the officer.

The "Bagnio."—In addition to a laboratory and a library, the Surgeons' new house seems to have been equipped with a "Bagnio" or Bath-house. A Minute dated 9th November 1697 states that, the house being nearly finished and the Bagnio ready for use, the Calling, in order to reap the greatest advantage, decided to roup it at the next meeting. Before this could be done, however, an important matter—that of supplying the Bagnio with water—had to be settled. Their own well, close at hand, being inadequate for the purpose, the Town Council passed an Act allowing them to obtain the overflow from the trough of the well near the head of Niddries Wynd. For that purpose the Calling was permitted to break the street and lay down pipes, provided it was done at their own expense. Patrick Skirving, plumber in the Canongate, offered to do the work at forty-four shillings for each stone of pipes laid, but as the Incorporation would only give forty shillings he offered to submit the difference to their discretion. His receipt for £636 in payment of his account contains a declaration that he was a considerable loser by the transaction and hoped the Incorporation would grant him an "extra supply" out of their own free motive will, in consideration of his loss. There is no evidence, however, that they did so. The building and furnishing of the Hall proved a costly undertaking. Money was constantly needed to pay the accounts, and frequently the Boxmaster or Treasurer was compelled to intimate that he was without funds.

A Perspective View of the Surgeons Hall -

Members of the Craft, however, usually came to his aid at these times with sums ranging from 1000 to 5000 merks. Failing them, a certain Pierre Castele, alias " La Pearle," who resided in the Canongate, seemed willing to finance the Incorporation to any amount. On one occasion when the Treasurer had again declared an empty box, it so happened that two unfree surgeons applied for admission to the Craft in the following circumstances. They had both served their apprenticeship to a master-surgeon who had neglected to register their names in the books of the Calling, thereby defrauding them of a certain revenue and also invalidating the right of the apprentices to the freedom of the Craft by examination. The Calling, after reasoning among themselves agreed, " as they had no more silver to finish the Bagnio without borrowing," to suspend the standing orders and admit them to trial. Both passed a successful examination and became master-surgeons on payment of 1500 merks each. The Calling then fined one of them £20 for having performed a surgical operation before his admission.

A final effort was now made to finish the Bagnio. For this purpose John Forrest, an Edinburgh merchant, was commissioned to go to Holland to purchase 400 black and 400 white marble stones about a foot square, all free from cracks and veins, for paving the floor of the Bagnio, and also to buy 700 white tiles five inches square, " without any painting on them," for lining the walls of the Bagnio. He received an advance of £800 before departing on his errand, and guaranteed to deliver the tiles at the Surgeons' Hall in Edinburgh at thirty shillings per gilden.

The Bagnio was now ready for use, with the exception of a few finishing touches, which were supplied by a coppersmith and a painter. The account of the former is for :—

A new copper globe	£12	0	0
For the sun *	12	0	0
For a bottom of copper to the Bagnio, weighing 51 pounds	63	0	0
For half a gallon of ale which you ordered the Lads	0	8	0
For gilding with English gold a large copper globe and the sun for the top of the cuppulla of the Bath house	23	0	0

* Probably the crest of the Calling.

On the 26th January 1704 the Bagnio was thrown open to the public.

The deacon announced the fact to the Incorporation by reading the following advertisement :—

"There is now erected at the Surgeon-Apothecaries' Hall in Edinburgh Two fine Bagnios after the Turkish Fashion, where all Noblemen, Gentlemen, Ladies and others may be conveniently sweated and Bathed—The men on Mondays, Wednesdays, Thursdays, and Saturdays, and the Women on Tuesdays and Fridays (on which two days no man is allowed to come within the garden). The price for each person is 3 pounds Scots. And if any person desires the use of a Bagnio alone they are to pay 6 pounds. The prices for the beds in the upper rooms of the Bagnio is to be two shillings ster. per night for a single person and if two shall lay together they are to pay three shillings ster. each night. There is nothing to be given to the Servants."

The building committee then reported that they had arranged with the following persons for working the Bagnios, but could bring them to no easier terms, viz. :—

"To John Valentine and his daughter, for each person that comes to the Bagnio eight shillings Scots, with the privilege of selling Coffee, Tea, Chocolate and other cordial liquors in the house, where he must have two rooms, one for his Coffee house and the other for his bed chamber. He is to sell no ale, but to take what he needs from Alex. Raeburn, the officer. To William Keir for making the fires and cleaning the Bagnios two shillings stg. per week. To Alex. Raeburn's wife's sister for washing the linen and assisting to bath the women Six pounds Scots per month."

The Bagnios were now a going concern, and for the next year or two—if we except a notice that members of the Incorporation attending patients there should be admitted free, no particular mention of them is made. Then in consequence of several complaints of abuses committed by the servants about the Bagnio, the officer was relieved of his duties and more stringent regulations were laid down for the prevention of like occurrences in the future. What really happened is not recorded, but the revised laws seem to have been drawn up especially to prevent men being admitted to the garden on women's days, and also to prohibit any man from entering the garden on other days unless accompanied by one of the masters. Before entering the Hall, the doors belonging to the bedrooms were now to be locked, so that neither master nor stranger could enter them. The Incorporation also ordered public placards and advertisements to be distributed declaring the price of the Bagnio to be four shillings stg. and one shilling to the servants, and certifying that if any servant about the place accepted of "drink money" they should be forthwith discharged.

In 1712, some disappointment was experienced on account of the Bagnios not yielding as much revenue as they had formerly done, and arrangements were made to bring the water pipes within the building "at an expense of half a crown for every ell of pipes of one inch diameter laid and soldered." The pipes were to be upheld by the plumber at half a guinea the year, and a pump was to be made use of to empty the cold Bagnio.

In 1718, an advertisement in the *Public Courant* gave intimation that "people are allowed to come in and wash themselves for half an hour in the little Bagnio and to have the use of a room to dress in, for eighteen pence, but if they stay longer, the haill dues are to be paid." During the next ten years no further reference is made to the Bagnios except "that Hew Patterson is not to have access to the Hall, nor to bath, nor sweat, in the Bath room without special permission, because he comes at night and in a masterful manner takes up his quarters in the Hall and obliges the officer to give him drink and vituals." The Bagnios, however, proved a failure, and, in 1740, it was decided to give them up. Both were taken down and the "marbles and piggs" were ordered to be disposed of to the best advantage.

Proposal to Sell the Hall.—The separation of the barbers deprived the surgeons of a very considerable revenue, and the Treasurer reported that the affairs of the Calling were in such a situation as required the most frugal economy. From a Minute dated 27th March 1729, it would appear that the Incorporation was bordering on insolvency. The Minute states that:—

"The Calling, for certain weighty reasons, agreed that their Large House, Yards and Two Pavilions should be exposed for sale the second week of July next, till which term the Bagnios shall be kept going, and remitted to the Deacon and his Council to draw up an advertisement and insert the same in the Edinburgh newspapers for that purpose, and empowers the said Committee together with the Committee appointed for falling upon ways and means to extinguish the Calling's debts, to condescend upon the place, day and hour of sale, and to have in readiness the Calling's Rights for inspection of any person that may be about to purchase the same."

Later the Bagnios, with certain furnished rooms, were let on lease at a yearly rental of £30, and the following advertisement was inserted in the newspapers :—

"That upon Wednesday next, 16th January 1734, at 3 o'clock afternoon at the Surgeons' Hall, High School Yards, Edinburgh, there is to be exposed to a voluntary roup the Large Beautiful and well aired House commonly called the Surgeons' Hall, with the Bagnios, two Pavilions and Gardens, all well enclosed with stone dykes and hedges, having a water pipe to it and several other conveniences. Any who inclined to purchase the same may enquire for Mr John M'Gill, Deacon of the Incorporation at his lodgings in Marlins Wynd, or for William Wardrob, Treasurer, at his house at Musewell in the Grass Market."

The following month the Treasurer reported that he and the Clerk had attended in terms of the advertisement, but that no offers of any kind were forthcoming.

The Incorporation then decided to retain the Hall for their own use, and to turn the remainder of the premises into dwelling-houses. The tiles belonging to the Bagnio, which had been brought from Holland, were to be sold, the stone dykes on each side of the entry taken down, and the place filled up with earth taken from the vaults in the south-east corner of the garden. The Treasurer was to get the Town Council's permission to break a hole in the east wall to the Pleasance in order to make an office there, as well as to raise an action in the Bailie Court against all those members who had not paid their quarter's accounts.

The financial crisis through which the Incorporation was now passing was serious, and it was only for want of a purchaser that the whole of the heritable property was not finally disposed of. As it was, the two pavilions, the gable ends of the large house and the rooms above the Hall were let to tenants on various terms. Mr John Lees, Rector of the High School, took the east pavilion for five years, at a yearly rental of one hundred pounds Scots. Lady Jean Home, Lady Henderson of Fordell, and Sir Peter Halket were also included among the Incorporation's tenants at one time or another. Mr William M'Dougall, merchant, rented the east gable at £18 stg., and agreed to pay 5 per cent. on a sum not exceeding £100, which the Incorporation advanced, for making a turnpike road to his house. In 1740, Lord Elchies, one of the Senators of the College of Justice, leased the western gable for twelve years at an annual rent of £27 stg., and as several alterations were required, including the building of a road similar to the one at the other end, he advanced the money free of interest, conditionally that it was repaid at the end of his lease. His Lordship, it appears, had entry to his apartments through the Hall, but as his servants were found to have been making use of the College furniture he was reminded that the privilege of passing through the Hall was invested in himself only, and was not extended to his servants. On one occasion when the Corporation met, the Hall was found to be crowded with Lord Elchies' furniture, and most of their own chairs were impressed with the marks of pots and pans, an unmistakable sign of their having been used in his Lordship's kitchen.

In 1745, the houses were insured against fire with the Edinburgh Friendly Insurance Company, the "Great House" being valued at £700 stg. and each pavilion at £100. In 1753, Lord Elchies was offered a new lease to include the use of the Hall, and the Managers of the Infirmary were asked for a place to lodge the library and collection of curiosities, in the event of the offer being accepted. Enquiries were also made as to whether sufficient money to liquidate the Incorporation's debts could be borrowed at 4 or 4½ per cent., and whether, as there was no immediate necessity to sell their subjects, the sum of £3000 stg. should be asked from anyone anxious to buy them.

As time went on without matters improving, a committee was formed to consider again the question of disposing of the subjects in the High School Yards. The committee, after thoroughly investigating the affair, came to the conclusion that it would be greatly to the advantage of the Calling if they could sell their houses for £1000 stg., and feu the area at the rate of £30 per annum.   This, it was said, would bring them in £80 a year, which was considerably higher than their present income, without any risk or trouble, for the gross rent of the houses was only £87, from which repairs and public burdens had to be deducted.   This, it was argued, if taken by the ordinary allowance made by landlords in Edinburgh —viz., 2/7ths of the rent—would come to £24, 17s. 2d., so that the net rent amounted to only £62, 2s. 10d.   But in this event the Corporation would want a hall.   To secure this, it was proposed to pay £300 for a commodious room, to be fitted up by the purchaser of the subjects.   Altogether this would give them £2, 17s. 2d. more than they were drawing at present, besides providing them with a good room, and entirely freeing them from all trouble, risk, and expense.

A statement of the rents and expenses of the houses belonging to the Incorporation from the time they were first let in 1722 to 1760, shows that the sum of £2043 was received for rent, but during this period alterations and repairs came to £897, leaving a net amount of only £1146.

A proposal to feu in part the areas adjoining the Hall for building purposes was negatived, the decision being that if they feued at all they should feu the whole, and if possible, to one person.   These views, however, were somewhat modified, and after consultation with an architect as to the best way of erecting houses with respect to their situation, elevation, etc., so as not to spoil the amenity of the houses already built, it was arranged to roup the areas in four lots—two upon the west end, and two upon the east end of the Hall.   The articles of roup were as follows:—

"That during the running of an half-hour glass, the areas are to be feued by public roup within the Exchange Coffee House of Edinburgh, and the person making the highest and last offer at the outrunning of the half-hour glass shall be preferred to the feu.   That the persons thus preferred to the feus shall within one calendar month from the date of the roup grant bond to the Corporation to erect buildings or houses, one or more, upon the areas similar conform to the houses lately built near the Candlemakers Row by James Brown, and commonly called Brown's Buildings."

The roup took place on 9th May 1764, when the whole area on the north-east was feued to Mr William Mylne, architect. Two houses were eventually built on the site, one of which passed into the hands of William Kerr, Esq., of Chatto, and the other to Mrs Congalton.

During the time these transactions were pending, the Corporation on one occasion was summoned to a special meeting by the deacon, but after waiting half-an-hour, as he had neither attended nor sent an excuse (although, it was said, he had some written proposals from Mr Mylne in his pocket to lay before the meeting, which was the only business they had in hand), it was proposed that he should be fined five shillings for having thus neglected the Corporation and made them wait so long to no purpose.

Efforts had been made from time to time to feu the ground adjoining the Hall with more or less success; but it was not until 1786, when these feus had been taken up and houses built upon them, that Surgeons' Square, the cradle of modern surgery in Edinburgh, came into existence. At this time the pavilions on the east and west of the Hall had probably disappeared. As far back as 1773, the one at the east end had been reported unsafe by the Dean of Guild, and in September of that year it was advertised to be rouped and the area to be feued against the end of the month. As this pavilion is not again mentioned, it probably changed hands, or, on account of its ruinous condition, was demolished. The fate of its neighbour to the west is also not quite clear, although everything points to its having been absorbed in the building of the New High School. It was in 1775 that the College, "in consideration of the many advantages that must result to the public," contributed £50 sterling towards erecting the new High School, which was to contain "large, airy and commodious rooms," and soon after we find the committee appointed for its building, offering to purchase the pavilion and some waste land adjoining it in order to give a free passage round the proposed new building. The College seems to have had no desire to dispose of the remaining pavilion, for two years later, Sir William Forbes, on behalf of the committee, again made proposals for its purchase, it being "of great use to their plan by enlarging their area and preserving the school more open and airy"—two circumstances, he claimed, conducive to the health of the boys. The pavilion and ground about it were then offered for the sum of £200 stg. but as there seems to have been some delay in accepting the offer, Sir William was requested to decide at once, or the house would be immediately let, which the College said was more agreeable to them than selling it. The probability, however, is that a settlement was arrived at, for we hear no more of this pavilion.

At the beginning of 1775, the Medical Society, finding their meeting house too small for their increasing numbers, determined to build a hall of their own. For this purpose they proposed feuing a piece of the College ground at a yearly rental of £5, but as the Society was not an Incorporated body with responsible office-bearers, the contract was not properly executed until after they had procured, in 1778, a Charter from the Crown. Some particulars of their difficulty, along with a brief narrative of their inception, may be gathered from a Memorial containing certain queries for opinion of Counsel, which somehow has found a resting place among the College papers for the last 130 years.

" The Medical Society of Edinburgh," it bears, " was instituted in the year 1737 for the laudable purpose of promoting an ardour for medical inquiries amongst those engaged in the study of the profession. Besides some students at the University, the greater part of the practitioners in Edinburgh and many of the most eminent practitioners in Britain are now members of it. The Society very early formed the design of collecting a library, to which purpose their funds for many years were solely given. A few years ago several circumstances determined them to build a Hall for their weekly meetings and a room for the reception of their books and on this building they have spent nearly a thousand pounds. The area on which the Hall is built was acquired from the College of Surgeons, but their only right to it at present rests upon a missive letter betwixt the Treasurer of the College and two of the members of the Society on their behoof."

" The Memorialists are now desirous that their right should be completed by a feu-contract from the College of Surgeons, which could not be hitherto done on account of their not having a *nomen juris*. This they earnestly wish to obtain by a Charter of Incorporation from the Crown, not only with a view to establish their heritable property on a sure footing, but that the moveable property may also be secured, which from the want of proper powers has at different times been subjected to very great losses—and this Charter they are further desirous of obtaining so that they may be enabled to extend their heritable property to £3000 stg."

"But before taking any steps for this purpose, they beg to have the opinion of Counsel upon the following queries : (1) Whether a Charter from the Crown will answer the above ends, and if so, (2) Is there reason to believe that such a Charter will be obtained."

The reply, which is in the affirmative to both questions, is signed by Henry Dundas and Henry Erskine.

Dr Duncan was closely associated with the Society at this time, and his name appears prominently in the above proceeding. He too became a feuar of the College and, in 1777, built a house on the west side of Surgeons' Square. In consequence, however, of his having circulated printed proposals for establishing a Public Dispensary, the College entertained a suspicion that he had intentions of using the building for that purpose. In repudiating the idea, Dr Duncan explained that he intended erecting a dwelling-house in accordance with a plan which he submitted ; in the middle floor of the house he intended to continue his lectures on the Theory and Practice of Physic, but at present he did not intend finishing the other two flats. He acknowledged having circulated a scheme for establishing a public dispensary, but it was impossible for him to say where the contributors might choose to have it. He assured the Incorporation, however, that unless he should be obliged to sell the property for some very urgent reason he intended to continue the sole proprietor of it, and while he was so, they might trust him to have a tender regard to their funds. In conclusion, he desired the favour of using their Hall for two hours in the day twice a week for three months, for the purpose of lecturing upon cases of patients labouring under chronic diseases, but if any objections should be made to his bringing patients to the Hall, he offered to provide another place for them and confine the use he would make of the Hall solely to the purpose of delivering lectures.

It was then agreed to insert a clause in Dr Duncan's feu declaring that the house should not be used as a dispensary or public hospital nor employed in any other way whereby it might become a nuisance to the neighbourhood. He was permitted to lecture in the Hall for the time specified but not to bring patients there, as the College considered that such a step would be obnoxious to their feuars and tenants.

In the same year Dr Duncan intimated his intention of keeping a register of the weather for insertion in his medical commentaries; for this purpose he had given orders for the necessary instruments, including a wind gauge and a rain gauge, and these he requested the permission of the College to place on the waste land at the east end of the area, behind the Hall. In 1790, Dr Duncan gave notice of his intention to dispose of his house, and about the same time a feu at the back of the Hall was granted to Mr John Bell. A year or so previous to this, in view of the City Wall being taken down, the College had considered a proposal to open up the ground behind the Hall for building purposes. By the demolition of part of the City Wall the privacy so long enjoyed by the tenants of the College no longer existed. A thoroughfare seems to have been made right through the property, and this led to complaints being made of the number of idle people that frequented the green at the back of the Hall in consequence of the place being laid open by Mr Bell's feu. To remedy this, the College offered to enclose the area with an iron rail, on condition that the feuars were unanimous in giving up the right of servitude upon the ground immediately adjacent to the Town Wall.

During the construction of his house, Mr Bell lectured in the Hall, but this caused so much inconvenience to Lady Henderson, the tenant who occupied the east end of the building as a dwelling-house, that the College undertook to accommodate Mr Bell with another room until his own was finished, and promised in future that no one should have the privilege of lecturing in the Hall except under unusual circumstances.

The New Hall at Nicolson Street.—About the beginning of the 19th century, it was evident that the Hall was rapidly falling into decay and that, in a very short time, attention

would have to be given to the providing of a new one. At
last, on the architect reporting that the building was unsafe
for the holding of meetings, a committee was appointed to
consider the whole question, and, if necessary, to build a new
Hall.

The committee decided that there was no alternative but
to erect a new building, although they experienced considerable difficulty in finding an eligible site. Several sites had
been suggested, but on professional inspection most of them
proved unsuitable. Thus, a new Hall built on the site of the
old one would now require an entrance from Drummond
Street, and consequently the expense of two fronts would
have to be considered. Minto House was another situation
seriously thought of, but on account of the rapid declivity
of the ground towards the Cowgate, a great amount of under-
building would be required, involving extra expense. The
old High School was then considered, but that too was
reluctantly given up, as the alterations and additions necessary
for the purposes of the College would have fallen very little
short of the expense of an entirely new building.

Another site had now come into the market — that of
the Riding School in Nicolson Street—and this the committee
unanimously resolved to recommend the College to acquire,
provided it could be obtained at a reasonable price. The
College soon came to terms with the proprietors of the
school, and, in May 1828, the property was acquired for the
sum of £3500.

Mr Playfair, the College architect, was then instructed to
make plans of a building to contain a hall for the meetings
of the College, a museum, and a lecture-room for the professors
and teachers. Estimates for the work were procured, when it
was found that the probable cost of erecting the whole building
would amount to £11,500 or, without the class-room, to £9500.

In describing his plan, Mr Playfair said that the principal
front, which was towards Nicolson Street, would consist of a
Corinthian portico resting upon a wall or pedestal, which
served to protect the interior of the grounds from intrusion,
and to raise up the columns of the portico to such a
height as would be necessary to produce a proper effect. By
means of this wall the portico was also allowed to project so

far forward as to be seen from a distance—an object of the first importance. Had the columns, he said, rested on a flight of steps, the opposite effect would have been produced—the building would have been pushed backward, and would have been obscurely sunk between the lofty houses standing on each side. According to the original plan, Mr Playfair, with a view to economy, proposed placing the meeting hall and the library considerably below the level of the adjoining street. In this way the expense of under-building would be avoided, and the ornamental front would be kept down in height. A strong feeling, however, having been expressed that the descent to various of the principal apartments would be undesirable, the plans were amended to meet this objection. Finding that this would lead to greater expenditure than had been anticipated, the design of the front had to be reconsidered. Eventually the fully enriched Corinthian front had to give way to a less expensive but more stately portico of Ionic design.

This important question having been settled, the foundation stone of the new Hall was laid on 27th February 1830 by Mr William Wood, the President, in presence of the members of the College. At this ceremony there was deposited under the stone a case containing a copy of the Charter, Royal Grants, and Acts of Parliament in favour of the College, besides various other documents and the newspapers of the day. Building now commenced in earnest, and continued for the next two years—the stone for the pillars and front entrance being brought from Humbie quarry.

On 16th May 1832, the College met for the first time in their new Hall, when, before proceeding to business, Dr Gairdner, the President, made a few remarks suitable to the occasion. " It was a matter of congratulation," he said, " that they now possessed a place of meeting worthy of their status as members of a liberal and scientific body. He believed that the fact of their having devoted so large a portion of their new building and of their funds to purposes of scientific usefulness could not fail to raise them in the estimation of the public."

Mr Russell, Professor of Clinical Surgery, and the senior member of the College, also addressed the meeting. He was old enough, he said, to remember the time when, instead of possessing funds which could be appropriated to scientific purposes, the College was deeply in debt, and when they had no means of providing for the widow of a deceased member except by the private subscription of individuals.   It was highly creditable to them to have applied so large a portion of their funds to the establishment of a museum, by which the acquisition of professional knowledge would be greatly facilitated.   He likewise rejoiced to see that in these few years there had arisen among the members of their body a number of distinguished lecturers on professional subjects, and authors of medical works worthy of the high character of the College, and calculated to increase the reputation of the Medical School of Edinburgh.

On Saturday 7th July, 1832 the Hall was formally opened, and a large number of guests were invited to luncheon.   Among those receiving invitations were the Professors of the University, the whole body of the College of Physicians, and several Officers of the Navy, Army, and East India Company's service. At the annual dinner which followed, the toast-list contained no less than 43 items, in addition to the replies.

Since the end of 1828 the College had held their meetings in the Hall of the Royal Medical Society, placed at their disposal in consequence of their own Hall in Surgeons' Square having been reported as so dilapidated that it was dangerous for a large assemblage of people to collect there.

During the cholera scare of 1832, the use of the Hall was applied for by the Board of Health; their request of course in the circumstances could not be complied with, but the house which had been purchased from Dr M'Cansh for a temporary museum was rented by the Board.

The College having no further use for their premises in Surgeons' Square, considered the advisability of disposing of them.   Under the feu-rights granted by them they had entirely deprived themselves of the power of feuing or building either upon the north or the south side of the Hall, and unless an access could be obtained from Drummond Street by an opening through the Town Wall, the property could not be expected to improve or become more valuable.   It was therefore decided to advertise it for sale either by public roup or private bargain.   For this purpose a valuation of the property was taken, when it was found that the Hall was only

E

worth the ground on which it stood plus the value of the old materials ; the former being estimated at £250 and the latter at £60. Mr M'Cansh's house was said to be worth £450 and the feus, amounting to £35 yearly, might fetch £750—in all a sum of £1510 stg.

Before the decision of the College was carried into effect, however, an effort was made to come to some arrangement with the feuars, whereby the amenity of the Square would be maintained. The idea was to apply to the Town Council for permission to pull down part of the City Wall and make an entry into Drummond Street ; the College offered the site of the Hall as an addition to the area of the Square. They offered to be at the expense of making the opening, on condition that the feuars would so far give up their rights of servitude as to allow the College to feu out certain other portions of the ground according to a plan to be approved of by all the parties.

The proposal seemed to meet with some approbation, but, as the Royal Medical Society saw some difficulty in legally alienating any part of their property, the plan fell through. Nothing remained now but to fall back on the former scheme of advertising in the newspapers, with the result that when an offer of £2100 was made by the Managers of the Royal Infirmary, the College had little hesitation in parting with the whole of their property situated in Surgeons' Square.

In course of time the old Hall passed into the hands of the University, to whom it still belongs. The upper part, which was falling into decay, was almost entirely rebuilt, but on the ground-level many portions of the original building may be easily recognised.

Conspicuous amongst these is the original doorway surmounted by the date 1697. This relic is still as it was when Monteath first fixed up his " Hot Pot " in the laboratory below, and Eliot, M'Gill, and the father of Monro *primus* passed beneath its venerable portals. Simple and unpretentious as it may be architecturally, this doorway has a peculiar romantic interest to Fellows of the College. Through it passed the Bells (John and Charles), Liston, Knox, Syme, and many others whose names are part of the history of the College. The late Principal of the University, Sir William Turner, a former

President of the College, recognising the historical association of the doorway with the Surgeons, undertook that when the building of which it forms a part comes to be demolished the doorway will be preserved and handed over to the College for preservation.

When the new building in Nicolson Street was finished, the oak panelling of the old Hall was transferred to the Council Room.

Meeting Places of the Council.—From the earliest time the Incorporation had made it a rule to meet once a quarter, but the day and hour of the meeting depended very much upon circumstances. As it was the practice of all well-governed Societies to meet on fixed days, and with the hope of it leading to a more punctual attendance of the members, the Surgeons, in 1743, decided to hold their meetings on the third Wednesday of February, May, August, and November, at 2 o'clock in the afternoon. The Deacon's Council was also fixed to meet on the Tuesday immediately preceding, at 6 o'clock in the evening, to prepare the business beforehand. The place of meeting of the Council was to be nominated by the Deacon on the day of his election, and any member who thought fit might attend to give advice.

John's Coffee House was the first place selected, and there the Council met regularly for many years. Situated in the north-east corner of Parliament Close, it is described as the "favourite resort of the judges and lawyers of the eighteenth century for consultations and for their 'meridian' or twelve o'clock dram, for in those days every citizen had his peculiar 'howff' or place of resort, where men of every station met for conversation or good fellowship." Muirhead's and the Laigh Coffee House are also mentioned as being used by the Surgeons for the same purpose.

In addition to the Statutory Meetings, an Extraordinary Meeting might be called at any time by the Deacon at the request of the members.

CHAPTER V

THE LIBRARY AND MUSEUM

The "Rarities of the College"—The Nucleus of the Library—Curators of Museum appointed—The Barclay Collection — Negotiations for Professor Meckel's Collection—Mr Cullen's Mission to Paris—Robert Knox's Contributions—Sir Charles Bell's Collection—Dr Macintosh's Obstetrical Collection—Transfer of Library to University—The College Portraits—The School of Medicine.

IN the new Hall at Surgeons' Square provision was made for housing such books as the Calling possessed, as well as certain other "rarities" which formed the nucleus of the Museum. In 1696, several books had been presented to the Incorporation. From this date onwards many donations were made, not only of books, but also of curiosities of a wide and varied description. As many of these gifts had not been recorded at the time of presentation, an Act was passed, in 1699, that in future, to enable the Calling to obtain a "thankful remembrance of all the benefactors and donations" all gifts should immediately be entered in their books. A long list then follows, noticeable amongst them being :—

Presented by :—

Alex. Wright, Merchant in Edinburgh.—*Josephus*: History of the Antiquities and Warres of the Jews, in folio, printed in London, 1576; with two shillings scots to buy a chain for it.

James Balfour.—A large African Gourd, with a silver head.

Thomas Edgar.—A case containing ten old german lancets.

Archibald Pitcairn.—Eight medical works, including Georgii Wolfgangii Wedely Phisologia Medica.

James Hamilton.—Four books, also a large eel skin stuft and taken in Cramond Water. A pair of tenailes incisive and a pair of tenailes for drawing of teeth.

Mr Lawrence Oliphant.—Culpeppers Herball, Bacons advancement of Learning, and some Sermons in Dutch.

Wm. Watson, Writer.—Answer to a Discourse of Celibacy of Clergy.

Reuben Makrabbi, Barber and Perriwig maker in Edinburgh.— Twenty-five books including Les Oeuvres de Ambrose Parie, Histoire generales de Angleterre, Ecosse, et Irelande, Le Remant de Chevaliers de la Gloire.

Robt. Swinton, Chirurgeon.—Six Pictures of Ancient Physicians, viz. Hippocrates, Galenus, Paracelsus, Avicenna Aesculapius, and Joannes Bocatius.

William Ross.—A vessel for Bathing.

William Bishop.—A fine english Bible and a french Bible with the Psalms.

Mr Patrick Mowbray, Clerk to the Incorporation.—A pair of Scots cocks spurs, clecked in Fife, prodigiously long.

Hugh Broun, Chirurgeon.—An anibi with its brachium.

Dr Drummond.—Several shells, plants of Spongia marina got in the north of Scotland.

John Adair, Hydrographer. — Vesprietinum American, or an American Wasps-Nest.

Alexander Monteith, deacon. — Some pictures with a glass cylinder by which they can only be discovered, and an American bird's beak—very curious.

Dr Charles Oliphant.—An Allegatory, or young Crocodile.

In October 1699, the following advertisement was ordered to be put in the *Edinburgh Gazette* :—

"These are to give notice that the Chirurgeon Apothecaries of Edinburgh are erecting a library of Physicall, Anatomicall, Chirurgicall, Botanicall, Pharmaceuticall and other Curious books. — They are also making a collection of all naturall and artificiall curiosities. If any person have such to bestow let them give notice to Walter Porterfield present Treasurer to the Society at his house in the head of the Canongate who will cause their names to be honourably recorded and if they think not fit to bestow them gratis they shall have reasonable prices for them."

At the same time the following laws were drawn up and approved of by the Calling, who ordained them to be "inviolably observed in all time coming."

"That the names and designations of every person who gives in any books shall be honourably mentioned in the Records of the Incorporation. Second. For the encouragement of those who have or shall hereafter give in any books, the Incorporation do discharge [prohibit] any book to be lent out of the library to any person whatsoever and if the donator will give in two shillings scots with each book, they shall be chained to the presses. Third. That the Bibliothecarius shall attend every lawfull day at the library, two hours. That every donator may have liberty to read what books they please. Fourth. That any who shall give books to the amount of £3 stg. or upwards, shall have their names put up in gold letters and particular mention made of their donations. Fifth. That any who either give in books to the value of ten shillings stg., or money for buying of them shall be Cives Bibliotherces. That no person shall be allowed to drink, or smoke tobacco in the library. That whosoever transgresses any laws of the Hall shall incur a set fine to be exacted for the benefit of the library."

In the course of time many additions were made, and many curiosities found a temporary resting-place in the Surgeons' Library. A writing master in Edinburgh sent "two brods or tables finely written, on the one was written the Ten Commandments and on the other the Royal Oake." With grateful thanks to the donors the Calling also acknowledged the gift of "a fine picture" from Alex. Mitchell, "a large fine case of Shottles [drawers] for containing the Materia Medica" from Robert Campbell, and an "Italian padlock for women" from David Fyfe.

A letter from Mr James Petiver, apothecary in London, testifies to the growing importance of the Library and points to it having roused a more than local interest. In reply to Mr Petiver's letter, the Calling admitted the great charges and expenses that he had been put to for several years in promoting natural history and collecting curiosities from all parts of the world, and that he had sent frequently some of them with his catalogue and figures to the Society. The Calling, therefore, for his further encouragement, subscribed a guinea, that they might have all his tables from the beginning and a dedication of one of them to themselves.

One of the earliest books purchased for the Library was the *Essays of Medicine*. It cost two shillings stg. The receipt is as follows :—

"Received from the Treasurer of the Surgeons of Edinburgh, one shilling stg. as the first half for the *Essays of Medicine*, being a Trans-

lation of "Tentamen Medicum de Medicastorum Audacitate" published
by the Approbation and Advice of learned Physicians, plainly detecting
by many Examples, the pernicious Arrogancy and inevitable insufficiency
of Quacks, or those who practise in medicine, being yet unacquainted
with the Institutions thereof and the mischievious Credulity of their
patients; Which Examples are Manifest Proofs even to the Unlearned
and necessary Cautions for Practice. In which Essay there shall be
some Additions to the Original and some variations Modestiæ causa;
and all in order to set Men above these little Crafts and Doubles of
Buffoons, bold Pretenders and the wrathful disingenuous Censures
of the Peevish and Men of Design, with which miserable world is
perplext; Medicine being a Mystery to all such as have not applied
to the Study thereof. Which I oblige myself to deliver to him or
his Assigns, stitcht, against the 25th December 1711, he or they
paying another shilling on delivery . . . "

The records do not contain many further references to the
Museum till about the year 1807, when nine members of the
College were appointed Curators, and in the following year it
was opened as a "deposite" for any anatomical or pathological
preparations which the proprietors of them might choose
to lodge in it. The sum of £30 was voted to pay the
expenses already incurred in providing spirit, and the same
amount for purchasing a case to accommodate the increasing
number of specimens. Ten years later a report shows
that the Museum contained upwards of three hundred
preparations of diseased organs and textures, many of them
very interesting and instructive, and generally in a good
state of preservation.

In 1821, an Extraordinary Meeting of the College was called
at the instance of the Curators of the Museum, to consider a
proposal to purchase the museum belonging to Dr Meckel of
Halle in Germany. The family of Dr Meckel had for three
generations employed themselves in forming an anatomical
museum, which both from its great extent—it contained upwards
of 5000 preparations—and from the skill and care which had
been bestowed in selecting and preparing the specimens, was
considered to be without a rival in Europe.

The collection was now for sale, and the price asked was
£5000 stg. In urging its purchase the Curators called attention
to the prosperous state of the finances of the College, the

accumulated funds of which, they said, now reached upwards of £9000 and its income for the last three years had averaged over £1100.   Against this, was a yearly expenditure of only £400, which showed a saving of between £600 and £700 exclusive of the interest on the sum already accumulated.   Various arguments in support of the proposition were brought forward, and the Curators thought that the College could not bestow a part of their funds in a manner more conducive to its own dignity as a scientific body, or to the collective and individual interest of its members, than by possessing itself of this collection.   It was then suggested that, in the event of the College acquiring the collection, the members should assess themselves in an annual sum for a few years for the purpose of defraying the extra expense likely to be incurred over and above the £5000 to be paid by the funds of the College, and that the sons and sons-in-law of members of the College should pay an increased entry fee more nearly corresponding to the value of the privileges they would obtain.

It was while this question was being thrashed out that Dr John Barclay made an offer to the College in the following letter addressed to the President :—

"Anxious to add, and yearly adding, to the number of my prepara-tions, notwithstanding that my rooms are already too crowded, I have long thought, to prevent my collection being scattered after I can make use of it no more, to have it deposited with some learned and respectable Society or body of men who could estimate its value and render it useful to themselves and others.   My first thoughts were to present it to the Royal College of Surgeons of Edinburgh, to which I am under so strong obligations, and for which I feel and shall ever feel a most sincere gratitude.   Recollecting, however, that morbid preparations, and not preparations chiefly anatomical, were what the College principally valued, it occurred to me that it might hesitate to accept my offer and grudge the expense of building a hall for its reception.   But these doubts having since been completely removed, upon knowing that the College has lately thought of purchasing at a very considerable expense a most valuable anatomical collection on the Continent, I feel encouraged to offer to it mine, and to bequeath it simply on the condition that the College shall build a hall to receive it, and the collection shall be allowed to retain my name, not doubting that the necessary degree of care to preserve it from hastening too fast into decay will be attended to.   I have nothing more to add than to assure you of my high respect for the College, of my warm gratitude for its former kindness, and to request that you will lay these proposals before it, and believe me to be, dear Sir,

Yours truly,

(Sgd.) JOHN BARCLAY."

6 ARGYLL SQUARE, 3rd July 1821.

The College, in thanking Dr Barclay for his munificent offer, referred not only to the liberality of his intentions, but also to the handsome and unqualified terms in which he had presented to them so valuable a gift, and assured him of the deep interest the College had taken in his success as a teacher of Anatomy. In conclusion, the College promised to embrace every opportunity of evincing the high sense it entertained of the manner in which he had fulfilled the object it had in view when upon a former occasion it placed his lectures on the same footing with those of most eminent teachers of anatomical science in the Universities of this and other countries.

Barclay's name is first mentioned in the Surgeons' books in 1804. He seems to have been held in high esteem by the College, for although not a Fellow of the College, the Surgeons unanimously approved that attendance on his lectures on Anatomy and Surgery should be held as equivalent to the lectures of members of the College of Physicians or Surgeons of London, Dublin, and Edinburgh, or of any other reputable College on the same subjects—rather an unusual proceeding in those days of monopoly. This act of the Surgeons appears to have been thoroughly appreciated by Barclay, who in reply said: "This attention from the Royal College of Surgeons is more than I had any reason to expect, and I cannot delay a moment in returning my sincerest thanks for such a mark of your approbation. It is the highest honour that has ever been conferred on me. I am sensible of its value, and you may be assured I shall always remember it with the warmest sentiments of esteem and gratitude while I live." Barclay became a Fellow of the College of Physicians in 1806, and in consideration of his gift to the Surgeons was made one of their Honorary Fellows in 1821.

Some further correspondence passed between Dr Meckel and the College, in which the former stated that he had considerable difficulty in making up his mind to part with his museum, and that he had not, in fact, finally determined to do so. In estimating the value of his collection, and in giving his reasons for disposing of it, Dr Meckel says : " I am persuaded that the price I ask is a very moderate one. For instance, the King of Prussia paid some twenty years ago 100,000 thalers for the Walterian collection, which could at that time be by no means compared to mine at this time ; suppose, then, the King might have paid far too much, yet my price would be very cheap. Neither should I choose to part with it for such a low price, if I did not desire earnestly to quit the service, in which I have been treated with the most abominable ingratitude and sacrificed to. a parcel of rascals who, infuriated by envy and malice, have dared against myself every conceivable villainy."

The Surgeons, however, did not acquire Dr Meckel's museum, but approved of a plan instead, of sending an agent to Paris to collect specimens from the various hospitals in that city. The suggestion was that Mr William Cullen (who made the proposition and was very sanguine of its success) should go to Paris for three or four years, and during that time endeavour to form a collection of anatomical and pathological preparations worthy of the dignity of the College. This object, he said, would best be effected by establishing proper relations with the young men connected with the hospitals as clerks or dressers, who, if properly managed, would not only give the specimens, which were useless to them, but communicate at the same time the records of the cases as put down in their note-books. With many of these young men, Mr Cullen said, he was formerly upon terms of intimacy, and no doubt could renew the acquaintance if he had any object in view. "The Physicians and Surgeons," he continued, "so far from opposing would gladly favour the enterprise ; he had often heard it regretted by many of them that they knew no one employed in forming a collection on whom they could bestow their specimens, and thus preserve much interesting information from being lost to science, as soon as acquired, for want of some such accurate record to preserve it." Besides the hospitals, Mr Cullen proposed visiting the public anatomical establishments, and from these sources he thought he could enrich the College with the gleanings of nearly 10,000 bodies. In Paris, too, bodies (entire and unopened) could be purchased in any number for one-twentieth of what he understood to be the cost of them in Edinburgh, and open bodies, which would serve all common purposes equally well, for one-thirtieth; morbid parts being obtained by private favour and individual exertion, would cost almost nothing, except when entire bodies had to be opened to remove them, or, in so far as it might be necessary, to bribe the subordinate agents about the hospitals into assistance and connivance.

Briefly, this was Mr Cullen's plan for forming a museum while in Paris, where, he said, such was the liberality of the French practitioners towards foreigners, and so great their public spirit, that they would vie with each other in assisting a stranger who made use of their resources for the purpose of science, and who appeared to find in Paris what he could secure nowhere else. "I know," he continued, "they entertained this feeling towards Professor Meckel, who spent among them the whole of last summer, and who was rewarded by being able to keep six men constantly at work and to carry off an immense treasure."

Eventually Mr Cullen's offer was accepted by the College, who were to allow him £300 a year as salary and £500 a year to be expended in procuring the preparations and transmitting them to Edinburgh.

Arriving in Paris on the 1st October, Cullen, who had previously become a Fellow of the College, at once set to work, but in a very short time realised the impossibility of his mission, and expressed his fears that owing to the unexpected obstacles he had met with he would have to solicit his recall.

To continue the narrative, we must now refer to a letter from Mr William Thomson (who happened to be in Paris at the time) to his father, Dr John Thomson, in Edinburgh :—

"You will have learned," he says, "from Sommerville's letter of yesterday (sent through the Ambassador's office) of our friend (Cullen) having suffered a few hours previously a stroke of apoplexy. I am happy to state that it has been in its effects and promises to be in its results as slight as from the nature of the event we could justly expect, since he was first bled (to the amount of 43 ozs.) he has improved, recognises those about him, answers any question distinctly as to his wants and feelings, and has the entire use of all his faculties. It is well known for some weeks to his most intimate friends that the apprehension of failure in this object has occasioned to him a great degree of anxiety of mind, and that this, along with the exertions he has made to overcome the difficulties he has encountered, has given rise to neglect and consequent derangement of his health . . . . In looking forward to the progress of his recovery I am much disposed to apprehend that it will be very liable to be retarded by the continuance of those feelings, which I am persuaded have been the cause of his calamity, and that much kind attention will be required to soothe his mind and to prevent it dwelling upon such disagreeable subjects. I cannot help thinking or suggesting that much might be done towards accomplishing this were the College to transmit to him an assurance of their being well satisfied of the zeal and judgment with which he has conducted his undertaking, and of their sense of the honourable manner in which he had without delay announced his apprehension of the probability of its failure."

In compliance with Mr Thomson's suggestion, a letter conveying their acknowledgment of his upright and honourable conduct and their regrets at hearing of his illness, was at once despatched by the College to Mr Cullen.

On his return to Edinburgh, some few weeks later, Cullen, in making a report of his mission, writes : " I deem it almost unnecessary to dwell on the causes of the failure, for they could not be duly appreciated by you here, at such a distance from the scene of the transaction. National prejudices, which I came too late to prevent, and was unable to remove, had been excited before my arrival. I exerted myself, however, to the utmost, and in the hope that they might ultimately wear themselves out I spared neither time nor toil, nor even my health, in the discharge of my duty. That I should have done so with no better success is a matter of deep concern to me, as it must have been of regret to the College . . . ."

So ended Mr Cullen's mission to Paris, which only lasted seven weeks. Its failure was a great blow to him. He was a grand-nephew of the Professor of that name, and resided at 22 Howe Street.

In the meantime the Curators of the Museum, in searching for suitable accommodation for their preparations, which were now steadily accumulating, fixed upon two rooms at the west end of their Hall. These were thrown into one and fitted up with glass cases and shelving with a view of holding Dr Barclay's morbid preparations, which he had promised to place in the keeping of the College.

It was at this time (April 1824) that Dr Robert Knox, the anatomist, first became connected with the College. In a letter to Dr James Russell, who was then Convener of the Museum Committee, Knox offered to bestow his whole time, labour, and energy towards forming a museum of comparative anatomy and physiology.

"I have felt," he said, "more than most anatomists, the great want of a proper museum and of an osteological collection, without which researches into comparative and human physiology cannot be carried out. But the formation and preservation of such a museum being altogether beyond the reach of individual means, I have ventured to submit through you the following brief sketch of a plan for the attainment of an object so desirable to science." Knox then offers to form a series of preparations illustrative of human and comparative anatomy and physiology, to be placed in the museum under the same regulations as the pathological collection, reserving to himself during his lifetime the use of the museum for the furtherance of "my favourite pursuits and studies." The expense necessary for the formation of the collection was to be defrayed by the College, whose sole property it was to be. Knox then presented some preparations of different parts of the eye of various animals, and also some skeletons of birds and serpents, in order that the College might judge of his qualifications for the task which he had proposed to undertake. In January 1825, in order that the College might secure his services on a more permanent footing, Knox was appointed Conservator of the Museum at a salary of £100 per annum.

No sooner was the appointment made than Knox received an opportunity for displaying those talents and energies for which he was remarkable. The College, through Dr Gairdner, had been negotiating with Mr Charles Bell for the purchase of his famous museum in London. In concluding this correspondence, Bell, at the end of 1824, wrote: "The subject of your last letter is a serious one to me. From habit, I have an unwillingness to part with my collection even after I am convinced I should do so. You speak of the midwifery preparations taken away as if this should diminish the value of the collection. But the spaces occupied by the midwifery preparations are already filled up with what to me and to surgeons should be more valuable. I mean by additional preparations of the bladder, prostate, and urethra. But a truce to this kind of argument. I shall take out of the collection certain preparations of the natural structure, and the remainder of the preparations (forming a complete set for the illustration of anatomy) and the whole of the morbid preparations I offer to the College of Surgeons for three thousand pounds."

At the same time Mr Bell intimated his willingness to make the College a present of his skeleton of his Makery Camel—" a beautiful creature which bore the same resemblance to the common camel that the greyhound does to the bull-dog," if they would make it up.

At the request of the Curators, Dr Knox and Mr A. Watson went to London to inspect the collection, and on their report that it would be a most valuable acquisition to the College, its purchase was decided upon.

During the discussions that ensued before finally arriving at this decision, many serious difficulties presented themselves, and the expediency of acquiring such an extensive museum as Bell's without first providing adequate accommodation for its reception was often questioned. The Hall, too, even if it admitted of extensions, had been reported as in a ruinous condition, and the Barclay Collection might at any moment fall into their hands. The question then resolved itself into this, that if the College seriously meant to maintain a museum of any consequence at all, a new hall was indispensable. In course of time several sites for this purpose were suggested. One on the " Earthen Mound " found particular favour, another was thought to be suitable upon the Calton Hill opposite to the new jail, while a proposal to acquire Minto House was negatived by the architect. Nothing, however, was decided upon, and the College at last came to the conclusion that considering the extent of the funds, and all other circumstances connected with the matter, no better situation could be procured than that upon which their Hall then stood.

It was while the College was debating this point, and considering the probable consequences of any step they might be induced to take, that a proposal was made to solicit a grant of money from Government, to assist them in carrying out their plan of building a new hall, with a museum and a class-room attached. In gathering information respecting the sums of money advanced to the London and Dublin Colleges of Surgeons for similar purposes, it was ascertained that the Government gave John Hunter's heirs £15,000 for his museum. The room to contain it, however, was built entirely at the expense of the College of Surgeons in London, while the sum voted by the Irish Parliament to the College of Surgeons in Dublin was £27,000, nine thousand of which was laid out in the purchase of grounds and eighteen thousand in building a hall and dissecting rooms.

With these precedents as a basis for their claim, the College had several conferences with the Lord Advocate and the Solicitor-General, when the latter assured them he would promote their application with all his influence. A memorial embodying the desires of the College was sent to the First Lord of the Treasury and the Chancellor of the Exchequer.

After detailing the object of the grant and their anxiety to extend their sphere of usefulness by adding to the system of medical education, the memorialists go on to say that the funds of the College were extremely limited, arising as they did only out of a small fee received for diplomas and from Fellows admitted into the College. Their annual income was little more than sufficient to defray the ordinary expenses of management, to afford a slender annuity to distressed members, and an allowance to the children of those who died in indigent circumstances. They pointed out that without the aid of His Majesty's Government they would be unable to place their museum in a situation where it would be accessible. It would be necessary to expend upon it a sum of money which was destined for the erection of a new Hall or College, their present house being in a state of decay and quite irreparable, and in reference to this they took the liberty to mention that the expense of erecting such a building, containing the necessary accommodation, could not amount to less than ten thousand pounds sterling. The value of the improvements which the College had already introduced was in some measure evinced by the increased demand for their diploma, as, in the three years ending 1803, one hundred and thirty-seven young men received the diploma, in the three years ending 1813 two hundred and seventy-four, and in the last three years (ending 1825) no less than three hundred and forty-eight, being an average of one hundred and sixteen annually, and that too in a period of profound peace, when the demand ought to be "considerably detailed."

To support the claims of the College and to strengthen the hands of those pleading its cause, Sir James M'Gregor, Director-General of the Army Medical Department, addressed a letter to the Lord Advocate and to the Solicitor-General, in which occurs the following passage:—

"I have reason to know that a great proportion of the Medical Officers serving in His Majesty's Army, and of those who have most distinguished themselves in the public service, have received their education in Edinburgh, where all the branches of the medical profession have for a series of years been taught by professors of such high celebrity as to establish Edinburgh as the first Medical School in the world. I would venture to say if any branch of the medical profession is studied with less advantage in Edinburgh than in other quarters, it is Surgery. One of the great advantages which London and Dublin, Paris and some other foreign universities have for the study, is in the noble collection which each of them possesses in morbid anatomy, by which the various changes effected in the human frame by disease may be studied."

The College, however, was doomed to disappointment, for information soon reached them that they had little prospect of success during that session of Parliament. They were further recommended not to push their application at that moment, for if it once received the serious consideration of the Treasury, and was then thrown out, the door was for ever shut, whereas by letting it pass over, the matter might be taken up again at a time when there was a better chance of success. The College were also invited to persevere in adding every procurable object or collection of objects of morbid anatomy and pathology to their present museum—thus evincing to the Government the sincerity of their views, and proving that they were less solicitous to advance their own individual and pecuniary interest than to promote the general welfare of chirurgical science and the education of those in their particular department.

In the meantime the arrangements for the purchase of the Bell Collection having been completed, Knox, who had now joined the College, proceeded to London to superintend its shipment to Leith, where it arrived in due course packed in 65 cases on board the smack *Robert Bruce*, and was safely conveyed to Surgeons' Square in spring wagons, lent by the Artillery for that purpose.

The accommodation at the west end of the Hall proving insufficient, a house in Nicolson Street was temporarily rented at £35 per annum, and later, when the whole of the Bell Collection (consisting of over two thousand specimens) was unpacked and ready to be placed in position, John Bell's house in Surgeons' Square, which had passed into the hands of Dr John M'Cansh, was purchased from that gentleman for £820 and fitted up to receive it. This house, which consisted of three flats, now became the museum proper, and eventually the whole of the pathological collection was removed to it; the morbid specimens being lodged in the upper flat and the healthy structures in the lower, while the middle floor it was thought would afford accommodation for the collection of Dr Barclay, who had just died. Other anatomical specimens were still in the apartments at the west end of the Hall.

During the month of April 1826, the museums were reported to have been visited by nearly five hundred students. A brief visit was also paid by Lord Melville and the Solicitor-General, both of whom expressed themselves highly gratified with what they had seen, and with the order in which the collections were kept.

Following the example of the College, the University now decided no longer to keep the doors of their museum closed, but to open them to the members of the two Royal Colleges and also to the medical public. Dr David Hay who was President at the time, in making this important concession known to the College, said that the arrangement had been completed principally, if not entirely, through the persevering exertions of their fellow-member, Mr William Wood; at the

F

same time both he himself and Mr Wood were duly sensible of the liberal and handsome conduct of the medical professors in the University, and particularly of Dr Monro, without whose aid it would have been impossible to have carried through the measure. A vote of thanks to Dr Monro was then agreed to, and soon afterwards, as the College were in possession of no less than four tattooed heads of New Zealanders, the Curators recommended that one of them should be presented to Dr Monro as a gift from the Royal College to the public anatomical museum.

The death of Barclay, in 1826, convinced the College more than ever that, even after acquiring the house in Surgeons' Square, their accommodation was altogether inadequate for their requirements, and that the question of providing new premises specially constructed to contain a large museum could not be deferred much longer.

The deed of settlement executed by Barclay in 1821, bequeathing the collection to the College, now took effect, providing that the following conditions amongst others were complied with :—

"If within six months after the date of the intimation the College shall give notice that they have built, or are in the course of building or purchasing a room or rooms or a hall sufficient for containing and preserving the collection in a proper and suitable manner, then the trustees are directed when the hall is in readiness to deliver over the museum to the President of the College . . . . The rooms or hall to be denominated the Barcleian Museum in all time coming . . . . If the College shall not within the space of two years after the date of intimation have duly received and accepted the museum, the bequest so far as concerns the College is to be null and void."

On account of a report by the architect, Mr Playfair, in August 1828, that the old hall and adjoining buildings were in such a state of decay as to render them unsafe for holding either the meetings of the College or any part of the museum, another house in Surgeons' Square, the property of Mr Lockhart, was rented at £60 per annum, and the museum at the west end of the College was transferred to it, as was also such part of the Barclay collection as could not be accommodated in the other house. By this arrangement the College came into undisputed possession of the Barcleian Collection, "which, they trusted, would long remain a monument of the industry and public spirit of the excellent individual whose name it bore."

For the next year or two (except for the building of the new hall and museum, described elsewhere, and now nearly ready for occupation) nothing worth recording happened with regard to the museum.

Many new specimens were added during this period, and the Conservator, Dr Knox, at perhaps the most trying time of his life, seems to have given much attention to preserving and arranging the various donations which were constantly being made.

In the beginning of 1831, however, in consequence of some misunderstanding between Dr Knox and Mr Syme, the latter summoned a meeting of the Museum Committee to receive a complaint which he had to prefer against the Conservator for incivility to him in the discharge of his duty as one of the Curators. The complaint and answer thereto having been submitted in writing, the Curators were unanimously of opinion that Dr Knox in not at once stating to Mr Syme "that he was putting up the preparation referred to by the advice and with the concurrence of the donor, forgot the respect which was due to the Curators collectively and individually, and that he ought to be admonished to avoid such conduct in future as being likely to produce consequences unpleasant in themselves and injurious to the interests of the museum."

Professor Russell and Dr Gairdner were requested to see this resolution carried into effect, after which it was determined that the papers connected with the affair should be destroyed. This was the beginning of the end of Dr Knox's connection with the museum. A month or two afterwards, while arrangements were in progress for removing the museum to the new premises, a report was read from the committee which had been appointed for that purpose, complaining in general terms that the Conservator had not shown a proper degree of willingness to meet the views of the Curators in their appointment, but had, on the contrary, thrown many obstacles in their way.

Dr Knox having been sent for and examined on the subject, admitted that his views differed from those of the committee respecting the removal of the preparations, and in effect stated that he saw no prospect of a cordial co-operation between them.

The Curators, however, were of opinion that, while the committee ought not necessarily to interfere with Dr Knox's ordinary duties as Conservator, it was indispensable that the latter should obey their instructions in those matters which the Curators had appointed them to superintend.

Dr Knox then resigned his office in the following terms to the President :—

"DEAR SIR,

I beg leave to acquaint the College, through you, that it is now my determination to carry into effect a measure I have for a long time contemplated, viz. :—the resignation of the Conservatorship of the museum of the College, and I request you will have the goodness to consider this notice as a resignation on my behalf of that office."

Mr W. Macgillivray succeeded Dr Knox as Conservator, and under his superintendence the entire collection was removed to the new museum in Nicolson Street, now ready for its reception. The formal opening of the latter took place on Saturday, 7th July 1832, when an addition to the staff was made by the appointment of an attendant, whose duty it was to maintain order and prevent the intrusion of improper persons. His salary was to be £15 a year, with a "coat, hat, and baton as his insignia of office."

With a view to increasing the utility of the museum, short lectures or demonstrations were permitted to be given by lecturers to their pupils in what is now the Reading Room, and which was temporarily filled with shelves for the purpose. A prize of ten guineas was also offered to the student of the medical school who should present to the museum the best series of preparations illustrating in experimental pathology : (1st) the processes of nature in repairing injuries of the intestines ; (2nd) the processes of nature in repairing injuries of the bones.

In 1837, a most important addition was made, by the College acquiring the obstetrical collection of Dr Macintosh, which included a number of specimens formerly in Sir Charles Bell's museum, but as the purchase money (some £400) would have to be borrowed to pay for it, it was agreed as a set-off that the expense of the biennial breakfast, which it was the custom of the College to give, should be defrayed by the members attending it.

CENTRAL HALL OF THE MUSEUM.

[*To face page* 84.

As showing the interest taken in the museum, both by the profession and the general public, it may be mentioned that in 1839 it was visited by no less than 10,256 persons, of whom 7926 were laymen. On one occasion a most unpleasant incident arose through the admission of the public to the museum. A pathological specimen—the head and neck of a man who had died of cholera and which bore peculiar contractions of the lower jaw, the result of a burn in childhood, was recognised and claimed by his relations. The head, which was none other than Broggans', the associate of Burke and Hare, was returned to his friends by order of the Curators. The skull, however, subsequently found its way back to the museum.

Mr Macgillivray resigned the Conservatorship in 1841, on account of having been appointed to the Professorship of Civil and Natural History in Marischal College, Aberdeen. The College placed on record the high sense they entertained of the value and efficiency of his services to the museum. John Goodsir succeeded Mr Macgillivray; James Spence was also a candidate for the office, but withdrew his name on account of the feeling of the College that the Conservator of the museum should not be engaged in practice. After two years' service Goodsir left to become Professor of Anatomy in the University, on the death of Monro *tertius* in 1846. In 1848, he underwent a full examination for the Ordinary Fellowship of the College. Harry Goodsir followed his brother John in the Surgeons' museum. His stay, however, was also brief, for he joined the ill-fated Franklin Expedition as medical officer and naturalist, and in 1845 sailed to the Arctic regions. There is a grim irony in recalling that as he was still anxious to have the honour of acting as Conservator, and "as his absence would only be temporary," he asked the College to give him leave until his return.

In December 1852, a letter was received from the Association for the Suppression of Drunkenness, requesting that the College would make arrangements for opening the museum to the public during the Christmas holidays. This was agreed to, and according to the Conservator's report "there was necessarily great confusion, and much dirt and dust deposited. Four policemen were in attendance to keep order. The only damage done was one preparation jar broken, but the preparation itself was not injured.   Some of the skeletons were also damaged, but the mischief could be easily rectified."

As far back as 1853 the Conservator gave demonstrations to advanced students of the College.

Transfer of College Library to the University.—In 1763, the Surgeons' Library and Curiosities were all made over to the University.   The particulars of the gift and the circumstances which determined it are interesting.

In the days of adversity, when, for want of funds, the College was compelled to rent its premises, the Hall was sometimes leased along with the dwelling-house adjoining it. A place of safety had therefore to be found for the collection of books and other articles it then contained.

When Lord Elchies vacated his house in 1752 it was taken by Sir Peter Halket of Pitfirrane, a gentleman who, after refusing to serve under Cumberland, embarked with his regiment for America, in 1755, where he fell in conflict with the enemy.   Upon Sir Peter taking possession of the premises, the Incorporation agreed to remove the library and rarities from the Hall so that he might have full use of it.   Captain Ferguson succeeded Sir Peter Halket, but soon incurred the Incorporation's displeasure in consequence of the way he abused the Hall and Gardens, and was informed that no wheeled carriages were to enter the latter.   The next occupant of the house was Mr Calderwood of Polton, who paid £38 a year for it.

Just previous to this it had been advertised that, if desired, the Hall would be let with the house to the Incorporation without any reservation as to its use.   As this could not be done without the removal of the books in the library, it was agreed in the year 1762 to offer them to the Managers of the Infirmary for the use of the students, on payment of a small sum annually.   The amount thus obtained was to be devoted to the purchase of other books under the direction of the Managers or the Professors of Medicine and Anatomy.   The scheme, however, fell through, and the following year the Incorporation considered whether it would not be to their advantage to join their library to that of the University, and to deposit their curiosities in the University museum.   As the proposal found favour among themselves, a committee was

formed to approach the members of the University and, if an
agreement with them could be made, to draw up regulations
for the transfer. The report of the committee was to the effect
that the Incorporation should enter into a contract with the
University for nineteen years upon the following terms:—

(1) That the library and curiosities belonging to the Incorporation
should be delivered over to the keepers of the University library and
museum by inventory, one copy of which, duly signed, should be
lodged with each party. (2) That the Incorporation should pay the
University for increasing the library £5 stg. annually. (3) That all
the members of the Incorporation should be free *cives* and members
of the University library and museum during the contract. (4) That
after the expiration of the nineteen years either party should have
liberty to resile upon giving the other two years' warning.

On this report being received, it was resolved to deliver over
the library and curiosities agreeably to the first article of the
report ; the second article, for payment of £5 annually, was
also agreed to, conditionally that all the members of the
Corporation now and in time coming shall be free *cives* and
members of the library and museum belonging to the University.
The surgeons, however, would enter into no contract for a
limited time, but insisted that it should be *in perpetuam.*

The University acceded to all the above conditions and
agreed to accept the donation in the manner proposed. A
contract was then signed by the two bodies, and ratified by
the Town Council on 7th September 1763, when the Surgeons'
Library passed out of their hands and became incorporated with
that of the University.

When the College agreed to hand over the whole of their
books to the University and to pay a yearly subscription of £5
on condition that the Fellows of the College should have free
access to the University library, it did not appear likely that
this arrangement would in course of time be considered "a
bad bargain" for the University.

In the *Story of the University*, however, it is related that
"in course of time the Senatus felt quite aggrieved at the
result of the bargain, and Professor Leslie stated to the
Universities Commission, in 1826, that "thirty was the number
of surgeons when this wretched contract was made ; but they
now amount to ninety, of whom about sixty are in the daily

habit of frequenting the library; they roam about the different rooms, distracting the attention of the under-librarian, and they borrow more than six hundred volumes of all kinds for themselves and their apprentices."

These remarks probably offended the sensibilities of the surgeons, especially as they had, since 1823, voluntarily increased the yearly subscription to £20. It is questionable, too, if the University fulfilled all the conditions; if they had done so, it would not have been necessary for the surgeons to apply to Dr Brunton, the Librarian: (1) for use of the periodical publications; (2) for power to obtain books from the library by a written order in case of sickness; and (3) for use of newly published books on an equal footing with the professors.

In answer they were told that at present there was no room except the Senate Hall in which the members of the College could have access to the periodicals, the room in which they were formerly placed having been taken away. To the second, Dr Brunton said, he had not the slightest hesitation in assenting, and as it was reasonable, he had no doubt the Curators would agree to it likewise. To the last, he replied that all parties, professors, members of the College, and students were placed in the same circumstances, and that no book was granted to one which was not accessible to another in priority of application. He also complimented the members making use of the library on their attention to the regulations.

When the intention of the University to raise the point before the Commission became known to the College, they, being unwilling to trespass on the time of the Commissioners, resolved to ascertain from them if a statement on the subject would be welcome, it being the opinion of the College that the Commissioners would not care to interfere with a bargain which, at the time it was made, was considered to be advantageous to both parties, and which had been acted upon for more than half a century.

The College, however, were prepared to defend their rights should occasion require it. Amongst their papers they had a number of letters addressed to successive Presidents of the College by Principal Robertson, in which he said he considered it his duty to give the College certain particulars regarding the library funds. As the practice had fallen into disuse, the

College thought it a good opportunity to apply to the Principal to be furnished with a similar statement annually; and to suggest to the Senatus that although in the present state of the library buildings it had been found necessary to keep the new periodicals in the Senate Hall, to which the members of the College could not. of course expect to be admitted, they trusted that in the new buildings a room would be provided for this purpose, to which they might have ready access.

Although it was known that the University intended making some representation to the Commission on the subject, the College does not seem to have known the exact nature of the report until some few years after it was made. It was not until March 1832 that the attention of the College was called to certain reports regarding an alleged improper use made by its members of the privilege of getting books from the University Library. Some professors and others, it was said, had circulated these reports, which it would have been highly injurious to the College to allow to pass unnoticed. A committee was consequently appointed to investigate the matter, and reported " That it was with regret and surprise, the College found that the Commissioners had received from the professors and their officers a number of *ex parte* statements, attributing to the members of the College abuses in the exercise of their privilege of borrowing books from the University Library, without affording them an opportunity of vindicating themselves."

In dealing with the charges in detail, the committee proved that, according to the library returns, only thirty-six surgeons were making use of the library at the time specified, and that the number of books standing against them amounted to 332 volumes instead of the 600 mentioned in the report. From the same report it was found that the Principal and twenty-seven professors (with whom the surgeons had equal library privileges) had borrowed no less than 976 volumes, or about thirty-five volumes for each, against ten for each of the surgeons. From this it was contended that Sir John Leslie greatly exaggerated both the number of surgeons using the library and the number of books borrowed by them, and that the dealings of the members of the College with the library were on a much smaller scale and on a more equitable footing than those of the professors. On the legality of the original bargain the committee had no wish to pass an opinion, but they thought that there were few bargains to which, after a lapse of about seventy years, both parties would be equally willing to accede as at the time when they were first entered into, and that neither law, morality, nor honourable feeling called upon an individual or an Incorporation to abandon a privilege merely because it was obtained by their forefathers at less cost than that at which it could now be procured.

The present value of the collection of books which was transferred to the University in 1763 was obviously a very unfair test of their value at the time the bargain was made, and it was impossible then to estimate correctly the motives which may have induced the University to accept the proposal of the College. Judging, too, from the talents of the persons engaged in the transaction on the part of the University—viz., Principal Robertson, Dr Monro, and Dr Cullen—there seemed no room for doubting that at the time the bargain was made it was considered as advantageous to the University as to the College. As the report had passed from the hands of the Commissioners into those of the Government, the committee advised that some communication detailing all the facts of the case should be sent to the Lord Advocate, and that, in consideration that these misstatements had never been met by any answer from the College, it would be proper to print and circulate the committee's report amongst those who were in possession of the report of the Commission.

Some months later the Town Council enquired of the College "whether, and upon what terms, the College of Surgeons would be disposed to renounce the right of access to the library now belonging to them." As the College thoroughly appreciated the privilege, and were in no hurry to part with it for any recompense whatever, they replied that as the question was of such importance they were not at present prepared to return any definite answer to the proposals. In this way the University was held to its bargain, but the College, realising perhaps that sooner or later they would be compelled to relinquish their title, now seriously set about forming a collection of books of their own, and, in January 1834, their Librarian reported that the College were in possession of a library containing about 150 volumes, most of which were either bound or half-bound.

In the meantime the College continued their yearly subscription of £20 to the University, but in 1849, in consequence of financial difficulties, it was reduced to £5, the amount under the agreement. This brought a remonstrance from the Town Council, and the College in consequence gave their assurance that as soon as their funds would permit the payment would be resumed either in whole or part.

In 1845, the Misses Abercrombie presented to the College their late father's library consisting of between 900 and 1000 volumes, and from this date the library was placed on a different footing. The year 1855 found the College still making the minimum donation of £5, when the old question was again raised by the University expressing their dissatisfaction that a privilege so valuable should continue to be used in consideration of such a small contribution. In reply, it was explained that although the obligation by the College was of the low amount stated, they had for several years voluntarily voted £20 annually, and that the cause of the discontinuance of that sum arose simply out of the low state of their finances and their greatly diminished income ; they were between £3000 and £4000 in debt at this time, but that as soon as the funds would permit the larger sum would again be resumed.

In this unsatisfactory way things ran on until a climax was reached, in 1860, by the Scottish Universities Commissioners addressing a letter to the College calling their attention to the agreement made in 1764, and stating that the library handed over by the College was of little value, as no use was then made of it. This state of affairs, the Commissioners said, appeared to them impossible to defend or sanction, and looking, as they were bound to do, to the interests of the University, they thought it right frankly to make that statement of their opinion before considering whether they should adopt the course of terminating the connection, or leave it to the College to suggest some arrangement for placing the relations between them and the University on a more equitable and reasonable footing. This might take the form of providing for the payment of an adequate subscription by Fellows using the library, by limiting the privilege now enjoyed, and by subjecting it to reasonable conditions.

In due course the College replied that they were inclined

to think that the Commissioners were neither aware of the precise nature of the transaction under which the privilege in question was acquired, nor of the causes which led to it.   They then reviewed the whole of the proceedings from the commencement, in the course of which it was remarked that it had always been understood that the proposal to unite the Surgeons' Library with that of the University emanated from Principal Robertson, and that the actual amount of the surgeons' subscription was also proposed by him.   For many years after the agreement, which was formally ratified by the Town Council, the College received from the Principal an annual statement of the progress of the library, including the amount of funds collected for its use, and enquiries as to what medical books the surgeons desired to have purchased, all of which indicated that the agreement was for the mutual benefit of both parties.   Whether such a transaction thus solemnly ratified by competent authority, is one deserving of being stigmatised in the unguarded language of Professor Leslie, whose exaggerated, and indeed ludicrous assertions are quoted with apparent approval in the former Commissioners' report, the College were willing to leave it to the Commissioners to say.   The College further stated that they would only consent to entertain the matter upon the understanding that their legal rights under the agreement referred to were distinctly recognised, in which case they were prepared to reconsider the conditions upon which they had access to the library, and to accede to such regulations as might be considered necessary for its beneficial management.

The Commissioners refused to recognise the agreement as legal and perpetually binding on the University, but invited the College to make some proposals which might lead to a reasonable arrangement being concluded between them.   In face of this, Dr Douglas Maclagan, who was President at the time, expressed his opinion that since the Commissioners declined to admit that the College had a legal right to the use of the library, the College ought not *in hoc statu* to make any proposals on the subject.   After some deliberation it was agreed that while reserving in full their legal right, the privileges of the library should be restricted to the resident Fellows, and the number of books which might be borrowed at one time be reduced to ten.   The payment of £5 was of course to be continued, and the question of any extra subscription was to be made a yearly consideration.   As might be expected, these terms were not satisfactory to the University, so the College, after some further negotiations, referred the following queries to Mr Dove Wilson, Advocate, for a legal opinion:—

First.—Is there a subsisting contract between the Corporation of Surgeons and the rulers of the University regarding the library in perpetuity on both parties?

Second.—What is the extent of the privileges acquired by the memorialists under this contract, having regard to the words made use of by the contracting parties and the custom by which these words have been interpreted?

Third.—Have the University Commissioners any jurisdiction or power in the matter which was not possessed by the former patrons of the University?

Mr Wilson's opinion in regard to the first question was that the contract entered into between the parties was as valid and effectual as if the agreement had been embodied in a formal deed under the respective seals of the two Corporations, but he entertained some doubt whether the University authorities in 1763, who were not in the position of absolute proprietors of the library but rather in that of trustees, had power to bind the University in perpetuity to an arrangement whereby the use of the library was (for a scarcely adequate consideration) to be diverted to a certain extent from the use of the University and to be shared with another Corporation . . . . and he thought it would be a question of very great difficulty and nicety to determine whether the University would not be entitled to set aside the agreement if it were found that the use made of the library under it seriously interfered with the primary purposes for which it was intended.

As this practically decided the question, there was nothing left for the College but to give way and to make the best terms they could.   At last it was settled that resident Fellows of the College, on payment of an annual subscription of one guinea, should be entitled to borrow books from the library, but not to have more than ten volumes in their possession at one time, provided that the College continued their yearly contribution of £5 and gave up their claim to any privilege granted to them under a former arrangement.   This concluded the matter, and the College then recorded their satisfaction that an amicable arrangement had been come to between them and the University.

The subscription was continued until 1887 when, as no books had been borrowed for eight years, and the College having in consequence paid £40 without obtaining any return, the agreement was annulled.

The College Portraits.—As the surgeons found it impossible to house the few hundred books which then composed their library, or to take care of the few curiosities consigned to their charge, it would not have been surprising had they failed also to preserve their collection of portraits, which now form such an interesting feature of the College.

The portrait of James Borthwick (the first surgeon-apothecary in Edinburgh), dated 1645, is the oldest by twenty years; the collection, however, may be said to have been formed between the years 1695-1710, when a large number came into possession of the College; they are mostly the work of Sir John Medina. After Sir John's death in 1710, they were washed and varnished by his servant, Andro Hay, who received "a guinea of gold" for his trouble, and the accounts show that Andro Sim of Carlton was paid £1, 18s. 6d. for taking down and putting up 37 pictures and furnishing them with iron rings, staples, and cleeks, a transaction which he described on receiving payment of the money, as "a guid bargain at six pence per piece." A note at the bottom of the receipt—stating that "the Calling having heard this account, it was agreed by them that each one shall pay for his own ring"—is scored out.

In 1720, an extraordinary Minute was registered calling upon five members of the Corporation to have their pictures drawn and placed in the Hall, or at least to satisfy the Calling that each of them had had a first sitting "before Whitsunday next," under the penalty that none of them should have liberty to book prentices or vote in the College affairs till such time as they obey this order. Although this order was never rescinded, not one of these gentlemen's pictures now appear in the collection, nor are they mentioned in any list now in possession of the College. After Sir John Medina's death, the old custom of members presenting their portraits fell into

THREE PORTRAITS FROM THE HALL OF THE ROYAL COLLEGE OF SURGEONS.

1. James Borthwick (1615-1675), the first special demonstrator of Anatomy in Edinburgh (Photo by D. M. Greig, Esq., F.R.C.S.).
2. Archibald Pitcairn (1652-1713), Professor of Medicine in Leyden and Edinburgh.
3. James Hamilton, Deacon of Surgeons' Incorporation when first Anatomical "Course" was held in 1702.

(*Blocks lent by Dr J. D. Comrie.*)

[*To face page* 94.

abeyance, and although, in 1724, there was a motion to have the pictures of the members drawn, and " Mr James Robertson recommended to talk with John Steill, vintner, concerning the fitness of a person to draw them," nothing was really done. Since that date comparatively few portraits have been presented to the Corporation.

When the College removed to the Hall in Nicolson Street, a curious incident occurred with regard to the portraits. When it was proposed that a sum of £30 should be expended in restoring the pictures, a member objected to the College being put to any expense in cleaning or preserving the portraits of John, Duke of Lauderdale, and the Duke of Cumberland, which he understood were in the collection. Strange to say, neither of these portraits now adorns the walls of the College, nor is there any evidence that they ever did; it is, therefore, curious that such a remark should have come from a Fellow who soon after occupied the Presidential Chair without first satisfying himself as to the accuracy of his information. There is certainly a record of some picture frames having been destroyed by fire in 1839, but as the pictures belonging to them are said to have been left in the Hall there is nothing to suggest that the offending portraits disappeared in that way. In the year mentioned, it appears that an examination into the state of the pictures generally revealed the fact that a number of frames had been sent "*some years ago*" to a Mr Hatton, but had never been returned. After having been repeatedly written to, Mr Hatton made a statement "that three years past in December last, his workshop was burned to the ground, that unfortunately he was not insured, and that everything contained in it was entirely consumed, that he remembered some oval frames being in the loft over the shop, which had been there for several years, that he did not understand for what purpose they had been sent, and no application was ever made for them till he received a letter from Dr Gairdner." As Mr Hatton was a carver and gilder, the frames were probably sent to him to be repaired. There was no need, therefore, for the pictures to accompany them, and as the fire was said to be purely accidental no legal claim could be made for their loss.

The School of Medicine.—In 1832, the ground behind the Hall was let to Dr David Boswell Reid on a lease of ten years, for the purpose of erecting rooms for teaching chemistry.   In 1849, Mr John Struthers, on behalf of the extra-academical lecturers, approached the College with a view to turning these rooms into a complete medical school.   The prospect of the extra-mural medical school at that time was not encouraging. The attendance at the classes was small, and the supply of teachers was said to be scarcely such as to afford even one lecturer on each branch of study, and as there did not appear any reason to expect much improvement as the school then stood, its extinction was not improbable.   That such a calamity would be prejudicial to the interests of the College was quite clear, as students would then resort elsewhere for their medical education, and probably also for their diplomas.

To prevent this, as far as possible, the lecturers proposed uniting together in a permanent school, and if the College encouraged them it was thought that the change would not only prove beneficial to the lecturers but to the College and the students as well.   In order to meet the lecturers, the College, although considerably in debt at the time, bought up the old premises of Dr Reid, and at an expense of over £1200 erected new buildings in every way suitable for the purpose.   The lecturers in this way became lessees of the school provided for them on a lease of ten years at £180 per annum.   The College some time previously had given their sanction to the advertisements of the extra-academical lecturers appearing under their name, but lest this might appear to identify the College too closely with one section of the lecturers, it was decided to withdraw the headline of " Royal College of Surgeons " and substitute that of " Surgeons' Hall."   In this way the lecture-rooms came to be known as Surgeons' Hall.

BORTHWICK'S TOMB IN GREYFRIARS CHURCHYARD.

[*To face page* 96.

CHAPTER VI

PERSONALITIES AND INCIDENTS

Alexander Monteath—Honorary Freemen of the Incorporation—Professional Disputes — Scarcity of Barbers — Augmentation of their numbers—John Baptista—Dr Taylor, the Itinerant Oculist—The Darien Scheme—Financial Position of the Calling.

Alexander Monteath.—As Alexander Monteath was Deacon of the Incorporation when the new Hall and Anatomical Theatre were erected in 1697, some facts regarding him may not be out of place here. He was a son of James Monteath of Auldcathie, the representative of the second (or Stuart) line of Earls of Monteath. After serving his apprenticeship to William Borthwick he went abroad for several years to study his profession. He was admitted a master-surgeon in 1691, and was deacon in 1695-96. He was one of the distinguished early teachers of anatomy, having, in 1694, obtained a special grant of anatomical material from the Town Council, as well as the use of a room for dissections. After three years, although he took part in the public dissections, he abandoned the formal teaching of anatomy and commenced a course of instruction in chemistry.

In 1700, he petitioned Parliament " that the art discovered by him to draw Spirits from malt equal in goodness to true French Brandie may be declared a manufactory with the same privileges and immunities as are granted to other manufactories."

He was elected deacon for the second time in 1699, but was removed from office by a decree of the Secret Council at the instance of the magistrates immediately after his election.

Before entering into the cause of Monteath's downfall, it might be well to explain that the Deacons of Trades had chosen Monteath to be their Deacon-Convener for the year, and at one of their meetings in the Magdalen Chapel in October—the month before he was deposed, a resolution was passed to take

certain proceedings against the Town Council. Before taking
active steps in the matter, each of the deacons had to obtain
the sanction of his respective Craft.   In laying the case
before the surgeons, Monteath read a note containing the
resolve of the Trades to raise declarator against the Town
Council.   Headed "Memorandum for the Trades of Edinburgh,"
it asks that a "declarator before the Lords of Session may be
raised upon the following articles, viz. :—

"First, of the fourteen deacons' rights and priveleges in electing the
Bailies of the suburbs and in filling up the Council of Edinburgh when
a vacancy is of an old Magistrate and in electing of the Dean of Gild's
council, in all which, by the Sett, the extraordinary deacons ought to
have a vote. Second, Against the Magistrates' extravagant expenses in
Taverns.   Third, Against the Magistrates' burgess ticket.   The
extravagant earnest penny at rouping the Common good; the Lord
Provost's wines, more than half a tun in the year and the extravagant
sums given to the Treasurer of gratuity at clearing his accounts.
Likeas the said Alex. Monteath, deacon, declares that it was the
unanimous resolution of all the deacons to call their respective
Incorporations and to repeat to them these articles, and if they be
satisfied that each Craft make an act empowering their deacons to
vote and consent to the laying on of what stent [tax] shall be found
necessary by the Convener and the rest of the deacons and Trades
Councillors at their meetings for carrying their declarator to its final
period."

The Calling agreed to the whole of the above articles and
were of opinion that the declarator should be carried to its
final issue.   Nothing, however, came of it, but it led to
Monteath being deprived of his office.   For the sequel of events
we must refer to a pamphlet entitled *The History of the Good
Town of Edinburgh ; Wherein The private Management as well
as the public Transactions of that City are clearly related*, first
published in the year 1700, ("Price Four Pence"), which, in
describing some municipal business, goes on to say :—

"The election at Michaelmas 1699 draws near; and although there
was no Provost to be changed this year, yet a Council must be had that
may be fit Tools against the next election, that a good Provost might
be secured to succeed himself; and although the ordinary Politics
were used at the election of the Deacons, yet things there succeeded
not as he intended; And particularly, Mr *Monteath* was chosen to be

Deacon of the Surgeons and Deacon Convener of the Trades, who though one of Sir *Archibald Mure's* Minions, being the only Man that was most active in bringing him on the Provostship for the second time at Michaelmas 1696: yet, having some Experience of his Carriage on the Council when he was former Deacon-convener, he was afraid he should be uneasy to him and thwart some of his Designs, not so much out of Zeal for the Town's Interest, as out of Ill-nature and the Ill-will he bore his Lordship; and really there may be some reason to believe it; For if Mr Monteath's Zeal for the Town's Interest had been what he pretended, the Declarator which he raised in Name of the Trades upon Points of Privilege and some Mismanagements, should have comprehended a certain Act of Council, which might, in Time, have been a Greater Bulwark against Faction and Mismanagement, than all these imaginary Privileges, scarcely worth a Farthing, and might have secured against Mismanagement in Time coming; and that is an Act of Council standing in full Force, never yet repealed, nor so much as ever proposed by any Man to be rescinded, though there is not a Member of the Council but knows it, *That no Deacon or Tradesman upon the Council shall be employed in the Town's Work.*

"This Act the Deacon-convener was not ignorant of and knew the bad Effects and Consequences of its not being observed, yet would not raise a Declarator upon that; So that most reasonably it may be concluded that the Declarator raised by him, was not so much out of Zeal for the Town's Interest as to gratify his own Humour. But whatever were his Motives, the Provost soon found a Way to get him turned out of the Council, by raising a Process against him before the Privy Council for protesting against the Bailie of the *Canongate's* being received, after he was, as he thought, illegally elected; so the Privy Council turns him out, and deservedly, for his Indiscretion."

While this was the ostensible cause of Monteath's expulsion, there is reason to believe that deeper political considerations were involved, for he was known to be an enthusiastic Jacobite. Monteath was unanimously nominated " Preses " of the Calling, in 1701, on the occasion of a member refusing to act as deacon after having been elected, which shows that he still retained the confidence of the Craft and that any differences that existed were between the Town Council and Monteath, and not between him and the Incorporation. In this case the Preses would preside over the affairs of the Calling but would have no voice in the town's concerns such as the deacon had.

Honorary Freemen of the Incorporation.—At no time

during its career had the Calling been on better terms with the Town Council than it was during the period when Sir Andrew Ramsay was Lord Provost of the City. During his term of office the Craft had the advantage of a friend at Court. He had assisted them in many ways, and so great was their regard for him that, when, in the year 1671, they decided to admit honorary freemen into their Incorporation, he was their first selection. In deciding to take this important step, which they conceived would promote the welfare of their famous Institution, their object was to select persons of power and place and of known good affection to their art and Society, who would help them in maintaining and preserving their liberties and privileges, "although they were not to use nor exercise the practical part of their profession." In honour of the occasion the deacon and masters invited Sir Andrew "to a treat," at which he was presented with the Diploma of the Incorporation with its seal attached. In choosing Sir Andrew Ramsay to be the first recipient of the greatest honour they had power to bestow, the Craft said they were mindful of the many eminent and singular favours conferred upon them by him, and his active and successful endeavours both in preventing many threatened encroachments upon their rights, as likewise in enlarging and amplifying them. He had also appeared as their patron and had evidenced his very great affection and respect for them and for the whole art of Surgery.

In 1672, the Duke of Lauderdale was admitted an honorary freeman, and two years later was presented with an address to commemorate the signal services performed by him in favour of the Trades in general and of the surgeons in particular. On this occasion the deacon and masters went in a body to the Abbey of Holyrood House and there with much pomp and ceremony presented his Grace with the following address :—

"Unto Your Grace My Lord duke of Lauderdale & His Majesty's High Commissioner for this his ancient Kingdom of Scotland. MAY IT PLEASE YOUR GRACE—The Deacon and Incorporation of the Chirurgeons of Edinburgh humbly shews that your Grace hath done our Incorporation that honor and favour to accept to be one of our number amongst us and opposed all infringements of our liberties in Parliament and of all the Incorporations of Crafts of Edinburgh and Kingdom of Scotland of which we are very sensible and heartily thank your Grace for the same   And for our Incorporation of the Chirurgeons of Edinburgh Our Kings and princes have been pleased to exercise that art and bestowed as large liberties favours and respects upon the same and several members thereof on all occasion as to any Chirurgeons within the Dominions as is evident in Records.   So amongst the rest of your Grace's favours We the Incorporation of Chirurgeons of Edinburgh humbly supplicate your Grace to represent to his Majesty that we are very sensible of his Majesty's and his Royal Ancestors the favours put upon us, and according to our power shall express our loyalty and obedience to his Majesty as is our duty at all occasions, and wish him long to be our King and Master, and earnestly and humbly long for the day that his Royal Majesty might honour this his ancient Incorporation to be a member thereof."

The Duke died in August 1682, and, on 3rd April 1683, the deacon acquainted the Calling that he had been invited by the Lord Provost, with as many members as he should think fit, to attend the Duke of Lauderdale's funeral "upon Thursday next, being the 5th of April," whose corpse was to be transported from the Kirk of Inveresk to his burial place at Haddington.   Eleven masters were selected and ordered to provide themselves with horses and wait upon the deacon to the burial, under a penalty of ten pounds Scots if he be absent.

Among some loose papers in the College archives is a document which bears to be an act of admission as honorary freeman in favour of Sir George Mackenzie, Lord Register, although this name does not appear either in the list of Honorary Fellows now recognised by the College, or in the College Records.   Drawn up in the same terms as other admissions, and certified to be "extracted forth of the Records of the Incorporation" by the Clerk, it appears never to have been engrossed in the Minute Book, although three other honorary freemen—The Duke of Queensberry, the Marquess of Atholl, and the Earl of Perth—were admitted on the same day, 13th December 1684.   Strangely enough the Minutes of that date, which include the names of the other three honorary freemen, are begun in the middle of the sheet, the upper part being left blank.   But as this blank space precedes the Minutes it can hardly have been left for the insertion of the Act in question if the original had been mislaid.   Again, the Minute ordaining the admission of the honorary freemen states

distinctly that three are to admitted, not four, which would
have been the number had Sir George Mackenzie been included.
It is matter for speculation as to whether Sir George refused
the honour, whether the Calling at the last minute resolved to
cancel the nomination, or the candidate failed to secure election,
or whether, having been elected, the fact was never recorded.

It may be mentioned that, on his return from Culloden,
the Duke of Cumberland was made an honorary freeman
of each of the City Crafts, as the best evidence they could give
of their "Dutiful Respect" and "sincere acknowledgments"
for his coming to that part of the Kingdom "to maintain,
protect, and defend our valuable Constitution of Church and
State, most unjustly and unreasonably attacked by the present
rebellion." The Act was presented to His Royal Highness
in a "gold box, properly ornamented," which cost 1212 pounds
Scots, the surgeons' portion being 105 pounds 3 shillings.

Professional Disputes.—About this time the Craft had
frequent occasion to exercise its authority in settling disputes
among its own members. It was found necessary, for example,
to ordain that "none shall take another man's shop over his
head, nor dwell in one stairhead without permission." It
sometimes happened, generally through some trifling misunderstanding, that two surgeons claimed the same patient.
If an amicable settlement could not be made between themselves, the matter was usually referred to the Calling. The
first case of this kind appears in 1663, when a man applied
to the Incorporation to decide whose patient he really was.
From a Minute it appears that during the absence from town
of a surgeon who had been attending him, the patient had
called in another surgeon who continued his visits after the
return of the original attendant. The patient's complaint was
that after he had been dressed by the second surgeon the first
removed the dressings and applied his own. The Craft enacted
a law to the effect that no prentice or servant shall dress a
patient or offer to attend him in any way unless his master
has been sent for ; and if the patient should send for two or
three masters, the master or servant arriving first shall consider
him as his patient, and none shall offer to take the patient out
of his hands until he has been satisfied by the patient and
clearly put off.

Another case which the Craft refused to deal with and ordered the defendant to be brought before the Sheriff of Edinburgh, occurred in 1698, when George Turnbull, surgeon-apothecary in Musselburgh, complained against Archibald Smith, surgeon in Fisherrow, for removing his bandages from off Margaret Wyllie in Musselburgh, her shoulder bone being broken, and putting on his own.

In the year 1678, the privilege of barbering within the town, which the Calling had enjoyed for so many years, was menaced by the Secret Council, who in a quiet way suggested to the deacon that a Canongate barber might be made a free barber in Edinburgh, but the surgeons deputed a committee to reply in the negative to the Laird of Lundie, " in such sober and discreet terms as they should think fit."

Scarcity of Barbers.—A few years later (1682), so great was the scarcity of barbers in the town that the Council made a strong representation on the subject to the Incorporation. The decrease in the number of barber-surgeons in the City was probably due to the advent of the surgeon-apothecary in 1657, from which date pharmacy had a greater attraction to the apprentices than the barber craft. Formerly the majority of surgeons were also barbers, for example, in 1658 out of a total number of seventeen members, thirteen were barbers as well as surgeons. From then onwards the number of barbers gradually became smaller, until at the time of the Council's complaint only six surgeon-barbers and three " relicts " (freeman's widows, licensed by the Incorporation) were following the trade within the City walls.

It may also be noted that, since 1658, surgeons on entering the Craft were no longer termed " free barbers " as well as " free surgeons " in their Act of Admission; but this did not prevent them from barbering if so inclined. In fact, one or two who became freemen after that date did follow the barber craft, but with these exceptions new members evinced no desire to combine the art of barbering with that of surgery, Consequently, as time went on, and the older members died off without their places being taken by younger men there was a scarcity of barbers.

The year 1682 thus saw the passing of the barber-surgeon not in consequence of any law or statute, but by the surgeon himself voluntarily ceasing to follow a trade which obviously no longer appealed to him. In their letter, dated 26th July 1682, the magistrates drew the attention of the Incorporation to the "scarcity of good and qualified persons within the City who have skill to trim and barberise, so that a considerable number of the inhabitants are forced to go to the suburbs to be trimmed, as also it has occasioned many complaints to be made by noblemen, gentlemen, and others resorting to the town, that they cannot be conveniently served by persons of that employment within the town, And to the effect that the lieges may not have sufficient ground to clamour upon that account, Therefor they recommend it to the Incorporation to take some effectual course that the City be furnished with a competent and suitable number of persons skilled in the art of cutting hair and taking off of beards . . . and if they do not speedily fall on some course to answer the expectations of the lieges, they will not espouse or own their interest in case any attempt should be made by application to superior judication." To this the Incorporation two days later replied that to prevent any danger, inconvenience, or hazard that they might hereafter sustain if they refused so reasonable a desire, they were ready to admit a number of able, expert, and qualified barbers in the City so that the inhabitants should have no cause for complaint in the future. The Calling lost no time in fulfilling their promise. The same day they admitted five barbers into the burgh on payment of 500 merks each. They also permitted to be barbers in the Canongate without payment of any kind, in consideration of their unfortunate position, two Frenchmen who, in their petition for admission to the Craft, declared that owing to the persecution of the Christian Protestants, they had been forced to flee their country for safety of their lives, their estates and means having been taken from them. They produced certificates from the ministers and elders of the places where they were born and where they had resided since they came to this country, that they had behaved themselves Christianly and soberly in the practice of the Protestant faith in "hearing of the Word and participating in the sacraments."

A Minute of 1684 shows that a few of the older surgeons still stuck to barbering, but they were in such a decayed state that the Calling, in consideration of simple barbers having been admitted into the town, dispensed with their quarterly subscriptions.

During the next few years the barbers seem to have been in a bad way. Trade fell off to such an extent that they alleged that they were unable to continue to pay their fees to the Incorporation. On this being represented to the Treasurer, the whole of the defaulting barbers both in town and in suburbs were ordered to appear before the Calling. Fourteen failed to comply with these instructions and were fined twelve shillings for absence. Three years later these same barbers were again summoned to answer any complaint that might be laid to their charge, but only one appeared—the remainder being again fined. The barbers were now required to sign an agreement that if they transgressed any of the Incorporation's laws, such as exercising surgery or (if a suburban barber) barber craft within the town, they *ipso facto*, without any further declaration or process of law, should at once lose their freedom.

The case of one George Smith, is probably typical of the condition of the barbers of Edinburgh about the year 1690. Admitted barber in 1683, upon a promise of payment of 800 merks, he paid 100 pounds Scots in ready money and gave for the use of the Craft " a skeleton with a fine case and a lock and key thereon." " But seeing," so runs the account, " that it is true that trimming, as an employment, is so dead and at such a low ebb, and that the supplicant cannot get so much by his calling as to maintain himself, and having a great charge of his poor aged mother, whose means, and his own, were for security put into the hands of the deceased George, Earl of Caithness, who being now dead had none to represent him, whereby the supplicant's expectation is now perished."

Another barber offered three dollars in payment of his indebtedness to the Calling, which were accepted. An immediate act of charity, however, acquits the Calling of any suspicion of avarice, for this very sum (perhaps the identical dollars) was given the same day to Lodovick Lindsay, a poor man, who submitted to the Calling a petition for charity.

A petition addressed to the Deacon of the Craft illustrates

a curious custom which prevailed amongst the Incorporated Trades in Edinburgh during the 17th century. Dated 18th March 1698, it runs as follows: "John Naysmyth, Wright, applied to the Calling that he was employed by the friends of the deceased Katherine Brown, widow of Peter Noyer (one of their own number) for making her dead coffin upon assurance that the Calling would pay for it as it was the custom and practice of all other Corporations in this burgh whose freeman and their wives and children are unable to do the same—which he very honestly and faithfully made but had received no payment or satisfaction from her friends who were not in a position to do so—and therefore made application to the Craft for payment, it not being reasonable that he being a mere tradesman should want payment." The Treasurer was instructed to pay him twelve pounds Scots.

In spite of all the Calling's laws and statutes, the barbers both in town and in suburbs practised their craft on the Sabbath day so publicly and openly that complaints were made by the Kirk Session. To guard against this "great scandal to the profession" visitors were appointed to search for the offenders and report them to the Calling.

In 1686, there was admitted, at the earnest request of James, Earl of Perth, Lord High Chancellor of Scotland, a free barber in Edinburgh by name Daniel Valentine. Some correspondence which passed between his Lordship and the Calling regarding Valentine's freedom is still extant. It consists of two letters addressed to Dr Christopher Irvine, Edinburgh. In the first, dated "Castle Drummond," 4th October 1686, his Lordship says:—

"My servant Daniel Valentine being already a freeman of the town of Edinburgh, and desirous to set up for a livelyhood as a barber there, but wanting his freedom in that trade, I earnestly recommend his affair to you, and desire that at your first meeting with the Society of Chirurgeons and Barbers, you would [tell] them that if they will give him his freedom for shaving and cutting of hair, or what els is propper for a Barber only, I will take it as a particular kindness done to Your affectionate Servt. PERTH."

The other, written a fortnight later, runs:—

"Sir, This comes to give you thanks for your endeavours with your Society in behalf of my servant Valentine, and so desire you to tell them that I am very sensible of their kindness in admitting him a member of their Incorporation at my desire, and that as occasion offers, it shall not be forgotten by   Your assured friend,   PERTH."

It is satisfactory to record that the position of the barbers soon improved.   In February 1696, the strength of the Incorporation had increased to twenty-six surgeons and thirty-four barbers.   The latter were distributed as follows: In Edinburgh 19, in the Canongate 10, in Leith 4, and in Portsburgh 1.   As their quarterly subscriptions had been regularly paid for some time, we may reasonably presume they were all prosperous.

John Baptista.—In 1676 the surgeons were confronted with an invasion of their liberties in a form quite new to them. A mountebank named John or Joanna Baptista had come to the town and applied to the magistrates for permission to set up his stage and sell his drugs and medicines to the public.   So seriously was the matter taken that the deacon convened a special meeting of the Craft, who at once resolved to oppose Baptista's action, and formed a committee to confer with the apothecaries, who agreed to unite with them and to pay one half of the expenses incurred.   A week later the deacon reported that he had consulted Sir George Mackenzie, and that he had drawn up answers for the Calling to be given to the Town Council for the mountebank to see and reply to by the next Council day.   It was also proposed by the deacon to write to the Duke of Lauderdale and to Dr Irvine to procure a warrant from His Majesty, prohibiting not only this mountebank but all others who might attempt to prejudice their liberties.   In the meantime, in spite of the combined efforts of the surgeons and apothecaries, Baptista erected his stage between the head of Niddry's Wynd and Blackfriars' Wynd, and there "vended his drugs, powder, and medicaments, for the which he received a great abundance of money."   On 31st January 1677, the committee craved the Provost to use his influence with the Council to give orders for the taking down of Baptista's stage, as the time allowed him by the Council had elapsed ; but apparently the Council conceived they had no jurisdiction over mountebanks and it was not until some weeks later that he was deposed.   On 21st March the Council reported that, in response to a letter written by the deacon to the Duke of Lauderdale enclosing a supplication to His Majesty craving warrant for the debarring of mountebanks and all others from encroaching upon their privileges, a reply had been received from His Majesty recommending the Calling to the Privy Council and Town Council of Edinburgh, who were thereafter to maintain them in their just rights. Although nothing more is heard of John Baptista, something of the kind was again attempted, in 1696, by Dr Arnold Kilmer, who desired to erect a stage and practise surgery within the town. The application for this privilege was made on behalf of Dr Kilmer by William M'Lean, "Master of His Majesty's Revells."

"Dr" Taylor, the Itinerant Oculist.—A similar incident agitated the Incorporation in the year 1744, when an oculist styling himself Dr Taylor came to Edinburgh and advertised himself as possessed of remarkable gifts in dealing with diseases of the eye. In order to expose his claims and publicly to disown all connection with this " doctor," seven of the surgeons, including Drummond and Monro, requested the deacon to summon a meeting of the Incorporation, but, as the deacon was supposed to bear a friendly feeling towards the object of their resentment, and might neglect to take action if he possibly could, they took the precaution of having their wishes conveyed in a somewhat deliberate fashion. At the meeting in question, the deacon explained that it had been called by him in compliance with a letter from his brethren—which had been left at his house by a notary public—to the effect that unless he summoned the Calling to a meeting by a certain date, they would themselves meet and proceed as if he were present with them. The deacon further represented that he was conscious of no reason for his being subjected to such an indignity, and challenged every member of the Society to give any evidence of his acting a partial, far less an arbitrary part in his office. He never did, and could affirm he never would have refused to call a meeting at the desire of any one member. He thought that most of those who had signed the letter had not done so with a desire to affront him. Probably, he continued, they did not so much as know it was to be delivered in the manner it was ; as for those who did, he left them—if they had any ingenuity left—to the cutting reflection that they did it without any cause and had only discovered their own temper. To which the reply was made that, at the last meeting, he (the deacon) had signified to some of the members privately, that he wished Dr Taylor had a diploma as an honorary member of the Incorporation. They therefore judged that he would not willingly call a meeting which was not intended for advancing the credit of the doctor, and, consequently, took that method of procuring one. It was then proposed that the following advertisement should be published in the Edinburgh newspapers and that copies should be transmitted to England and elsewhere at the Incorporation's expense :—

"Surgeons' Hall, 9th July 1744.—Whereas the itinerant Oculist, Dr Taylor, has of late represented himself in the Edinburgh newspapers as a most applauded and successful Operator and Physician for the Diseases of the Eye ; and as he has caused a paper to be clandestinely printed here, in imitation of a column of the newspapers, with a design of dispensing it in the places where he intends to go in quest of patients, and thereby to persuade the public, 'That his lectures have been constantly attended by the Chief of the Faculty in this University, and by the most eminent of the Faculty, etc., that he has extraordinary abilities in the cure of Diseases of the Eye' ; and that he has performed what he promised at his arrival here, of curing all the poor, gratis ; We the Surgeons of Edinburgh, think ourselves obliged, in justice to the public, and in vindication of our own characters, to give the following acount of the matter—

"Dr Taylor's earnest solicitations, his strong assertions of the SURPRISINGLY curious things he was to say and do, moved the Curiosity of some of our members so far as to make them attend his lectures and operations, but to their great disappointment his lectures contained little more than his own Encomium and a frivolous Theory ; none of the Professors of Physic and Surgery of the University have given him so much countenance as to be present at his lecture. The Doctor's Operations and Medicines have been attended with remarkable little success ; few, very few, have been cured, several have been hurt ; and many, after having long undergone very violent pain and evacuations, have been thankful for being restored to the state in which the Doctor found them, by their ordinary Physicians and Surgeons, who saved others from suffering by hurtful operations which the Doctor proposed. The Operation for Cataracts, which the Doctor says is attended, when he performs, 'with little if any pain or inflammation, and without even a possibility of a relapse,' has created excessive pain and inflammation to many of his patients ; and we are informed only of two of the many Cataracts which he has couched that have not returned; all the others having already returned, after a first, second, or even third Operation;—After the strictest enquiry we cannot learn that one person under any degree of a Gutta Serena has been cured.—None, so far as we know, have been healed by him of the Fistula lachrymalis, Squinting, and other cases which he undertook to cure.—At his first arrival he performed Operations to some Poor, gratis; soon however he took money from everyone who could procure it by either borrowing or begging, and some, so very poor, that Gentlemen who were informed of what he had done obliged him to return the money:—and at present he has presented Bills and commenced Lawsuits for obtaining exorbitant Fees for the most trifling Operation."

It was then moved that the following memorial should be given to the Town Council, with one of the foregoing advertisements:—

"The Incorporation of Surgeons humbly presume that the Hon. Town Council ordered a Burgess Ticket to be made out for Dr Taylor, Oculist to His Majesty, from the generous principle of encouraging virtue and merit; The Incorporation is persuaded that the Hon. Council is now convinced, from the want of success in his Operation, and from the general opinion of the proper Judges of the matters, how much they have been misled in this particular by wrong information. The Surgeons, therefore, humbly request the Hon. Council to do what is in their power to prevent the bad uses which Dr Taylor may make of that honour, and to vindicate the honour of our Society from the Imputation of having been aiding in procuring it."

At the next meeting of the College the deacon reported that he had presented the Memorial and Advertisement to the Town Council, and moved that the Council would consider their merits, but as none of the Council seconded his motion the Lord Provost gave it as his opinion "that they had nothing to do with that affair, and ordered that nothing relative to it should be recorded in their books."

The Darien Scheme.—Like so many more in Scotland, the Surgeons became involved in the affairs of the Company of Scotland Trading to Africa and the Indies, commonly known as the Darien Scheme. In this venture they invested the sum of £600 stg., and Monteath, the deacon, was appointed to represent the Calling at the meetings of the Company. When the bubble burst this money was looked upon as lost, but about ten years later some £362, 8s. were recovered.

Financial Position of the Calling.—The various calls upon the funds of the Incorporation left them for a time in rather low water, and within a period of twenty years from 1686, they had borrowed no less than 25,000 merks. One half of this amount was advanced by various members of the Craft in sums ranging from 1000 to 5000 merks, Pierre Castele, alias "La Perle," being responsible for the remainder. On one occasion 5500 merks were obtained from the latter to pay the wrights and masons, the African Company, and for defending the rights of the Craft. Even as late as 1707 they were so short of money that each member paid two years' subscription in advance. In spite of all this the surgeons, in 1692, found it convenient to lend 3000 merks to the "guid toun," which was repaid in one year, plus 120 pounds Scots interest.

CHAPTER VII

THE SURGEON-APOTHECARIES

The Surgeon-Apothecaries—Incorporation of the College of Physicians by Royal Charter—Visitation of the Drug Shops—The New Charter.

The Surgeon-Apothecaries.—It has already been mentioned (Chap. III., p. 36) that about the year 1657 a rapprochement took place between the barber-surgeons and the apothecaries, and from that time onwards a certain number of persons combined the practice of pharmacy with that of surgery.

To understand the position of the surgeons and the apothecaries, however, we must go back to the year 1643, when, in consequence of threatened differences between them, the Town Council convened a meeting of representatives of the two parties, which resulted in a mutual agreement that the application of searcloths to dead bodies, all manual operations and applications about dead or living bodies, and the curing of diseases such as "tumours, wounds, ulcers, luxations, fractures, and the curing of virolls, etc.," should belong to the surgeon, while the administration of medicine inwardly was to be the only liberty of the apothecary.

This agreement, which became an Act of the Town Council, clearly defined the respective privileges of the surgeons and the apothecaries. The union which took place between them in 1657 resulted in what, until then, had been unknown in Edinburgh—the surgeon-apothecary.

This combination was due to the efforts of a small body of surgeons who recognised the danger of an uncontrolled sale of drugs by inexperienced persons. The apothecaries, fully assured of the necessity of the movement, joined with them, and together made application to the magistrates to grant to them (the apothecaries) the right to examine and test the abilities and qualifications of all who intended to practise the "arte of apothecarie" within the burgh ; and

112

that all who were not so found qualified should be prohibited from practice.   They also requested that the Council
should from time to time choose two apothecaries "to
visit the sufficiency of all sorts of drugs, and where they
find any fault or insufficiency to report the same to the
magistrates."

The petition bears sixteen signatures, four of which may
be recognised as belonging to surgeons, including James
Borthwick and Thomas Kincaid, who assumed the additional
title of apothecary from that time.   In granting the request
the magistrates declared that the Act in favour of the surgeon-
apothecaries and apothecaries is "in no way of intention to
erect them into a Corporation, but merely for the improvement
of the said art, and good of the people."

As a result of this Act pharmacy received more attention
than had hitherto been bestowed upon it by the surgeon, and
apprentices had now the option of serving their time either
with the surgeon-barber, or with the more advanced surgeon-
apothecary, whose curriculum included the combined arts of
surgery and pharmacy.

The Act of the Town Council was ratified in Parliament
in August 1670, in the following terms :—

"That whereas OUR SOVERAIGNE LORD and estates of Parliament
Understanding That the Art of Chirurgie Is an Ancient worthy and
free art most necessary for the health and lives of his Majesties subjects And that the Incorporation of Chirurgeons and Barbers of
Edinburgh Are an able and famous Incorporation Whereby the leidges
have found large experience of their abilities in peace and war to their
great advantage.   And SICLYKE Understanding That the Art of
Pharmacy Is an Ancient free and necessary art for the health and
lives of his Hienes subjects And that the brotherhood of Apothecaries
and Chirurgeon Apothecaries are an able and famous brotherhood.
And that they have given good .proof thereof.   THEREFORE for
conservation of the healthes and lyves of his Majesties leidges And
for the greater encouragement and increase of their skill and knowledge
in the said Arts respective And for preventing the dangerous practice
of Ignorants and unskilfull people that assume the practice of these
Arts to the loss of the lives of his Majesties good subjects which
having been too frequent OUR SOVERAIGNE LORD with advice and
consent of the estates of this present Parliament has Ratified and
Approven," etc., etc.

H

It will thus be seen that the apothecaries, although under the protection of the surgeons, were not an Incorporated body by themselves, and had no liberty to perform surgical operations even of the simplest kind.

In 1680, a serious dispute arose between the surgeons and the apothecaries, owing to a member of the latter body usurping the functions of the surgeons.

Patrick Cunningham, the offending apothecary, was the son of John Cunningham of Hillness. He had been apprenticed in 1661 to James Borthwick to learn "the Art and Calling of Chirurgie and Pharmacy." In June 1680, Cunningham was charged with opening a vein of the Earl of Carnwath, and with letting the blood of the Lady Lee, thereby encroaching upon the privileges of the surgeons. In consequence of the difficulty in obtaining evidence in cases of "blood-letting, giving of salivations by pills and applications of ointments" by barbers and apothecaries, the magistrates had recently decreed "that any unfreeman found carrying basins or a great case or truce with razors and lances" should be holden as guilty without any further evidence. Being ordered by the deacon, Mr James Nisbet, to appear before the magistrates, Cunningham gave in a bill of advocation to the Lord Ordinary, who remitted it to the bailies as competent judges. Cunningham then appealed to the Court of Session, and eventually the case was ordered to be tried by the whole of the Lords of Council.

In a lengthy plea, Cunningham protested that the surgeons had no legal right to exact an oath from those who desired to practise surgery. To this the surgeons replied that the method of procedure adopted against Cunningham, viz., that of summary citation, was perfectly just and legal and that the Town Council having allowed them the privilege of pursuing unfreemen, they (the Council) allowed a way of procedure suitable to the crime, otherwise, as surgery was so unlike any other trade, a conviction would scarcely ever be obtained or a fine exacted. For example, in the case of a tailor, who dealt in clothes, and a shoemaker in boots and shoes, the clothes or boots might be confiscated, but in the case of the surgeon nothing could be seized upon by way of reparation. The surgeons also explained the difficulty of obtaining witnesses, as in most cases, such as in blood-letting and applying of plasters, no one but the patient and the contravener would probably be present.

The appeal in due course came before the Judges of the Court of Session, but in the meantime the case had taken on a more serious aspect, as it now appeared as the Apothecaries against the Surgeons, the Surgeon-Apothecaries, and the Provost, Bailies, and Council of Edinburgh.

In their pleadings the surgeons asked the Court to decide : "*First*.—Whether surgery and pharmacy were compatible in one person, or if they should be divided in the future. *Second*.— Whether the surgeons might force the apothecaries to depone upon oath when they were pursued for exercising the trade of surgery, time, place, person, and operation being condescended upon. *Third*.—Whether the privileges of the surgeons of Edinburgh extended only *inter concives* or to strangers, so that unfreemen, whether apothecaries or others, could be employed within Edinburgh to exercise any surgical operation."

The apothecaries claimed that the callings of pharmacy and surgery should separate, they being two distinct trades and employments, the attending and following of either of which was sufficient for any one man, that the combining of those trades was allowed by the magistrates to conciliate the deacon of that trade in order to favour them in the election of the magistracy. The present surgeons and their successors who jointly practise both trades should make their selection and be restricted to one only in time coming. That apprentices should then be booked to the trade chosen by their master, and not in respect to the two employments at one time.

"That the trade of surgery having been erected by the Seal of Cause as a distinct employment in the Kingdom ought not to be confounded with any other. That the declarator is founded upon the Decreet-Arbitral of King James VI. whereby all trades are ordained to be erected and distinguished from others."

The surgeons based their reply on the terms of their Seal of Cause, which gave them the right to receive apprentices into their trade, to make them freemen, and to pursue all unfreemen. They claimed that they had always been privileged to practise pharmacy, and that as surgeon-apothecaries they were eminently capable of exercising both employments.

In the end their Lordships found for the apothecaries, viz. : That the two callings of surgery and pharmacy were no longer to be used by one and the same person, although the surgeons might buy and sell simples as a druggist or merchant did, and compound such drugs as were necessary for surgical and external applications, yet they were not to compound a medicine to be taken inwardly by the mouth.

In the course of the argument on the count relating to the privileges of the surgeons and the limits of their jurisdiction, a suggestion was made that the advice and counsel of some " disinterested, learned and skilful physicians " should be taken, and the judges recommended that three of the Lords should call Dr Stevenson, elder, Dr Hay, Dr Balfour, and Dr Burnet to give their opinions on the points controverted.

To this course the surgeons objected : they "humbly con- ceived no necessity to call for the opinion of the physicians about the bounds and limits of their calling, seeing their gifts and grants were as specially, distinctly and clearly designed as men's wits or words could express them, for since the question was not whether the apothecaries had as much skill to apply a searcloth or draw blood as a surgeon had, neither was the question whether an apothecary might apply plasters as well as make them, or cure tumours, etc." The only question was whether manual operations and applications upon the body, and particularly phlebotomy and the application of searcloths and curing the specialities mentioned in their Charters, was not only proper and due to them to exercise exclusive of the apothecaries and all others . . . though all the physicians in Scotland should affirm that an apothecary may apply a searcloth, draw blood and cure the viroll, yet certainly the Lords, in point of right, must find that the apothecaries cannot do the same . . . ."

The surgeons feared that the physicians would be biased in favour of the apothecaries, who were to some extent dependent upon them ; and "they thought it possible that the physicians bore them no good will" for having opposed all attempts to erect a College of Physicians in the town.

The physicians, however, were called, and after hearing their views the Lords declared that the surgeons had the only right of phlebotomy within the town and upon the burgesses except in cases of necessity and charity, and where there was no incision made upon the dead bodies and only wrapping to be done, the apothecaries and makers of the searcloth might wrap the body, but when incision was made the application of searcloth to the body was proper to the surgeon.

In terms of the decreet all the surgeon-apothecaries who were actual masters at the time were permitted to pursue both employments during their lifetime, but they had to make their election at once as to which table they would sit at—the surgeons' or the apothecaries'.

In giving judgment the Court ruled that the Act of the Town Council of 1641 ought to be rescinded, as the ratification of it was but surreptitiously purchased by the surgeons from the Parliament without calling the physicians and apothecaries to hear what they had to say; or at least it ought to be restricted to unfreemen and apprentices, and not be extended to skilful and experienced apothecaries.

The Act of 1643, it was declared, should also be rescinded, as it was against common sense and reason to think that the application of a searcloth to a dead body, upon which no anatomical dissection had been made, could be called a surgical operation. "As to the Act of 1655 no shadow of reason can be given for it remaining, except the unwarrantable gratifying of the surgeons for the countenancing and continuing of the factious designs of the magistrates."

The settlement of the litigation was followed by a number of minor domestic quarrels arising out of it.

The finding of the Court was made known in February 1682, at which time the members of the Incorporation included ten surgeons, ten surgeon-apothecaries, and six surgeon-barbers, besides simple barbers.

For declaring in the presence of the Calling that the surgeon-barbers were not concerned in the plea between the Calling and the apothecaries, and that they, not being apothecaries, objected to any money coming out of the Incorporation's box for a matter that did not concern them, one of their number was ordered to be fined and lodged in the Tolbooth during the Calling's pleasure; his conduct, they said, being destructive to their interests and contrary to his oath.

A surgeon and two surgeon-barbers were also summoned for acting in opposition to the Incorporation during the process, joining the apothecaries in presenting a bill to the Lords in the name of the surgeon-barbers, without warrant or commission from them, and with disowning and disclaiming the interest of the Calling in craving a separation, not only of the two employments of surgery and pharmacy, but also of the two tables, thereby doing what they could to destroy and take away from the surgeons the interest of the guildry, notwithstanding they were all guild brothers. They were also charged with having, since the close of the process, behaved insolently at the meetings of the Calling, with questioning their authority to meet, protesting against all their procedures and refusing to pay their quarter's accounts.

At the same time John Jossie, a surgeon-apothecary, who elected to join the apothecaries in accordance with the decreet of the Court of Session, is described as having deserted the Calling, and the Clerk was instructed to delete his name out of the Rolls and declare that hereafter neither he, his children, nor his apprentices were to have any privilege or interest in the Calling. This John Jossie, who thus seceded from the surgeons in favour of the apothecaries, was an old master and deacon. Son of John Jossie, a bailie of the town, he was apprenticed to James Borthwick in 1654, gratis, without any fee for booking in consideration of the many courtesies and favours conferred by his father upon the Calling. During the twenty years he was with the surgeons, he more than once complained of the misconduct of his brother surgeons towards himself. On one occasion he became embroiled with a certain George Scot, who after a long examination was found to have transgressed against the act of deportment by his "uncivil, obscene, and unchristian miscarriages, not worthy to be repeated, named, or again heard of," and also to have given the lie again and again to John Jossie, and swearing with a great oath that he would "break his head," besides threatening him with violence afterwards, which the Calling said was a great disgrace to the art of surgery and to every member of the Incorporation. At another time Jossie complained that a master had abused him, by calling him "an incendiary and firebrand in the Calling, as his father was before him in the town."

Incorporation of the College of Physicians by Royal Charter. — In 1681, shortly before the Lords issued their judgment in the case of the apothecaries, the physicians of Edinburgh sought to obtain a Charter erecting them into a Royal College. Foremost among those who promoted the petition were three of the four "disinterested physicians" who had been consulted by the Court with regard to the claims of the apothecaries and whose advice had contributed to the defeat of the surgeon-apothecaries.

On hearing of the intention of the physicians to seek incorporation, the surgeons nominated a committee of sixteen members to oppose it with all their might, being afraid that if the Charter were granted "it might mightily encroach upon their privileges and tend to other prejudices." In September 1681, a copy of the Patent was served upon the Calling, with instructions to lodge answers thereto by the next meeting of the Privy Council. Two months later the deacon announced that, despite all their opposition, the physicians' Patent had passed, but, so far as was possible, the surgeons' rights and privileges had been reserved.

The surgeons now determined to obtain a new Charter for themselves, and having procured a "signature"[1] ratifying the whole rights formerly granted to them, it was read in their presence. The deacon, however, said that as he had been instructed by the Secret Council to send it to the physicians and others, there was nothing to be expected but a great deal of trouble. In this the deacon was right, for the "signature" still lies in the archives of the college unsigned and useless.

Visitation of the Drug Shops.—About this time a bitter controversy arose between the surgeons, the physicians, and the apothecaries, regarding the inspection of the drug shops of the town, " for purging them of rotten and insufficient drugs." The Court of Session had ordained "that the magistrates should in future nominate a visitor from the apothecaries to visit the drug shops in the town," but the magistrates nominated a surgeon-apothecary instead. The Court interposed, they themselves nominating one of the apothecaries.

The surgeons based their claim to perform this duty on the Act of the Town Council of 1657, the physicians on their

[1] A writing prepared to be sealed as the warrant for a proposed Royal Charter.

Royal Charter of 1681, and the apothecaries on the decreet of the Court of Session just made.

The case for the surgeon-apothecaries is set forth in the following petition to the Privy Council:—

"That albeit the Surgeon-Apothecaries have brought their trade to that perfection that those bred with them are preferred to any other of their trade in any army or navy abroad, and that his Majesty's ships and navies have been to their great satisfaction served by them the conjunction of these trades being able to encourage young men to go abroad to Paris and elsewhere to perfect themselves in their trade to the greatest height that can be, and to be able to be a patrimony to the sons of very worthy and honest parents, yet that trade is now like to fall into an absolute decay by the designs of the Phisitians who think they have too much respect among the people because of their knowledge, but of all the prejudice that has ever been done to the Surgeons the greatest was a late act which probably has been suggested by the Phisitians in which the examination of the drugs in their shops is referred to the President of the College of Phisitians and their two Censors with liberty to them to throw them out if they do not please them. Against which power granted to them the Surgeon-Apothecaries humbly offer these reasons: 1st. That every Surgeon-Apothecary is sworn when he is first admitted to have sufficient drugs and to be faithfull in the administration of them and is more severely examined upon his skill in them than the Phisitians are. 2nd. They are for many years bred up in the skill of them and it a science that requires long and great experience, whereas a Phisitian will be graduate upon a year's study, and that which they chiefly study is not so much the knowledge of drugs as the general theory of Physic. 3rd. Upon these considerations in their erection of their trade or Seals of Causes from the King their shops are only to be visited by those of their own trade who are sworn upon oath and by the custom of all Nations all tradesmen are to be tried by their own trade, and at London there is no trial of drugs but by the Surgeons and Apothecaries. 4th. By the erection of the College of Phisitians it was appointed by his Royal Highness's special determination that notwithstanding of that erection the Surgeon-Apothecaries' shops should not be visited without the concourse of the ordinary visitors of their trade . . . . And lastly it is not just that it be left arbitrary to any of the Phisitians (who have a prejudice at the Surgeon-Apothecaries which is but too nottourly known) to throw out their drugs upon pretence that they do not please them and thereby do defame themselves and their shops and ruin their trade and their prentices' education, for there being no certain measure in the goodness or illness of drugs it is absolutely arbitrary, and to refer the determination of things that are arbitrary to those that are known to have prejudices, looks not like that great justice which your Lordships upon all occasions, . . ." etc., etc.

The controversy, after being dragged out for a number of years, seems to have ended inconclusively, and there is little evidence that the drug shops were ever visited at all.

The New Charter.— In 1686, an attempt was made by the surgeons to obtain a new Charter, and this was so far successful that His Majesty, King James II., granted a new gift and Patent which was signed by his royal hand and passed the Great Seal of the Kingdom. As its ratification in Parliament was refused in 1693, this Charter did not, however, become effective, and as the surgeons neglected to pay the necessary fees attached to it, it was retained by the Deputy-Keeper of the Great Seal. Through the courtesy of Mr H. Home Drummond this interesting document came in 1820 into possession of the College.

A more successful attempt was made in 1694, when King William and Queen Mary granted a gift and Patent in favour of the surgeons and surgeon-apothecaries which was ratified in Parliament on 17th July 1695. The grant was not opposed by the physicians, who, since obtaining their own Charter had established more friendly relations with the surgeons. The Minutes of the Royal College of Physicians (6th August 1695) show that Dr David Dickson was commissioned to negotiate with the surgeon-apothecaries, and he, being satisfied that all the rights and privileges of the physicians were reserved, agreed not to oppose ratification. His action was approved by Dr Trotter, the President:—

" I do declare in name of the said College that whereas we have rid marches with the Surgeons of Edinburgh we will not in any manner of way oppose the reuniting of Chirurgy and Pharmacy."

The Patent of 1694—better known as King William and Queen Mary's Diploma—besides confirming in general all the grants in favour of the surgeon-barbers and the surgeon-apothecaries, reunited the arts of surgery and pharmacy, and described the duties of the surgeon and physician and the manner in which the grants made to them should be understood. In addition, it contained a clause which considerably extended the privileges of the surgeons and gave them a new authority. They were authorised to proceed against any person or persons, not only within the Burgh of Edinburgh, but also within the Sheriffdoms of the three Lothians, of Fife, Peebles, Selkirk, Roxburgh, and Berwick, who should in future practise surgery and pharmacy without first being approved and admitted by them and obtaining a certificate under their seals.

In order to advertise their new liberties, Letters of Publication were obtained under the Signet of the Privy Council, and published at the Mercat Cross of Edinburgh by a macer and by sound of trumpet, and also at the Mercat Cross, of the head burgh of each of the several shires mentioned in the Patent.

The Calling at once took steps to get in touch with the surgeons practising in the shires over which they now had jurisdiction. On 6th August 1696, a committee was nominated to meet a deputation of the country surgeons who desired further information concerning the examination of those already in practice, and how far the same might be extended.

An arrangement was concluded, which, judging from the number of applications for admission that quickly followed, was most satisfactory. On 26th May 1697, the first certificate was granted, the recipient being James Porteous of Peebles; and within a few weeks several others had received the College diploma. A few months later the surgeons in Fife came over in a body, but as they refused to pay the Clerk's fee of two rix dollars for making out their diploma special articles of agreement had to be made with them. The licence issued to the country surgeons was as follows:—

"Whereas the Incorporation having seriously considered the literature and qualifications of . . . . and being certainly informed that the said . . . several years bygone has exercised the arts of Chirurgie and Pharmacy in that place (with the blessings of God upon his endeavours) with very good success to the great satisfaction and approbation of the whole country amongst whom he lives:—Do therefor authorise and empower the said . . . . to practise and exercise the said arts of Chirurgie and Pharmacy within the said town of . . . . or within any other part within the liberties and jurisdiction where he shall happen to reside for the time (the town of Edinburgh and suburbs thereof being always excepted) without trouble or molestation."

Between the years 1695 and 1705, nothing seems to have marred the relations between the physicians and the surgeons. In the latter year, however, hostilities broke out afresh when James Nisbet, a surgeon, was fined by the physicians for practising in medicine. Nisbet appealed to the Court of Session, and from his petition we get an insight into what had happened.

"In anno 1705," he says, "I being called to see one Helen Heriot, a poor girl, and finding that she was in extremity under all the symptoms of poison and immediate death if some present remedy had not been adhibited; and also that she neither would send for a physician, nor in that season of the night could expect one, at least as soon as her circumstances required, your petitioner did administer what, by the blessing of God, recovered her to perfect health, . . ." etc.

Trivial as this matter may appear, it led to considerable trouble; actions were raised in the Court of Session, petitions and counter-petitions were made to Parliament, arbitrators were called in, with the Lord High Chancellor, the Earl of Seafield, as umpire-in-chief, but all without bringing peace.

CHAPTER VIII

THE SEPARATION OF THE BARBERS AND SURGEONS

The Barbers' Complaint—Action in the Court of Session—Separation of the Crafts—Résumé of the Association of the Barbers with the Surgeons—Revision of Constitution of the Surgeons.

The Barbers' Complaint.—We must now leave the apothecaries and physicians and turn to the barbers. Of late years they had become a numerous body, far exceeding the surgeons in number, and on the whole seemed fairly prosperous and contented until, in August 1708, they complained to the surgeons of the many grievances they suffered at the hands of unfreemen barbers as well as from the surgeons themselves.

In the first place, it was alleged that a number of unfreemen trimmed and shaved without the Calling's liberty. Also that in regard to the fees of entrants, no distinction was made between those who had served five years' apprenticeship to barbers and those that had served no apprenticeship at all. Further, that there were a great many barbers exercising their employment whose fees had been paid by bonds still lying in the hands of the Calling, which was hurtful to those who had paid considerable sums for their freedom. And lastly, that the widows of freemen barbers took daily into their service prentices and servants contrary to the Acts of the Calling, which allow them only one journeyman, who is to be entered in the books of the Calling. These grievances the surgeons were asked to consider, and to provide for them a remedy.

This was done to the satisfaction of the barbers, who in future were themselves to be permitted to search for unfreemen without reference to the Calling, and to visit the widows suspected of having apprentices and servants in their employment. It was also arranged that the sum of five hundred merks should be paid by all who had served no apprenticeship; three hundred merks by those whose names had been entered in the

books of the Calling and who had served five years' apprenticeship to a master-barber; one hundred pounds Scots by the
sons of freemen and those marrying freemen's daughters; and
all who had bonds lying in the hands of the Calling for their
fees were ordered to pay up the same at once to the
Incorporation.

All now went well with them until March 1718, when a
wigmaker named William Carss was fined forty pounds by
the magistrates for trimming without a licence. To prevent
the sentence against him being executed, Carss locked up his
shop and kept out of the way until such time as he might
obtain an order of suspension which he intended to apply for.
The surgeons, however, obtained from the Court of Session
"letters of open doors," and ultimately arrested two wigs, which
were returned to Carss on payment of the forty pounds. Carss,
who it appears had on three occasions unsuccessfully applied to
the Lords of Session for suspension, now influenced about a
dozen other wigmakers to join with him in presenting another
petition to the Lords, and gave into them a most "clamerous
bill" against the Incorporation. The deacon explained to the
Calling that he had lodged answers in their name, and that he
and the Council had consulted as lawyers, Sir Walter Pringle,
Mr Robert Dundas, Solicitor, Mr Walter Stewart, Mr Duncan
Forbes, Mr Charles Erskine, Mr John Fleming, young Pencaitland, and Mr Hugh Dalrymple, Advocates, and had employed
Mr Alexander Hamilton of Dechmont, My Lord Pencaitland's
second son as Writer, and the Clerk as Agent for the Calling.

Nothing more is heard of this affair, probably from the fact
that more important events intervened.

The condition of the Calling for several years past had
considerably improved. With the growth of the population
their numbers had steadily increased until, in 1718, the surgeons
numbered 29, while the barbers in town and suburbs totalled
no less than 99. This extraordinary addition to the number
of barbers, who, as a rule, paid a larger sum for their licence
than the surgeons did for their freedom, materially contributed
to the prosperity of the Incorporation. In spite, however, of
the heavy tax laid upon them, the barbers had not the slightest
say, either in the administration and application of the common
funds, or in the management of the affairs of the Incorporation

in general.   This unequal division of governing power seemed to them so unjust that at last they decided to raise an action in the Court of Session to ascertain the extent and limits of their rights.

Action in the Court of Session.—The first signs of the coming storm are contained in a commission dated 3rd April 1718, and signed by forty-one barbers, in favour of Alexander Baillie, Writer in Edinburgh, who was granted full power and warrant to prosecute before the Lords of Session such an action as should be thought necessary to relieve them of the hardships imposed upon them by the Incorporation of Surgeons ; and to that end to employ lawyers and to pay any necessary sums for defending them, or any of them, against any action the surgeons might bring against them.

Ten days later, the barbers executed another warrant appointing eight of their number to meet with any of the surgeons having authority to treat with them concerning the matters disputable in order to come to a friendly agreement, and to report their procedure to their constituents before coming to a final conclusion.

On 20th May the surgeons declared that the barbers had raised an action against them, but as they had now made some proposals for taking the plea away in an amicable manner, a committee would meet them if the barbers really meant it. "But," concludes the Minute, "in case the barbers insist in their plea, the Calling resolve that they will, both out of their public stock and out of their own private pockets, maintain and defend to the utmost their rights and privileges against the unjust demands brought against them."

Accordingly, three surgeons (including Alexander Monro) were deputed to meet the barbers in conference, and "without appearing to have a commission from them (the surgeons) endeavour to find out the conditions upon which the process might be abandoned."

A "scroll of terms" was then submitted to the surgeons' committee, who had been authorised to dispense with the barbers' accounts in case the process could not be otherwise settled.

Meanwhile an Action of Reduction had been raised at the instance of George Manson and seven others on behalf of the Freemen Barbers.

In opening their case the barbers set forth that the surgeons' Charter of 1694, and the Ratification which followed it, should be set aside, inasmuch as they were both made without reference to them, and also because, while they confirmed the rights of the surgeons, who were now joined with the apothecaries, the barbers themselves had been entirely left out. It was also claimed that the Seal of Cause was equally in favour of the pursuers, as barbers, as of the defenders, as surgeons, and that all members, both barbers and surgeons, had equal rights to a vote, and to be voted for, in the election of the deacon and other office-bearers, and to the administration of the common funds. The pursuers also said that the inequality of the management of the affairs of the Incorporation was manifestly a grievous oppression to them, whose fees for admission since the year 1682 amounted to more than the value of the whole stock then belonging to the Society. The surgeons were likewise charged with making Acts at their own convenience for obtaining money, and then suspending those Acts whenever it suited their purpose. In this manner their patronage was said to have been extended to as many as would pay for it, without respect to their pretensions of right by apprenticeship or being servants to a free barber.

The surgeons replied that only those found qualified by examination could pretend to any privileges of the original Seal of Cause, and that the barbers were only dependent upon them. In support of this statement they quoted a letter written by King James VI. directly to the Lords of Session explaining that the surgeons, out of *pity* and *compassion*, had admitted certain simple persons to be barbers, "to poll, shave, wash, and make aquavite," which, they said, were all the privileges that any barber, not qualified in surgery, could formerly take advantage of.

The barbers maintained that the two Crafts were distinct, the one from the other, and ingeniously quoted a passage from the Seal of Cause that "no barber-master or servant shall use nor exercise the craft of surgery unless he be expert," which, they said, made it beyond question that he might, without that knowledge, be a barber. The custom of admitting barbers upon petition, covering only a licence to trim and shave, was described as depending upon the arbitrary management of the surgeons themselves who, in the several Acts of Admission granted to barbers, dispensed their favours in every conceivable way. To some of them the freedom of the trade had been given to the entrant and to his widow, excluding both his children and his apprentices, while in other cases the freedom was granted to the entrant, his widow, his sons, sons-in-law, and apprentices. To one the privilege was only granted during the life of his wife, and yet, continued the pursuers, others, who had no more title than the recommendation of a nobleman, are found to have been admitted even gratuitously and their privileges extended without any rule.

This last hit obviously refers to the transaction between the Earl of Perth and Dr Christopher Irvine, regarding the Earl's servant, Valentine (p. 106), who was admitted a free barber without payment of any kind in consideration of the "great obligations they lye under to the said Lord High Chancellor of Scotland for his eminent favours and good offices conferred upon and done unto the Incorporation and in testimony of their just resentment and thankfull acknowledgement of the same."

In continuing their case, the surgeons held that the barbers were admitted as dependants upon the surgeons, which could never be the relationship of co-ordinate members of the same Society, and said that they (the surgeons) were unjustly taxed with pride "in not opening their door and making one for the pursuers." The barbers were further charged with being the provokers, and "having waxed wanton by too gentle treatment, did now pretend to insult their Superiors, who were obliged to uphold the honour of their Society, and to keep the successors of the simple barbers mentioned in King James's letter, to trimming and shaving, and not allow them to go beyond the line."

After some very plain speaking on both sides, the barbers applied for access to the Minute Books, wherein, they said, it would be seen that they had paid over 140,000 merks since the year 1682, and that the books would also show the mis-application of the money, which to them was a "mighty grievance." After the books had been opened to their inspection, the barbers declared that for an uninterrupted period of 150 years simple barbers like themselves had enjoyed the whole privileges of the Craft, had frequently been elected Boxmaster [Treasurer] and on more than one occasion had been raised to the Deaconship itself—in fact, were in every way equal to their brethren the surgeons.   They also contended that the Act passed by the Corporation, in 1648, prohibiting the entry of simple barbers, was illegal, it having been made by one part of a Society against the other at a time when there were only six barbers and ten surgeons, the latter taking advantage of their superiority in numbers; to which it was replied that no simple barbers were admitted between the Acts of 1648 and 1682, and that it mattered not to the surgeons what rights the old incorporate barbers had—*they* were quite another class of practitioner modelled upon the footing of the Act of 1682.   Why then, inquired the surgeons, " did they pretend to say to those who were their makers, that they ought to have made them in another form, or that they must alter their shape and turn them from shavers into members of an incorporate body? It was no use for them to jangle in words and to say that because they were admitted freemen barbers, they must therefore be members of the Incorporation and have its privileges."

Their Lordships, however, found that all masters should be examined in surgery and anatomy and be capable of exercising both crafts; that the Act of 1648 was consistent with and conformed to the Seal of Cause; and that the title of the barbers conformed to the Act of the Town Council of 1682, which did not entitle them to the full privileges provided to the masters of crafts.

The surgeons then expressed their willingness to relieve the barbers of any apparent hardships; but the latter asked the Court to make reasonable regulations for preventing in the future the abuses from which they suffered through the pretended superiority of the surgeons, and they submitted a statement containing certain articles which might form the basis of a settlement.

This was met with counter proposals by the surgeons, who declared that a private settlement had been made with the barbers and asked that judgment might be given in terms therein stated.   The barbers now repudiated the agreement which, they said, had not been signed by them as a body, and,

I

as they were not yet formed into a society which was regulated by plurality of votes, it could not be said to have been signed by the barbers of Edinburgh. The surgeons, they said "ought truly to be ashamed of mentioning the affair at all, seeing that the proposals were at most merely passed to one of the surgeons on the High Street, not in name of the barbers, but upon the express conditions of being returned the next morning. But instead of this being done, they were clandestinely and unfairly entered in the surgeons' books, where they appear now, forsooth, extracted by their Clerk."

A long debate then ensued as to the disposal of the quarterly subscriptions originally intended for the relief of the poor. In endeavouring to get this entirely into their own hands, the barbers declared that no pensions were ever paid to their poor by the surgeons; on the contrary, they always supported their own poor according to their ability. Some of them, they said, were now begging in the streets, "and the children of Alexander Cruickshank, who died in June 1718, were turned by their landlord out of doors; and when they applied to the surgeons, they got a crown of charity, but with the express condition 'never to trouble them again.'"

Separation of the Crafts.—Eventually the Court gave its decree in 1722, which, with the exception of some minor details, completely divided the Crafts, a decision which probably gave entire satisfaction to neither party. At least, the conciliatory attitude of the surgeons showed no desire on their part for the introduction of such a drastic measure.

Résumé of the Association of the Barbers with the Surgeons.—In considering some of the points raised by the barbers, it is presumed that the period during which they claim to have shared the privileges of the Corporation equally with the surgeons, was the first century and a half of the Craft's existence, viz., from 1505 to the passing of the Statute of 1648. The College Records, however, would only carry them as far back as 1581, and as they fail to quote any circumstances prior to that date, in all probability they made no reference to the Burgh Records from which they might have gained some additional facts.

In looking at the conditions surrounding the union of the two Crafts in 1505, we may safely suggest that the barbers were then more numerous and of more influence than their intended colleagues. The union should not be looked upon, as is customary, as a *mésalliance* for the surgeons, for if we remember that the barber of that day was also the surgeon of the monastery— and thus the first to specialise in surgery—we realise that the coalition which took place was no more than a union between the chirurgeon of the laity and the chirurgeon of the priesthood. The duties of the latter were many and various. About the period of which we speak, several references to him appear in the Accounts of the Lord High Treasurer in connection with the making and selling of aquavite, and as fourteen shillings were paid to one for "taking furth the Kingis tuth," it is evident that his professional abilities were not confined to the trimming of beards. Then there was the King's barber, who, besides supplying His Majesty with "holland claith at ten shillings the eln" supplemented his income by selling crossbows and daggers. All this in addition to his clipping, polling, and shaving, stamps him to have been a busy man whose trade appealed to one and all, from the highest in the land to the meanest citizen. On the other hand, his newly made brother the surgeon would not be nearly so much in request, he having to depend more upon the cracked heads and broken bones consequent upon some night brawl in the High Street, or the more serious tumults which were then of no rare occurrence in the Scottish capital.

It is easy, then, to conceive that the barber would be the better known and the more popular of the two, and this may account for the Incorporation being almost invariably styled the "Barber Craft" whenever reference was made to it in the early days.

Almost the first time the Corporation is mentioned in the Burgh Records is in the year 1530, when, at a meeting of the Trades, the "Barber Craft" is said to have been represented by a certain John Arras. Again, in 1558, when the Crafts furnished a contingent for defending the town, a number were found by the "Barbers," while, in 1570, the "Barber Craft" made a gift of three pounds Scots to the sustentation of the ministry. The same thing occurs in most of the old documents belonging to the College of Surgeons. For instance, a deed of bequest by George Leith, in 1533, of some houses in the

High Street is in favour of the " Chaplain of the Honest Craft of Barbers," and, in 1556, a sum of money is acknowledged to have been received from Alexander Bruce, " Dekin of the Barbers." Other instances could be cited indicating that the barbers, at that time, were more closely identified with the Incorporation than were the surgeons.

That the two Crafts were distinct for some years after their union is probably correct, for it cannot be supposed that the mere granting of a Charter transformed the surgeons into barbers. It is still more unlikely that it turned the barbers into surgeons, and whatever claim the former may have had to blood-letting before 1505, was forfeited by the Seal of Cause, for, as bleeding was a surgical operation requiring some knowledge of anatomy, the surgeons would claim it as belonging to them alone. The trades, however, can scarcely be said to have been kept separate after it became the custom for both to be pursued by the same individual, and this really began soon after the union, for, as the barber became expert and passed whatever examination was required of him to assume the *rôle* of the surgeon, instead of discarding his razor in favour of the scalpel, he continued in the practice of both Crafts simultaneously. Likely enough, this led to the extinction of the simple barber, for it may reasonably be assumed that very few failed to pass the test. Be that as it may, it is certain that about the middle of the 16th century the title of the Incorporation was subject to a complete change. We no longer read so much of the Barber Craft nor of the barber; slowly, but surely, he is superseded by the surgeon, or, to be more accurate, the surgeon-barber, until, in 1567, we find a Charter granted by Queen Mary to the surgeons in which the barbers are ignored altogether. Later on, in the Decreet Arbitral, Gilbert Primrose is described as deacon of the " Chirurgeons " and it was the " Craft of Chirurgeons " that was granted pre-eminence amongst the trades, in 1583. Turning to the surgeons' own records, we find the names of the whole of the Masters of the Crafts in 1581, and as they were all surgeons or surgeon-barbers, it is quite clear that no simple barber existed at that date. The barbers, however, in their action in 1718, claim that one on this list, who was elected deacon in 1584, could only have been a simple barber because of his inability to write. This certainly seemed to be a point in favour of the barbers, for according to the Seal of Cause, no master was permitted to "tak ane prenteis or feit man in tyme cuming to use the surregeane craft without he can baith wryte and reid." It is true that on referring to the Minutes of that date we find that the deacon—Henry Lumsden by name—signed an Act "with my hand at the pen" [led by the Notary], but, as he is reported in the Burgh Records as one of the "Chirurgeons" who attended a wounded man at the instance of the Town Council in 1580, this claim must be dismissed.

It is probable, therefore, that the original simple barber died out soon after 1550. As the Surgeons' Records describe the condition under which everyone of their members entered the Society, we are able to fix the date of his reappearance, and also to give an account of the number of simple barbers, simple surgeons, and surgeon-barbers so entering, from 1581 down to the year 1648, when the former were prohibited the *entrée* of the Craft. Of the simple barbers, Alexander Rattray was the first. He was admitted to the "Barber Craft" in 1584 with permission to "clip, cow, and shave only and not to use any point of chirurgie." After eight had been admitted on these conditions in the space of twenty years, the terms were slightly modified. Admission in the future was to be "without prejudice to him to crave admission to the *art of chirurgie* when it shall please God that he be able to discharge his duty therein." Under these combined headings thirty-five were admitted, of whom twenty-two subsequently passed the "tryall" and so became surgeon-barbers. Ten entered as masters of surgery only, and nineteen were admitted masters of both Crafts at the same time.

With regard to the barbers' claim that their predecessors equally shared the privileges of the Craft with the surgeons, careful investigation certainly leads to that impression. At any rate, during the period under review, viz., 1581-1648, three simple barbers held office as Boxmaster [Treasurer] on nine occasions, and seven barbers, who became surgeons afterwards, occupied the same post on fourteen occasions. To this extent the barbers were permitted to hold office, but the position of deacon or councillor was never held by any but a surgeon.

What the privileges of the barbers were prior to 1581 cannot even be surmised, but in 1601, 1605, 1606, and 1607 they were certainly present at the meetings and voted in the election of office-bearers, in fact, on one occasion they were in a majority of six to four.

If they attended the meetings during these years they were probably present at other times, for although the terms generally employed in the Minutes describing the meetings are that "the whole brethren of the Chirurgeons" convened in the deacon's house, or that the "Deacon and Masters of the Chirurgeons" convened, etc., it must not be taken that the barbers were not also there, for the headings of the Minutes do not always agree with the text. For example, in a list of the names of the "haill Masters of the art of Chirurgie" given in December 1601, there appear the names of two undoubted simple barbers. So many slips, contradictory in themselves, occur in the early Minutes that it is sometimes difficult to arrive at a definite conclusion as to what is really meant, but judging broadly from the data at our disposal, there is no reason to doubt that at the time in question the barbers had equal privileges with the surgeons, with the exception, perhaps, of actually occupying the deacon's chair.

So much for the early barbers. But the simple barbers of 1682 were raised upon quite a different footing to their predecessors, that is if they can seriously be said to have had any, for if we carefully distinguish between the old simple barber and those entering the barber craft preliminary to becoming surgeons, we find that the appearance of the former —previous to 1682—was so spasmodic, his life so transient, and his number so small, that no actual body of them can be said to have existed until the formation of the one above mentioned.

When the Town Council had their attention called to the inconvenience the public were put to through the scarcity of barbers in the town, the magistrates plainly told the surgeons that unless they quickly remedied the defect "they would not espouse nor own the interest of the Calling in case any attempt should be made by application to superior judicatories for causing the Incorporation to receive into freedom such number of barbers as they should think fit." The magistrates also declared that if the Calling would voluntarily admit a competent number of persons skilled in barber craft at present or at any future time, "that these persons should be holden as depending upon the Incorporation and be liable to all its Laws and Acts." This was the foundation, then, upon which the barbers of 1682 were established. Their Acts of Admission, although varying in detail, are all alike in principle and contain no expectancy of their entering the craft of chirurgie "when it shall please God that they be able to discharge their duties therein," as we find mentioned in Acts of a former date. At the time they were raised there were nine barber's shops in the town, six of which were kept by surgeons and three by "relicts" or freemen's widows; none of the old simple barbers—with whom they might have claimed a kinship—therefore existed. Taking into consideration all the facts of the case, it is surprising that the simple barbers of 1682 should have expected—much less demanded—equality with the surgeons.

Taken altogether, the numbers of the Incorporation were very small—seldom exceeding fifteen at one time. Once, in 1647, they had dwindled down to eight. Although the majority of these were barber-surgeons, there were always a few surgeons content to follow their own profession alone.

The notion, generally accepted, that the separation was brought about by the surgeons cannot be entertained. They did their best to avert it, and, after the Court had decided some points in their favour, endeavoured to settle the question in a friendly way. The barbers, however, refused to listen and preferred to place themselves in the hands of the judges. After all, the barbers do not seem to have had so much to complain about. Their fees, certainly, seemed very high and probably required adjusting, but their claim for equal votes and privileges with the surgeons, was, for obvious reasons (especially when it is remembered that the barbers were in a majority of about three to one), out of the question, and although the fact that they had no voice in the affairs of the Incorporation may have appeared to them a hardship, yet many larger bodies occupy a similar position at the present day. When the action was first raised in 1718—it lasted four years—separation was probably never thought of. The separation was a loss to both parties. By it the barbers forfeited caste and the surgeons suffered financially. Deprived of their revenue, the direct effect of the separation was to plunge the surgeons into such financial difficulties that, after unsuccessfully offering their hall and lands in the High School Yards for sale, they were obliged to turn the former into dwelling houses, retaining but a single room for their own convenience. The land adjoining the hall was then cut up into feus and eventually developed into the famous Surgeons' Square. In this way a small yearly income was assured, but the Incorporation was many times reduced to the utmost necessity before they recovered from the effects of their separation from the barbers.

The long tedious process by law at last came to an end, and to all intents and purposes the barbers were now separate from the surgeons, not by any movement of the latter, it will be observed, but by circumstances entirely brought about by themselves.

Revision of Constitution of the Surgeons.—Immediately after the partition the surgeons began to revise their laws and draw up such acts and rules as they conceived most likely to promote their interests in the altered conditions. These new Regulations deal with every department of the Incorporation and contain many interesting particulars. In dealing first with admission of Entrants it was ordained:—

"That no person who has served as Apprentice hereafter be admitted a freeman till eight years be fully elapsed after his being booked Apprentice for freedom; nevertheless he may be admitted any time after his Indentures are discharged upon paying Two hundred pounds Scots for each year that is unexpired of the eight years.

"That no man's bill be heard till such time as the person who is on his trial be either received a freeman or rejected Excepting honorary freemen and country surgeons residing within the Calling's privileges, concerning which two classes of surgeons, the Calling have made the following rules:—

"That such Liberties and Privileges as are granted to them cannot be communicated or conveyed to their Children or Apprentices, but must die and extinguish with themselves; That the Licentiat Country Surgeon And Hon. Freemen be not obliged to attend any meetings or be capable of any office of the Calling, nor pay quarterly or other payments whatsoever.

"When any Apprentice gives in his bill to be received a freeman He shall produce his Indentures with a sufficient discharge of them written by the Calling's Clerk, and, before he be received freeman and have the oath of the Calling administered to him, he shall produce his Burgess ticket, and before he can have a vote in the Calling he shall produce his Act of Admission.

"When any person having a title to be a freeman applies to the Calling for that end, His first lesson shall be appointed against that day four weeks from the deliverance of his bill.

"That the Intrant's first lesson shall be a discourse upon any Chirurgical or Anatomical subject and he shall be obliged to answer all practical questions in Chirurgy; that his second lesson shall be Anatomical, the third and fourth Chirurgical Operations.

"In case any Examiner be absent he shall get another Examiner to take his place, but if he neglect to do so, he shall pay a Crown to the Treasurer, and he shall be debarred from voting until it be payed.

"That the Preses of and at each examination (which the Examiners are to be per vices according to their seniority) shall make a speech upon any part of Chirurgie or Anatomy except the Intrant's lesson, and upon neglecting he shall pay a Crown to the Box.

"That each prentice shall pay Two hundred pounds scots of upsett each freeman's son forty pounds scots; their sons in law Two hundred pounds scots, which shall be paid before they shall have their Act of Admission.

"That Chirurgeons within the Calling's Privileges shall pay to them for their freedom to practise within the several jurisdictions within which they reside, the sum of Five pounds ster.

"That four of the Members be appointed Examiners for every two Intrants in the following manner, viz. Beginning at the two eldest and two youngest successively, and in case any examiner be chosen Deacon or Treasurer the next on the roll to him shall succeed as examiner."

APPRENTICES AND SERVANTS

"No Master shall have Privilege to Book an Apprentice for freedom oftener than once in three years.

"That every Master be obliged to Book his Apprentice and Servant in the Books of the Incorporation at furthest within twenty days after he has indented, and to prevent any difficulty that may arise to the Master in complying with this Regulation, it is ordained that the Prentice or Servant may be booked before the Deacon, Treasurer and two Masters and the Clerk who are authorized to enter them respectively into the Calling's books, for which booking an Apprentice shall pay six pounds to the box, one pound four shillings to the Clerk, one shilling to the Officer and six pence to the Magdalen Chapel, and a Servant

138 ROYAL COLLEGE OF SURGEONS OF EDINBURGH

Three pounds to the box, 12/ to the Clerk, 6/ to the Officer and 4/ to the Magdalen Chapel.

"That each Master, the day of election of the Deacon, give a note of his Apprentices and Servants under a penalty of eight pounds scots.

"The time of service for freedom shall be declared in the Indentures to be five years, and it is hereby declared that if the Prentice serve his Master faithfully, though he has not been entertained by him at Bed and Board yet notwithstanding of anything contained in the Indentures thereanent he shall have a just title to the freedom forsaid.

"That it shall not be in the power of any Master to transfer his Prentice to another Master, but shall be obliged himself to teach and instruct him, and the freedom is hereby declared to be communicated to the prentice only by the Master with whom he indents and serves.

"That all Indentures shall be written by the Clerk, for which he is to be payed at least for each pair, 12/; as also that he write the discharges thereof for which he is to get at least a Crown from an Apprentice and 3/ from a Servant.

"In case a Master die during the currency of the Indentures betwixt him and his Apprentice or Servant, application should be made by bill to the Incorporation for another Master with whom by Indentures he may serve out the remainder of his time.

MEETINGS

"The Calling appoint four meetings to be held yearly upon or within eight days, Lambmass, Martinmass, Candlemass and Whitsunday, upon which days each Member shall pay 2/6 as their Quarter Account.

"Such as come to the Meetings after prayers said and rolls called shall pay 4/.

"That each Member for absence from a meeting shall pay 1/.

"And it is hereby statute That the Quarter Account shall be payed at the Quarterly Meetings. The Seros at the Members immediately entering the Meeting. The absents at or before the next meeting, under the penalty of being debarred from booking Apprentices or Servants, or voting in any of the affairs of the Society, such as go from the meeting without liberty shall pay five shillings ster.

"One third of the whole Members shall be a Quorum of the Society for carrying on their ordinary business, but no act shall be repealed, or new ones made but in a meeting consisting of more than the half of the Calling.

"No Member shall be allowed to vote by Letter or Proxy in any matter whatsoever except in the election of Deacon.

"That in all debates each member shall address himself only to the Deacon and keep silent among themselves under the penalty of six pence ster.

"Toties Quoties; and none shall interrupt another under the same penalty which shall be instantly paid.

"That none of the Members use indiscreet or unmannerly expressions or swearing in the Calling under the penalty of [   ]

"If any be found guilty of any of the above Trespasses, the deacon shall stop debate till the fines be paid, and if any member refuse to pay a fine without a vote of the Society and yet be found guilty, he shall pay double of the said fine.

"That none shall be chosen a deacon except such a member as is actually in the exercise of his Business.

"There shall be chosen annually when the Deacon is elected, a Committee of Accounts consisting of five, whereof three shall be a quorum who shall examine the Treasurer's accounts and the Necessity or Advantage of the Works before tradesmen be employed therein, and shall examine Tradesmen Accounts and report to the Society the Necessity or Advantage of employing Tradesmen before they be actually employed, and the state of their accounts before they be payed by the Treasurer, who shall call a meeting of the Committee as oft as he pleases, and if they refuse to meet with him, they shall upon conviction thereof pay £1 ster.

"There shall be annually chosen a committee to be the Deacons' Council consisting of six including the Treasurer for the time, whereof three with the Deacon shall be a quorum, to meet the first Tuesday of every month.

"And it is hereby Statute that no money shall be allowed any of the said Committees who shall be sent to examine or treat with the Surgeons in the country, and that any Member of the Society may be present either at the Deacons' Council or any Committee.

"That the Clerk in time coming Minute affairs as they shall be offered to or Tabled before the Calling, and that according to the order of the said Minutes the Affairs of the Calling be considered and Discussed before Intrants be examined, and that all Minutes be written by the Clerk in a book for that purpose apart, and read immediately by the Clerk to the Calling and then the Deacon shall sign them, and shall be read over again in the next succeeding meeting before they be approven. And if approven shall be transcribed into a Minute Book to be signed by the Deacon, if not approven shall be expunged."

CHAPTER IX

POLITICS AND APOTHECARIES

The Apothecaries' Appeal—Admission of Simple Apothecaries—
Political Activities of the Incorporation

THE apothecaries whom we left in 1682, vainly endeavouring
to get the magistrates to recognise their fraternity, were now
in a bad way. Their claim to have one of their number
appointed Visitor to preside at their meetings and visit the
drug shops, etc., in accordance with the decreet pronounced
by the Court of Session, was never seriously regarded by the
magistrates, while the granting of the Surgeons' Charter of
1695, re-uniting the arts of surgery and pharmacy, had completely upset their calculations. Thoroughly disheartened by
their humiliating position and the discouragement they had
received from the magistrates, the fraternity had dwindled
almost to nothing, and anyone who pleased practised pharmacy
without censure. At this stage, as though in desperation, and
perhaps taking advantage of the litigation going on between
the surgeons and the barbers in the Court of Session, they made
a strong appeal to Parliament to keep the two employments
distinct or to pass an Act enabling them to practise both
pharmacy and surgery when necessary.

The apothecaries held that the arts of pharmacy and
surgery were distinct, and that in the City of Edinburgh
the business of pharmacy was carried on by a Society of
persons long before the surgeons had any title to be an
Incorporation. They recalled the fact that when the Scots
army went to England, some of the apothecaries' prentices went
with it as mates to the surgeons, and that when the wars
were over, two apothecaries — James Borthwick and Thomas
Kincaid—were received by the surgeons into the Incorporation
and were largely instrumental in securing, in 1657, the Act

from the Town Council which combined the surgeon-apothecaries with the surgeon-barbers. They complained that this
composite body "neglected and condemned" the simple
apothecaries, and "allowed none to practise pharmacy, but
such as subjected themselves to trial before them . . ."

Amongst the many instances of their oppression, the apothecaries begged the Honourable Estates of Parliament to take
notice of these two, which they claimed could be instantly
verified.

(1) "A poor man met with an accidental strain, which called for
speedy help and application; an Apothecary in Edinburgh, being first
found, not without importunity, was prevailed upon to go along, and
being aware of the necessity applied a plaster to the strain, which
coming to the knowledge of the Incorporation of Surgeon-Apothecaries,
they, of their own accord, without applying to any Magistrates for their
concurrence, sent him to prison, where he was detained till they were
ashamed of their lawless procedure.

(2) "A relation of James Chisholme, Apothecary (bred with
Thomas Edgar, Surgeon), dying of an Hydropsie, and the swelling
being such as to necessitate an operation in order that the coffin might
receive her, which the said James Chisholme did, was convened a few
days after before the Magistrates, and ordained to answer, as an
unauthorised practiser of Surgery summarily, and the libel was sustained relevant by Mr Chisholme's oath which he was instantly
ordained to give, *super inquirendis*, without so much as allowing him
a sight of the libel or time to consider the same, and upon his refusal,
he was unlawed in an exorbitant fine, which put him to the expenses
and trouble of suspension, which lies still undiscussed.

"The Apothecaries further asserted that, besides all this, the
Surgeons have their emissaries and agents in all the Courts of
Judicature within their bounds, and wherever an Apothecary pursues
for payment of his Account, they [the Surgeons] take up the process
to see if in the accompt there be the least item for Surgery such as
blood-letting, which frequently happens, and which the Apothecaries
are allowed to do in cases of necessity, the Apothecaries' libel is made
a ditto against themselves, which they must either forgo, or undergo an
unreasonable and exorbitant fine.

"In conclusion, it was urged, that before the conjunction of these
arts, there were eminent Surgeons in Edinburgh who lived well and
purchased large estates, such as Pennicuik of Newhall and Arthur
Temple of Reveltridge, but they, like their predecessors, kept Barbers'

shops according to their Seal of Cause, and by applying themselves to surgery alone they became perfect in it—'Arthur Temple,' they said 'cutted an horn from a woman's head'—but there is not a surgeon now in town that will offer to cut or cure the stone, which is as common abroad where surgery and pharmacy are separate employments, as phlebotomy is in Scotland. The Apothecaries therefore prayed that the employments might be kept distinct and not exercised by one man—'the Pharmacian being kept to his Materia Medica and Dispensatory, and the Surgeon to his Fractures and Luxations, Astrology and Dyets of the Moon, as appears by his Seal of Cause.'"

An old account rendered by an apothecary to his patient, in 1714, shows how careful the apothecaries were not to make an open charge for bleeding, for although the other items are carried out in full, the fee for the operation mentioned is left blank—to be arranged, no doubt, at the time of payment. The bill includes:—

A vomiter to Mrs White	.	.	.	£0 18	0
Stomatick Materials	.	.	.	0 8	0
A gl. Syrup of lemons	.	.	.	0 12	0
Purgeing potion	.	.	.	0 12	0
Three ounces Electuary	.	.	.	1 4	0
Three ounces Syrup of Poppies	.	.	0 4	0
Hysterick Jelup	.	.	.	1 15	0
Hysterick Plaster	.	.	.	0 18	0
A vomiter to Mary	.	.	.	0 10	0
A blooding to Janet	.	.	.		
Jelup against Worms	.	.	.	0 15	0
Ane Interscapulium	.	.	.	0 14	0
Militet plaster	.	.	.	0 6	0

Crippled by their long and expensive process with the barbers, and fearing to be drawn into another litigation with the apothecaries, the surgeons resolved to settle their differences by absorbing them into their own Society. Accordingly, at a meeting on 25th April 1721, the whole of the Apothecaries in Edinburgh, fifteen in number, on representing they were desirous of becoming members of the Incorporation, were admitted surgeons, without examination, on payment of £50 each, the Calling being satisfied of their "sufficiency and qualifications to be free surgeons in and among them."

As if in acknowledgment of the irregularity of such a

proceeding, the following naïve explanation was ordered to be inserted in a Minute Book :—

"April 19th, 1721. The Calling judging it proper that the occasion of the agreement with the Apothecaries on the terms foresaid should be set forth in their books, have ordered it to be done accordingly. And it is this—That they consider it to be their duty to husband the Calling's money with the utmost frugality and for this reason with the greatest care to avoid as much as may be expensive law suits, they having a feeling sense of the inconveniences arising from them, and particularly with respect to the decreet of separation pronounced by the Lords of Session anno 1682, not that the Calling at present apprehend any danger from the said decreet, being assured by their lawyers that the same is ill founded and will consequently be reduced, but that by the litigious strugglings of the Apothecaries the charge thereof may prove very considerable. Besides by this arrangement, the Calling have it in their eye how they may effectually prevent and discourage any unfree practisers for the future, either in surgery or pharmacy. The Calling, further considering the true state of their circumstances, are satisfied this agreement is very rational, a great part of their debts being thereby paid and the Calling thereby much strengthened."

The surgeons, now united with their old opponents the apothecaries, decided again to challenge the physicians on the pharmacy question, and after holding many conferences with them, at which no amicable arrangement was come to, the Incorporation applied to the Town Council for an Act to regulate the exercising of pharmacy within the City.

They asked that the practice of the art of pharmacy should be confined to those who were entitled to the freedom of the Incorporation of surgeon-apothecaries after being examined by the said Incorporation; and that they should make up their medicines according to the new Edinburgh Dispensatory.

The physicians were up in arms at once against this proposed Act, representing it to be an encroachment upon their privileges, and claiming that the right of examining apothecaries should be invested in themselves.

In their answers to the representation of the physicians, the chirurgeon-apothecaries said they "should be exceeding sorry if the proposition they have made by their petition offered to the Town Council should occasion any difference or misunderstanding betwixt them and the Royal College, for whom they have all the Regard due to that Learned Body . . . " and that " it was far from their intention in the least to hurt or incroach upon the rights and privileges of the Royal College."

Throughout the lengthy argument that followed, this amiable attitude was not consistently maintained, and Acts, Charters, Ratifications, and Letters Patent were quoted by both sides at great length, without carrying much conviction as to the merits of the case, or indicating how it all ended.

Political Activities of the Incorporation.—About the year 1740, the Incorporation became deeply involved in politics. As the Parliament under Walpole was then on the point of being dismissed owing to its unpopularity, the surgeons considering the affairs of the Kingdom to have been grossly mismanaged, decided to put forward a candidate of their own at the next election. With this object in view and by way of opening their political campaign, they held a meeting for the purpose of considering the " State of the Nation," when it was agreed that their deacon, as deacon-convener, along with the other deacons of trades should lay a resolution before the Town Council, and move that they, as representing the community of the City, would concur in giving these or other instructions for the same end, to Patrick Lindsay, Esq., the then representative of the Burgh.

In this long and rambling Resolution, after drawing attention to the unhappy state of the Kingdom and the dangers threatening the Constitution, they go on to suggest :—

"That it is of the highest importance that those whom the nation entrusts with the power of making all Laws upon which our Lives, Liberties, Properties and Trade do entirely depend, should be absolutely free and uninfluenced by any lucrative considerations. . . . It is therefore, in our humble apprehension, absolutely necessary that some new and more effectual provision be made to limit and restrain the number of Members who partake of the bounties of the Crown by the enjoyment of Places, Grants, Pensions, Quarterings, or otherwise, and that some effectual method be taken for the more certain and easy discovery of all such as do enjoy these Places and other private Transactions. They further 'craved that the representative of the good town might be instructed to use his utmost endeavours to promote a Bill for limiting the over-grown number of Place-men who had seats in the House of Commons.' "

The nature of the response given to the Resolution by the magistrates may be gathered from a singularly incoherent, almost maudlin, Minute, which records that :—

"These our warm applications were but coldly received both by the Magistrates and the City's Representative in Parliament, and had not the desired effect, our Member being left at liberty to vote as he thought proper, went into all the contrary measures directly opposite, not only to our just sentiments in particular, but also to the sense of the far greater part of the nation in general, and left us still in a worse and worse condition. . . . And now that things were brought to this sad pass . . . When behold, a sudden and an unexpected event began to revive our drooping spirits, and to dispel the clouds of fear that had damped all our hopes. For the kind Providence of Almighty God, ever watchful and ever fruitful in expedients, and never failing to send seasonable relief and help to those It designs to preserve and protect, put it in the heart of an Illustrious, Noble, Generous, Worthy and Disinterested Patriot, the Duke of Argyll, to appear amongst us, and to espouse our just Cause and that of his Country, the Glorious Cause of Liberty . . . When we reflect on this extraordinary event . . . our breasts are filled with Joy, Love and Gratitude to our great bene-factor . . ."

For his vigorous attack on the Ministry, which contributed so much to its downfall, the Duke of Argyll received an address from the surgeons in which they applauded his "steady adherence to the cause of Liberty, his true interest in King and Country, and his endeavours to maintain the privileges of the City."

To which the Duke replied :—

"That since they were pleased to think him their friend and servant, he wished to advise them to behave themselves with the greatest duty to the King, with the strictest regard to the laws of their Country, and to give their assistance in their elections to such persons only who, they were persuaded, would serve the King and Country with true zeal unalloyed with private interest."

On the fall of the Ministry, the surgeons on 1st May 1741 invited Mr Alexander Nisbet, their deacon, to contest the City on behalf of the trades, it being their duty, they said, to pro-mote the election of one who would serve his country with true zeal uninfluenced by any lucrative consideration, and, that the

K

election of a tradesman to represent the City was of the greatest consequence to the several Incorporations, as preserving and establishing their privileges which had been so much infringed.

The object behind this movement was to re-establish the privilege of the tradesmen or craftsmen (among whom the surgeons ranked) of sharing equally with the merchants in the representation of the City. By the Treaty of Union the representation of the City in Parliament had been reduced from two to one, and from that time the merchants had succeeded in monopolising the representation, in spite of the protests of the tradesmen, whose right, under an agreement of 1583, was in danger of being lost by proscription.

At a meeting of the deacons held in Magdalen Chapel, Mr Nisbet was thanked for his offer to represent them and was urged to prosecute his election at once, and to encourage him in doing so the deacons agreed to convene their respective Incorporations and set the case before them for asserting their right, and to contrive methods whereby money might be advanced for bringing the matter to a head.

The surgeons unanimously resolved to stand by their deacon, and to bear a proportion of such expense as should be necessary for maintaining the privileges of the trades, and also to collect from each member of the Incorporation, or from other well-disposed persons, such sums as they should be pleased to advance.

After the election, in which Mr Nisbet was defeated, it was reported to the Surgeons that the Deacons of the Goldsmiths, Skinners, Furriers, Wrights, Fleshers, Weavers, and Waulkers, besides two Trades Councillors had, in direct contravention of the solemn promises given by each of them at their election to support the interests and privileges of the Crafts of the City, and also in opposition to the declared sentiments of their several Incorporations, vigorously opposed Mr Nisbet's election, and joined, aided, and voted for Mr Archibald Stewart, merchant, his opponent. It was therefore agreed by the members of the Incorporation to adopt this fixed resolution, viz.: that they, neither in this nor in any other Society of which they might happen to be members, would give their vote or interest to any of the persons named to bear any office of trust in time coming.

CHAPTER X

SOME SOCIAL AND DOMESTIC ACTIVITIES
OF THE COLLEGE

The Apprentices' Banquet—Dinner to the Magistrates—Social Gatherings
—The Botanical or Physic Garden—Act and Resolve against Im-
moralities—The Trades Maiden Hospital—The Widows' Fund—
The Establishment of a Lunatic Asylum — Public Vaccination—
Licensing of Midwives.

The Apprentices' Banquet. — In the Seal of Cause it is
stipulated that on his admission to the Craft the lawfully
begotten son of a freeman master shall be exempt from any
money payment "Except the denner to be maid to the
maisters efter he be exemmit and admitted by them . . . "
This old established custom of the apprentices celebrating
their entry to the Craft by entertaining the deacon and
masters to a banquet seems to have been maintained. In
1588, it is recorded that an apprentice after examination had
payed "his dewty for his bancat." As no specified sum is
mentioned, it may have varied according to circumstances.
Later on the amount seems to have been fixed at forty pounds
Scots, and this sum was paid by each apprentice along with
other fees at the time of his entry. In 1616, it was ordained
that there should be no prentice banquet in future unless the
deacon, the four masters, and most part of the brethren were
present, and that if the deacon should happen to be absent
he should be censured at the will of the brethren of the Craft.
This custom was continued through the whole of the 17th
century, and towards the close of it seems to have been
extended even to the period of examination. At last the
subject was taken up by the Calling, who appointed a committee
to consider ways and means of curtailing the practice or of
putting a stop to it altogether. The report of this committee,

147

which afterwards became an Act, was that, in their opinion, feasting and drinking with the entrant was extravagant, and tended to the dishonour of the Incorporation and to the detriment of the entrant. The practice ought therefore, the report continued, to cease, and instead of the hundred and forty pounds which the entrant usually paid at his admission, he should in future pay two hundred pounds for his upset and banquet, out of which thirty shillings stg. should be allowed for the purchase of books for the use of the Incorporation ; and the three examiners were allowed "every one of them to pay a pint of wine and the entrant also one pint of wine and no more, and that there shall be no feasting and drinking with the entrant until he be admitted."

Despite the air of festivity with which the examination seems to have been surrounded, it must not be supposed that the examination itself was a mere formality, for the rejection of a candidate, although not of frequent occurrence, was not unknown. An instance of this is recorded in 1672, when a candidate having been examined by the deacon upon the "containing and contained parts of the breast, and after other members had also examined him and seen him demonstrate upon the same," they declared themselves not satisfied and suspended him until he became better qualified. After the examination a question was raised as to whether or not an examiner might bring his lessons to the meeting house in writing, in whole or in part, and read the same off his papers when he examined.

Dinner to the Magistrates.—Another of the early dining customs of the Incorporation was to entertain the magistrates. When this custom originated has not been traced, but it was discontinued, about 1777, in consequence of the incidental expenses incurred in that year being as much as could be conveniently spared out of the College funds ; when the dinner was abandoned, a polite note was sent to the Lord Provost informing him of the reason. Soon afterwards it was agreed, that instead of supping together at the admission of each member, the College should have one stated supper meeting on the 1st August yearly, and that the expense of the supper should be defrayed by the members who attended it.

In 1784, it was agreed to resume the former practice of

giving a dinner yearly to the magistrates, and to allow a sum for that purpose, not exceeding five pounds stg.

Social Gatherings.—At an earlier date the surgeons made an arrangement to encourage more social intercourse between the members of their Society, by meeting in a neighbouring tavern and there spending the evening in a friendly fashion. In proposing the subject at one of the meetings, the deacon said he had observed with great satisfaction the harmony and good agreement that existed among them, but, at the same time, he had also noticed a sort of negligence in every individual in promoting a general and more intimate acquaintance which might be of good service to each other and for the general good of the Society. The best method that had occurred to him to remedy this evil, and to render the members more sociable and communicative, would be to appoint meetings at set times so as to pass the evening together in a cheerful manner. He therefore proposed that the Incorporation should meet at Lammas and Candlemas respectively, and that each member should pay 2/6 towards discharging the bill. After this had been agreed to, the deacon gave notice that the first meeting would be held at John Clearihue's at eight o'clock in the evening.

John Clearihue's tavern was known as the " Star and Garter." Situated in Writer's Close, and frequented by the magistrates and leading men of the day, it was perhaps the most popular resort in the city. A vivid description of its interior is given by Scott in *Guy Mannering*. Colonel Mannering, on searching for a friend (a lawyer) there, said he " could hardly conceive how a gentleman of a liberal profession and good society should choose such a scene for social indulgence. Besides the miserable entrance, the house itself seemed paltry and half-ruinous. The passage in which they stood had a window to the close, which admitted a little light during the daytime, and a villainous compound of smells at all times, but more especially towards the evening. Corresponding to this window was a borrowed light on the other side of the passage, looking into the kitchen, which had no direct communication with the free air, but received in the daytime, at second hand, such straggling and obscure light as found its way from the lane through the window opposite. At present, the interior of the kitchen was visible by its own huge fires—a sort of pandemonium, where men and women, half-undressed, were busied in baking, broiling, roasting oysters, and preparing devils on the grid-iron; the mistress of the place, with her shoes slip-shod and her hair, like that of Magaera, from under a round-eared cap, toiling, scolding, receiving orders, giving them, and obeying them all at once, seemed the presiding enchantress of that gloomy and fiery region."

Such was Clearihue's, the "howff" of the surgeons until 1777, when an Act was passed that all tavern meetings should be discontinued.

A receipted account, signed by John Clearihue himself, bears evidence of the abstemious habits of the surgeons, for at one of their meetings held in No. 9 room, their libations for the evening were settled for the modest sum of £1, 18s. 6d. Of this, eleven shillings was for supper, eighteen shillings for three bottles of claret, one and sixpence for bread and beer, and three shillings and sevenpence for punch, porter, biscuits, and a broken cup. It took two shillings and fivepence, however, to assuage the drouth of the officer, who appears to have been present, and two shillings to tip the waiter.

Dr Alexander Wood, who was Deacon of the Incorporation in 1762, while upholding the best traditions of his profession, also found time for social relaxation and "high jinks." "Lang Sandy"—as he was more endearingly called—is described by his bosom friend and life-long companion, Dr Andrew Duncan, as one of the most eminent and active surgeons of Edinburgh, and one of the most zealous promoters of those social meetings, which tend both to diffuse the knowledge of medical science and to promote harmony among the practitioners of the healing art. At one of those social functions at which he so ably presided, after the "lang craigs" had circulated too freely, Dr Wood no longer sat upright in his chair, and at a mock examination which was immediately held, he was reported to be dead, and the following verses were composed and sung by the assembled company to the tune of "Toby Philpot"—

> "Here lies Sandy Wood, a good honest fellow,
> Very wise when sober, but wiser when mellow;
> At sensible nonsense by no man excelled
> With wit and good humour dull care he repelled.

In the cure of diseases, his talents long shone;
As a good operator, he was second to none
A friend and a bottle were long his delight,
He could toil all the day, and yet laugh all the night.

But though now he's laid low, we must not complain
For after a sleep, he'll be with us again,
Shed no tears, my good friends, wear no garments of sable
Sandy Wood is not dead, but laid under the table."

The Botanical or Physic Garden.—The Incorporation played a useful part in promoting the study of botany by their apprentices and members.

Somewhere about 1664, a botanical garden had been established close to what is now the North Bridge, where students and others might obtain instruction from the Intendant, Mr James Sutherland.

An Act of the Town Council incorporating this highly useful institution into the University, evoked the jealousy of the surgeons, who, conceiving a possible encroachment upon their liberties, represented their suspicions to the magistrates. The Lord Provost promised that nothing should be done to their prejudice, and that the Act should be stopped until they be heard.

As the surgeons had already cultivated a physic garden of their own, it is obvious they could not with any chance of success oppose others following their example. As far back as 1664, their Minutes disclose that they then had a garden furnished with all kinds of "medicinall herbs and flowers that can be had anywhere," while, in 1668, a signed agreement with George Cathcart, their gardener, describes his duties in detail. First he is to occupy the gardener's house beneath their own convening room, at the entrance of the yard that lies in the High School Yards, commonly called Curryhill Yards, and to plant the whole yards with medicinal herbs and flowers for the use of the Calling, except a part of the high yard which is allocated to himself for his own particular use to be planted with pot herbs; he is to keep clean the banks, bunkers and valleys, and has liberty to sell drink within the house, and also to keep "kyles" [a game of ninepins] in the entry of the yard, "providing he suffer not the vulgar sort of persons and the scholars of the High School to play thereat."

Such was the surgeons' garden in the year 1668. Nearly thirty years later, when the arts of surgery and pharmacy had again been joined together, Mr James Sutherland, who had now been appointed Professor of Botany by the Town Council, solicited the patronage of the Calling in the following terms : That at great labour and expense he had brought the Botanic Garden in order and furnished it with a great number of plants as could hardly be expected in any garden in this country and goes near to equal several botanic gardens abroad. And besides, planted the dispensatory plants, first, by themselves after the order of the Latin alphabet such names as they usually prescribe them in the shops for instructing his scholars in the beginning, and has afterwards ranged them and classed all the whole plants in the garden into several tribes, as they nearest resemble each other in flower and seed, so that at first sight of a plant in its full perfection one may easily know to what family it belongs, and under what genus it is to be planted. He had also planted all the pleasant flowers and sown all the annual seeds in several compartments by themselves, so that nothing was wanting in the garden to make the study of botany both pleasant and easy. As all this was chiefly intended for the information of apprentices and servants and those that had the liberty of the shops, he therefore desired the Calling to take the garden into their collection (seeing what was done was for the great advantage both of the masters and of all those under their charge) and by their act to ordain all the prentices and others who had the liberty of their shops to pay a guinea to him, for which he undertook to own all the masters of the Calling as his patrons, to attend them in the garden and demonstrate the plants whensoever they pleased, besides waiting upon them at a "solemn public herbarizing in the fields" four times in the year, and to teach their apprentices and servants who have paid their money at such hours every day as the masters shall appoint.

In 1705, Sutherland was superseded by Dr Charles Preston, who craved the Calling to confer upon him the privileges held by his predecessor. The surgeons, finding that the knowledge of botany was absolutely necessary for all their apprentices, and being fully convinced that Dr Preston was well qualified to teach the said science, granted his request.

That Dr Preston fulfilled the surgeons' expectations and succeeded in making botany a pleasant study is amply borne out. So interesting indeed were his lectures that considerable difficulty was experienced in getting the pupils to leave the garden after their conclusion. This happened so frequently, that at last, on account of the long absence of their apprentices when they attended Dr Preston at the Physic Garden, the surgeons ordained that " five of the youngest of their brethren with the deacon go to the garden by turns every morning by four of the clock and dismiss their apprentices and servants at seven, and recommend that they go straight to their masters' several shops."

On Dr Charles Preston's death, in 1711, his brother George succeeded him, and drew up the following regulations, which the Calling approved and ordered to be observed in the future :—

" 1st. That all apprentices and servants are obliged to come to the gardens between the hours of five and seven in the morning during the teaching time, which is from the middle of May till the end of September. 2nd. That no apprentice or servant shall come to the garden any other time than what is above mentioned without acquainting their masters, and the Intendant is to attend the garden for that purpose three days in the week, Monday, Wednesday and Friday from three to five in the afternoon. 3rd. All prentices and servants are prohibited from plucking up any tree, shrub or plant without leave given by the Intendant, and as oft as any of the prentices or servants shall be found plucking or pulling any of the trees, they shall be obliged to pay sixpence to the gardener every time and lose the benefit of being taught in the afternoon and coming to the garden at any time except between the hours of five and seven in the morning. 4th. All prentices and servants are prohibited to ask from the gardener any plant or root without a line from their Masters directed to the Intendant, and for the encouragement of this order Mr Preston obliges himself to give to the Masters a part of such plants, roots, etc., growing within the garden as may be best spared. 5th. For further encouragement of the prentices and servants and their giving all due respect to Mr Preston, he hereby promises that after such time as the garden is in good order, to teach the Materia Medica, the diets of which shall afterwards be appointed."

Act and Resolve against Immoralities.—So unsatisfactory was the state of affairs in the City in 1703 that the Town Council conceived it to be their duty to draw the attention of the inhabitants to the many misfortunes which had befallen it, and to call upon them to join in a general supplication to the Almighty to deliver it from further calamities. To this end the Incorporations were desired to adopt an Act submitted to them by the Town Council, but as the surgeons considered there were many sins and judgments in which this Act was defective, they proposed drafting one themselves "more comprehensive of the wrath of God, as occasioned by the prevailing sins of the Nation and the City, and to enumerate them in the Act, with a special regard to their present circumstances." Accordingly the following Act was passed and ordained to be read in the College once a year :—

ACT AND RESOLVE AGAINST IMMORALITIES

"At Edinburgh the 13th July 1703. The which day the deacon, masters and brethren of the Surgeons of Edinburgh, being convened in their Hall—Taking to their serious consideration the many and dreadful judgments and tokens of the wrath of an angry God which hath overtaken this sinful Nation and City, such as many years' scarcity of victuals and dearth whereby not only this Nation and City have been mightily impoverished, but many thousands of Christians perished with famine to the desolation of some corners of the land.—The disappointing and blasting that great design of advancing the trade and wealth of the Nation by the loss of the African and Indian Company's Colony of Caledonia in America, Whereby this Nation and City have lost not only many brave men, but a great part of their treasure without any hopes of recovery—Several dreadful fires which within these few years have consumed the most glorious of our buildings and best part of our City whereby many families have been brought to ruin—The present low estate of the common good of this City whereby the poor and decayed burgesses are defrauded out of their just birthright by the mismanagement of those who sometimes have had the charge thereof, notwithstanding the pious endeavours of many honest neighbours to prevent the same who have still met with disappointments by ambitious and designing men—The terrible blowing up of several barrels of gunpowder in our suburb of Leith whereby a great part of that place was reduced to a ruinous heap—The great losses this City and Nation have of late and daily sustain in their trade by taking many of our ships by

French pirates—and that even in sight of our harbours so that trade and commerce even in our own parts are obstructed. And farther considering that not only these but many other dreadful judgments do still threaten us because of the wickedness and abominations of city and country which are but too evident such as woeful defection of all sorts and ranks of people. The crying sins of profanity, blasphemy and vile hypocrisy, Sabbath breaking, lukewarmness and formality in public and private worship, and immorality of all sorts which overflow this City and Nation like a flood—We do therefore in the first place earnestly beg of the Eternal God that He would divert His deserved rods and for His own holy Name's Sake yet preserve a remnant for himself in this poor afflicted Nation and City—And in the next place we do resolve in the Lord's strength, every one of us for our own selves to be more watchful over our hearts and ways than formerly. And we do again earnestly beg of the same holy God of all Grace that He would give us grace, zeal, and prudence in our several capacities to advance His glory and so far as an opportunity shall be put in our hands to suppress and rebuke all sorts of vice and immorality. Amen."

The Trades Maiden Hospital. — The Trades Maiden Hospital was founded by the Crafts in 1704, for the purpose of maintaining and educating the daughters of decayed tradesmen. Some particulars of its inception and early history are recorded in the surgeons' books in September 1704, wherein it is stated that although the sons of indigent craftsmen were taken care of in Heriot's Hospital, no provision of any sort was made for their daughters, who were altogether destitute of a public fund for a similar purpose. The Incorporations, therefore, resolved to found an institution where the female children and grandchildren of their brethren who were in need of assistance would receive the same benefits. The Deacons of Trades, the two Trades Councillors, and nine others to be chosen—in all twenty-five persons—were to form the Governing Board, from which a Treasurer was to be elected to receive all monies and to defray the necessary charges of the Hospital. For carrying out this pious work the Incorporations were invited to contribute what they thought fit, and any person subscribing a certain amount would be permitted, in virtue of his donation, to make a nomination of his own.

The surgeons, in recognising the charitable design of the

undertaking, agreed to pay 320 pounds Scots yearly as their quota for the support of four girls to be presented by them from time to time. The first nominee of the surgeons was elected in 1708. On another vacancy occurring in 1710 it was filled by "Anna Balfour, grandchild of the late Sir Andrew Balfour, Doctor of Medicine." When the barbers were separated from the surgeons in 1722 it was arranged that each Society should make a presentation alternately, but in 1782, in consequence of the establishment of the Widows' Fund whereby the orphans of surgeons were provided for, it was arranged that, when the surgeons had no daughters of their own to present, all vacancies should be filled up by the barbers.

In 1803, Mr John Bennet, Deacon of the College, was charged with neglect of duty as one of the Managers of the Hospital for not attending more to the comfort of the girls, and particularly in permitting them to be seated at the same end of the church as the 42nd Highlanders. The reflections cast upon the deacon, however, were probably due more to private animosity than to facts, for upon investigation it was proved that "the behaviour of our brave countrymen had been most devout in church and decorous in every respect to the girls of the Hospital."

In the year 1845, a clause was inserted in the Medical Bill then before Parliament to the effect that, while the College were most anxious to forfeit their Incorporative standing, they wished still to reserve their right of presentation to the Trades Maiden Hospital. This, it must be explained, was not so much on their own account, as no surgeon's child had been presented for more than fifty years, but because of the obligations they were under to the barbers of presenting children of members of that Society, failing their own. The convenery objected, however, that the College should disjoin itself from their body and at the same time retain one of its privileges, and stated that if the College had come under obligation of presentation to other parties, which interfered with their renouncing these rights, it was for them to satisfy these obligations with which the convenery had nothing to do. The College were now in a dilemma, for unless they appeased the convenery, and at the same time came to an amicable arrangement with the barbers, the Bill, then in Parliament, might receive such active opposition when it came to the Lords as to endanger its success.

The College dealt first with the barbers, and eventually the latter Society agreed to surrender its contingent right to the presentation to the Hospital and all other claims which they had on the College, provided that that body paid an annuity of £10 to the Barbers' Society yearly "in all time coming." The barbers were further to be free from all obligations to the College either as regarded the election of the Clerk or any other matter. Of course, there was still the possibility of the convenery or the Hospital Governors objecting to the barbers making any presentations at all, if the surgeons ceased to be an Incorporation, as the barbers' privileges only came to them through their connection with the surgeons. However, as soon as it was ascertained that there was to be no objection to the proposed arrangement, and that it could be carried through without compromising the rights of the barbers in regard to the Hospital, the transaction was concluded. The annual payment of the £10 was now the only existing connection between the surgeons and their old dependents the barbers. On coming to terms with the barbers, the College at once withdrew their claim to any Corporative privilege, and as this satisfied the convenery, the clause in the Bill was accordingly amended, and so the matter ended. This brought the career of the College as one of the old Incorporated Trades to a close, and when the City was honoured by a visit of her Majesty, the late Queen Victoria, it was proposed that in case of any public demonstration taking place it would be more fitting that they should appear in their proper character of a Royal College, and as such they ought to act along with the sister College of Physicians. On a previous occasion when King George IV. visited Edinburgh it was arranged that the different Incorporations and public bodies should be drawn up in the High Street upon the day on which the King was to go in procession from Holyrood to the Castle and back again. The members of the College were therefore requested to be in their place on that day as one of the Incorporations of the City, and the Treasurer was instructed to provide a new cloak and hat for the officer.

The Widows' Fund.—A fund for the benefit of the widows

and children of deceased members of the Incorporation, known as the Widows' Fund, was established in 1778, the prime mover of the scheme being Mr Thomas Hay, a most energetic member of the Calling, who, after acting as Deacon in 1784-5 and again in 1794-5, when he was also chosen Deacon-Convener of the Trades, served the City in the important office of Burgh Chamberlain. Before this fund was instituted, charity was dispensed in many directions from the quarterly payments which every member of the Craft was liable to under the Seal of Cause, and from the time Minutes were first kept numerous grants of varying sums were recorded. In the early days the bare fact of the gift was simply noted, but as time went on the circumstances in which the grants were made were fully described. Almost the first recorded act of the Calling is one of charity to the widow of a deceased member. Assistance, nevertheless, was not confined to craftsmen and their families, for, in 1616, one John Stewart was awarded twenty pounds Scots because he was " spuilziet [plundered] by piracie," and a Frenchman was given five shillings at the "Craftis command." In 1632 twenty merks were contributed as the surgeons' share towards purchasing a bell for the Magdalen Chapel, while twelve pounds Scots were presented to an old woman "to relieve her necessity," and the deacon promised to speak to the Kirk Treasurer "to restore her to her pension" which, for some reason, seems to have been withheld. These and many other instances of the Craft's benevolence appear on almost every page of the early Minutes. A case of shipwreck and another of piracy may not be altogether uninteresting, as they illustrate the varied nature of the demands made upon the Craft's purse.

In 1694, a petition was presented by a merchant of Thurso "craving a supply" in respect of his misfortune in having lost two ships at sea, of one of which he was quarter owner and of the other sole owner. He was awarded ten rix dollars. Another request for assistance was made by George Hailes, apothecary in London, on behalf of his father and a lady who were prisoners with the Turks "at Marmora in Barbarie." They were represented to have lost three thousand pounds sterling by fire, and by a ship, " richly ladened from the West Indies—wherein both they themselves, ship and cargo to the value of five thousand four hundred pounds stg. were taken by the Turks and carried into Marmora, where they were in great misery and would inevitably perish unless relieved and ransomed with four hundred pounds stg." Towards this sum the Incorporation subscribed twelve pounds Scots. Another entry states that a generous donor offered five pounds eight shillings to the surgeons' poor-box, with the promise that "as God shall move his heart he would contribute more."

An appeal by a barber in distress reveals the condition to which a member of the Craft was reduced in the year 1670. As it attracts attention for more reasons than one, it is given verbatim :—

"The humbell petition of William Sinclair, barbour in Leith. Sheweth,   That I your poore petitioner am reduced to extreme great povertie with my wyfe and children by my infirmitie and sicknes, so that I am not able to doe anything for the supplie of meself and familie, so that we are in ane most lamentable condition without hous or being or any uther comfort, els we being rendred most unexpressibell poore and licklay to starve, which hath urged me your poor supplicant to lay oppen my condition unto your honours, humblie desyreing that ye will be graciouslie [pleased] to conterbut something, according as your honours shall think fitt, for my present supplie, my neccessaties being so urgent.

" May it thairfor please your honours, for Gods cause seriouslie to tak the premiss to consideration, and in regard thairof be graciouslie pleased to extend your bowels of christian pittie and compassion towards your foresaid petitioner whose pressing neccessities wold constrain the hardest hert to pittie."

The result of this petition was three pounds Scots ; while another barber in a similar condition was allowed a pension of twelve shillings per week, and the Treasurer was instructed to provide him with shoes and stockings and a pair of breeches.

The Society for the relief of the poor Episcopal clergy for many years received an annual gratuity of two guineas, and, as a sequel to the '15, a sum of five pounds stg. was voted in aid of " several gentlemen, prisoners within the Castle, Tolbooth, Canongate, and other places, who by the late troubles were reduced to the utmost extremity and were now called up to Carlisle in order to be tried."

Thus it will be seen that the surgeons, besides ministering

to the needs of their own indigent members, had many calls upon them from outside ; and when it is remembered that the funds of the Incorporation were frequently at a low ebb, it is apparent that the value of the sums disbursed depended more upon the state of the poor-box than upon the claims of the applicants. For this reason many deserving cases probably suffered, so that when it was proposed to inaugurate a new system, whereby all the widows of their deceased members would share alike, the proposal was warmly received.

The subject of the Widows' Fund was first brought before the Incorporation, in April 1777, by the deacon, who explained that he had called the meeting to take their opinion upon a proposal made to the Council by Mr Hay for raising a fund to support their widows and children. Mr Hay then laid his proposals before the meeting, remarking that the many advantages derived from the scheme for supporting the ministers' widows, and from others of a similar nature, induced him to think that a fund might be established in their own Society with the same happy result. After considering the scheme and taking the opinions of the Lord Advocate and Mr Ilay Campbell upon some legal difficulties which were likely to arise, it was decided to apply for an additional Charter containing such powers as were necessary for the proper execution of the scheme and the applying of a part of their funds to support it. Briefly, the idea was that each member should pay five pounds yearly into the fund, and that twenty-five pounds should be annually taken out of the Society's fund for the same purpose, and that on the death of a contributor his widow should benefit to the extent of twenty-five pounds per annum. Trustees and a collector were then appointed, and Mr James Chalmers, solicitor in London, was authorised to take steps to obtain the Charter which was found to be necessary.

It then occurred to the Incorporation that as it had long been their wish to have the title of Royal College of Surgeons conferred upon them there could not be a more proper time for making the application. Accordingly a petition was presented to the King, bearing :—

"That the Surgeons of the City of Edinburgh were created and erected and incorporated into a Society or College, and various privileges conferred upon them by several grants made by your

Majesty's Royal predecessors, Kings of Scotland, and by Acts of the Parliament of that Kingdom, and particularly by Letters Patent of their Majesties King William and Queen Mary bearing date 28th February 1694 confirming all the former Grants, and these Letters Patent were ratified in Parliament 17th day of July 1695.—The Petitioners hope that they have been no less deserving of Royal Patronage than their predecessors, Their numerous Pupils serving in your Majesty's Army and Navy may be mentioned as an evidence of the attention bestowed by the present members of the said College to improve the art of Surgery.   That they may maintain an equality with similar institutions in several neighbouring Kingdoms they are solicitous that your Majesty may be graciously pleased to confer upon them the Title of Royal College of Surgeons—When they reflect upon the liberal patronage and support your Majesty has been uniformly pleased to bestow on literature and useful Arts They are encouraged to hope this their request will not be refused . . ." etc., etc.

It had been the wish of the Incorporation for some time to amend their title.   A few years previously the question had been referred to Mr Henry Dundas, whose attention was directed to the Charter of 1686, which contains the following :— " Damus concidimus ratum facimus et approbamus prædicte *Societati et Collegio* chirurgorum ibideni et aliud ejusdem Magistratus et Senatus Civitatis Decretum in favorino Pharmacopieorum et Chirurgorum Pharmacopieorum 25 februarii 1657," etc., etc.   As in this Charter they are frequently called " illa Societas seu *Collegium* Chirurgorum " and as they were fully empowered to teach surgery and pharmacy as a collegiate body by their Charter of 1694, they submitted they were entitled to assume the appellation of Royal College of Surgeons.

Mr Dundas said they did not owe their existence as a Society to those Charters ; their original foundation was the Seal of Cause, and all the Charters and ratifications in Parliament related to them as a Society already incorporated.   He therefore was of opinion that the legal denomination of the surgeons in Edinburgh was the denomination given them in virtue of their original Seal of Cause which was that of Corporation ; but as the title of Collegium was given in the Charters from the Crown, he did not think that anyone would have a right to object if they were to take the title of College, but as to the use

L

of the term *Royal* College he could see no foundation either from the Seal of Cause or in the later Charters.

There the matter ended, until it became obvious that a new Charter would have to be obtained before the Widows' Fund could be established when, as before stated, they decided to include in their petition an application for a new title. No difficulty was found in the matter, and, on 22nd May 1778, a Charter was granted in their favour incorporating them anew under the name and title of Royal College of Surgeons of the City of Edinburgh and authorising them to carry into execution the scheme for making a provision for their widows and children.

The Widows' Fund, now fairly floated, became a great success. Four years after its inauguration, the trustees reported the fund to be flourishing beyond their expectation and showing a credit balance of over £120. In 1787, it was apparent that some alterations were necessary for the improvement of the scheme and for making it permanent. For this purpose another petition was drawn up and entrusted to Mr Hay to deliver to Sir Adam Ferguson in London, who had promised to present it to the House. On his return, Mr Hay informed the College of the passing of the Act which, he said, was so framed that no accident could now materially affect the fund, as it did not depend upon the number of contributors, the number of widows, nor the interest of money falling below what it then was. These circumstances, he explained, might vary the amount of the annuities paid, but that if in any one year the sum calculated upon was, from these causes, not fully paid up to the widows, they became creditors upon the surplus funds of future years to the amount of arrears due to them. His great object, he said, was to raise the capital by slow stated payments, and to relieve the contributors after a certain number of payments from their annual rates. These two objects he had attended to, and congratulated the members on their now being rendered permanent by an Act of the British Legislature. Mr Hay then moved that letters of thanks be sent to the following members of both Houses of Parliament for the assistance they had given him in carrying through the Bill, viz., the Earl of Moray, Lord Elphinstone, Sir Adam Ferguson, Sir James Johnston, and Mr Skene of Skene. After this had been agreed to, Mr Alexander Wood represented the College as being highly indebted to Mr Hay, not only as the original proposer of the scheme, but in virtue of the uncommon attention he had all along bestowed upon it, and in particular for the great zeal and activity he had shown in getting the Bill passed through Parliament. He therefore moved that the thanks of the College be returned to Mr Hay and, as a further mark of their approbation, that they should make him a present of a piece of plate.

The motion was unanimously agreed to, and the thanks of the College having been given to Mr Hay, a piece of plate to the value of £50 was ordered to be presented to him bearing the following inscription :—

"Nero optime de Collegio Regio Chirurgorum Edinensium merito
THOMÆ HAY.
Quia vidius quæ Maritos, atque liberis qui Parentes,
Amissos diflerunt,
Labore indefessus consuluit ;
Nas houe Argenteum, grati animi monumentum,
Publico Fratrum consensu
donatum est

A.D. 1787."

The Establishment of a Lunatic Asylum.—Since the death of Fergusson the poet in the City Bedlam or pauper hospital for the insane, in 1774, the necessity of providing a suitable place for the treatment of lunatics above the position of pauperism appealed so strongly to the kindly disposition of Dr Andrew Duncan that he determined, when opportunity offered, to erect some such place in the vicinity of Edinburgh. No such opportunity, however, presented itself until he was President of the Royal College of Physicians in 1791. In the meantime we find that the matter was discussed by the surgeons, to whom it was introduced by Mr Thomas Wood, who informed them that he proposed to institute an asylum for lunatics, and as he thought the success of the undertaking would in a great measure depend upon his receiving the sanction of the College, he hoped they would favour him with it, in which case he requested that they would take an opportunity of intimating to the public that the proposal met with their approval. This the College agreed to do, and also thanked him for engaging in an undertaking which might be attended with such beneficial consequences. Whether Dr Duncan's intention was anticipated by Mr Wood, or whether the action of the latter forced Dr Duncan's hand is of no importance, but no sooner had Mr Wood's proposal been made public than Dr Duncan launched a more extended scheme, in the name of the College of Physicians, proposing that an institution should be established under the direction of the Lord Provost, the Lord President of the Court of Session, the Presidents of the Colleges of Physicians and Surgeons and other trustees whom they named. On this second proposal coming before the surgeons, Mr Hay who was deacon at the time, observed that as the College had already pledged themselves to Mr Wood, he could not see how they could, with propriety, take any part in the establishment then suggested. Mr Wood thereupon informed the meeting that upon reconsidering the matter, and upon the advice of his friends, he had resolved for the present to drop his proposed scheme, and moved that a committee be appointed to deliberate with a committee of the Physicians upon the proposals now made. As the result of these meetings, the joint-committee concluded that, as the trustees were taken from several different Societies, the best method of promoting a general subscription would be by getting them to appeal to their own Societies in whatever manner they thought best. It was also of opinion that if the Royal Colleges were to set the example by being the first to adopt the plan the best consequences would probably arise from it, as this would demonstrate to the public at large how far a lunatic asylum was considered as a most necessary institution in Edinburgh.

This is the origin of the Royal Edinburgh Asylum, and although the attempt to establish it proved abortive owing to the unsatisfactory response to the appeal for subscriptions, a more successful endeavour, aided by a Government grant, was made in the year 1807. The failure of Dr Duncan's efforts, however, left Mr Wood free to prosecute his original plan; that he did so is evident from a report made by a small committee of surgeons who inspected his institution in 1797. In consequence of this report, which was openly read at one of the meetings, the members of the College said they were happy to find that an asylum for the reception of patients in a state of lunacy had lately been opened in the vicinity of the City by Mr Thomas Wood, and that they were satisfied that an institution of this kind, conducted by a professional gentleman of character, was calculated to be of great benefit to unfortunate lunatics. They further testified to the excellent regulations for the internal government of the house, and warmly recommended the undertaking to the earnest support and protection of the public.

Public Vaccination.—As early as 1771, the Surgeons promoted a scheme for introducing inoculation on a general scale. A letter from Dr Boswell, President of the College of Physicians, whose co-operation had been solicited, acknowledging the receipt of a communication from the Surgeons states:—

"That the College have desired me to return you and the much respected Society of Surgeons their respectful compliments and thanks for the honour they have done them in consulting them about an affair of so great consequence as the setting up and establishing of an hospital for inoculation. They approve much of the design and will heartily concur with them in promoting it to the utmost of their power and have appointed a committee to take it into their consideration and to make report to the College, who will with all convenient speed acquaint your committee of their resolution, both as to the scheme in general and also first as to the ways and means for bringing such a design to a hearing and then of supporting it . . . 17th April 1771."

Ten years later, an advertisement was drawn up for insertion in the newspapers intimating to the public that the members of the College of Surgeons had been hitherto in the practice of inoculating the poor of the City, and, being convinced of the great benefit which must accrue to them from inoculation becoming as general as possible, they have resolved to continue the practice and to furnish them with medicine and assistance gratis. Eventually, as the result of several conferences with the Physicians, it was proposed that one or more convenient apartments should be hired on the outskirts of the town at which the operation might be performed. Also that four members of the College of Surgeons be elected every half-year or appointed by rotation as inoculating surgeons, each of whom would take charge of patients in a certain quarter of the town, and that four members of the College of Physicians be appointed in a similar manner, each to visit the patients of a particular surgeon when he should think it necessary or proper.

After the lapse of another decade, in 1791, the question was again taken up by Dr Andrew Duncan who, as one of the Managers of the Public Dispensary and also President of the Royal College of Physicians, proposed to the surgeons to concur with the physicians in offering their services to inoculate and to attend the children of poor people at their houses, during the months of September and October, without putting their parents to any expense. It was also proposed to send a letter, signed by the Presidents of both Colleges, to all the ministers in the City, informing them of the steps which had been already taken to encourage the practice of inoculation among the lower ranks, and recommending them to exert their endeavours in attempting to remove the prejudices which had hitherto prevented the practice from becoming general.

In 1806 the College of Physicians of London, in compliance with an address from the House of Commons, undertook to inquire into the state of vaccination in the United Kingdom and to report their opinion upon the causes which had retarded its general adoption. In order to make these reports as complete as possible and to collect information from different parts of the country, the co-operation of the Surgeons of Edinburgh was cordially invited. In this way we get an insight into their views before the practice was generally approved of. Since the Vaccine Institution was established in 1801, vaccination, they said, was increasing so rapidly that for two or three years past smallpox had been reckoned rather a rare occurrence even amongst the poorer classes in the City, while among the better-off class the disease was unknown. From experience, they had no doubt of the permanent security against the smallpox which was produced by the constitutional affection of the cowpox, and, so great had been their success in vaccination, that for some years past they had not been required to inoculate any person with smallpox who had previously undergone inoculation with the cowpox. They further observed that they met with no recurrence in their practice of cowpox inoculation which would operate in their minds to its disadvantage, and they begged particularly to notice that they had seen no instance of obstinate eruptions, or of new or dangerous diseases which they could attribute to the introduction among mankind of this mild preventative of smallpox.   The College knew of no causes which had retarded the adoption of vaccination in Edinburgh ; on the contrary, the practice had become general within the City, and judging from the amount of vaccine matter that had been sent to the country by members of the College and the Vaccine Institution, they had good reason to believe that the practice had become as general throughout that part of the Kingdom as could have been expected.   This led to a National Vaccine Institution being established in London under the direction of the Government, and the Board, which then consisted of the President and Censors of the Royal College of Physicians and the Master and Governors of the Royal College of Surgeons, invited the surgeons of Edinburgh to communicate from time to time any observations they might deem important on the subject.

Midwifery and Midwives. — In 1752, the Incorporation granted its licence for women to practise midwifery.   Mrs Anna Ker, the first lady to receive the licence, in her petition for examination, states, that as the office of midwifery was of the greatest consequence to mankind and one of the most useful branches of surgery, it behoved everyone who intended to practise it to be previously instructed in the principles of the art, and not to follow the common method of women, of beginning practice without either study or experience.   After being examined upon all the different sorts of births, natural, laborious, and preternatural, and on the methods of treating women after delivery and new-born children, the examiners (of whom Prof. R. Smith was one) said she was in every respect extremely well qualified to discharge the office of midwife and well deserved the favour of a licence, which was accordingly granted.

In 1769, when the Incorporation consulted Counsel upon some privileges contained in their Charter of 1694, which settled the boundaries between the physicians and surgeons, they touched upon the question of midwifery and requested an opinion as to whether the practice of that art did not belong exclusively to themselves, for according to the physicians' patent the latter were excluded from performing any sort of manual operation and consequently that of midwifery. In reply to this query, Mr Henry Dundas (to whom the questions were submitted) said :—

"I apprehend this query is the one of most importance to the Memorialists, and therefore should have wished it had been in my power to give them an answer to the question more agreeable to their wishes than I find myself at liberty to do. So far, I am of opinion that if midwifery did exclusively belong, either to the Physicians or the Surgeons, it does seem more naturally to belong to the art of the latter than that of the former. But my difficulty consists in this, that I do not see the grounds upon which to be of opinion that it falls under any exclusive privilege. If midwifery had been understood to fall under the exclusive right of any of the Societies, it was a matter of too general and notorious importance to escape a particular mention being made of it; but so far is this from being the case, I cannot discover any word which can be so tortured as to comprehend it, and indeed, if I am not mistaken, the history of the art renders it impossible that it should have been mentioned, for at the time that both the Societies were erected, midwifery was not practised and understood to be a male operation, and accordingly the uniform consuetude, which is the best interpreter of all writings, has uniformly explained this matter agreeable to the opinion which I now give, for it has never been claimed as exclusive right either of Physicians or Surgeons, but has been practised by any woman in the country who choosed to think herself qualified for it. For these reasons I am of opinion there is no room for entering into a discussion to settle the boundaries betwixt the Physicians and the Surgeons as to this point, because I do not think it falls under the exclusive privileges either of the one or of the other."

CHAPTER XI

THE DIPLOMAS AND EXAMINATIONS OF THE COLLEGE

Recognition of Diplomas for Public Services—Nominations to Navy and Army — Revision of Laws regarding Diplomas, 1806—Recognition of Lectures by Licentiates—Duration of Qualifying Courses — Class Certificates of Attendance — The Title Licentiate — Fraudulent Diplomas — Revision of Regulations for Examinations, 1816 — Examiners Assaulted and Threatened.

Recognition of Diplomas for Public Services.—Towards the end of the 18th century, when an invasion of India by the French was considered probable, candidates for service with the East India Company holding the diploma of the College of Surgeons of Edinburgh were required to pass an additional examination conducted by the College of Surgeons in London. To obviate this the Edinburgh College, in 1798, petitioned the Company that their diploma might in future be deemed sufficient evidence of qualification for appointment to their service without the necessity of a further examination in London. In putting their case before the Court of Directors, the College observed that a considerable number of those who had annually been appointed to serve in the different Presidencies, and also in the shipping service, had received their education in the University of Edinburgh. After this education had been completed, they applied to the Royal College of Surgeons for diplomas, and were required to produce certificates of attendance at the medical classes and at the hospitals for a specified number of years before being admitted to examination. When so admitted they passed a very strict examination in anatomy, surgery, botany, and pharmacy before receiving the diploma of the College. Yet, notwithstanding this testimony of their qualifications, they were then required, at an expense which their circumstances in many instances could not well afford, and with inconvenience to themselves, to submit to an examination before the College of Surgeons in London in order to obtain from them a similar testimony of their professional abilities— a hardship sufficient to keep back some of the most meritorious candidates from applying to the Company for employment. The College therefore hoped that the respectability of their Institution, added to that of the University with which they were so closely connected, and the degree of credit which the medical world had always attached to their diploma, would strongly plead in their favour in the present instance. In this case the request of the College was granted.

The same regulations, however, held good with regard to appointments in the public service. This led to another memorial being presented to the Duke of York, as Commander-in-Chief of the Army, in 1808, under the direction of Mr Henry Dundas. Drawn up in terms somewhat similar to the one already described, it bore that the College was formed into a body corporate as far back as 1505, for the purpose of instructing pupils in surgery and granting licences to practise to such as should on examination be found properly instructed in that art; those holding their diploma were fully qualified to practise indiscriminately both medicine and surgery. As showing how thoroughly the latter was taught in Edinburgh, it was pointed out that no fewer than three public courses on surgery, apart from those on anatomy, were now delivered there, viz., lectures on the Principles and Practice of Surgery, on Clinical Surgery, and on Military Surgery. The diploma of the College, nevertheless, was not accepted by the Army Medical Board without an additional diploma from the College of Surgeons in London, and as the distinction between the two diplomas was considered to be injurious to the character of the Edinburgh School and detrimental to the public service, the memorialists prayed that the two diplomas might be placed upon the same footing. Similar petitions were also submitted to the Board of Admiralty, to the Army Medical Board, and to the Commissioners of the Transport Service. The Admiralty was the first to give a definite reply, which in effect was, that their Lordships, having considered the petition, together with a letter which was transmitted to them at the same time from the Secretary of the Royal College of Surgeons in London stating their objections to the measure, were pleased to concur in the opinion of the London College, and had informed the Board that they did not mean to give their sanction to any alteration in the manner or place of examinations for surgeons for the Navy. Naturally enough, in order to see what these objections were, the surgeons applied for a copy of the letter mentioned, but were informed that the established custom of their office did not permit of this being done.

The reply of the Army Medical Board was more favourable, but before submitting the questions to the Commander-in-Chief, they wished to be informed upon certain details concerning the subjects of the examination, such as who the teachers were, and whether the examination was conducted by fixed members or by all the members in rotation. In reply, the College explained that their examination was by no means confined to anatomy and surgery strictly so called, but included questions on chemistry, pharmacy, materia medica, and the medicinal treatment of surgical diseases — in fact that it extended to all branches of education necessary for those who were to act as surgeons in the Army or in private practice. The College also stated that it never meant that every person calling himself a teacher should be deemed competent for the instruction of those who were qualifying themselves for its diploma, but referred only to members of the Colleges of London, Dublin or Edinburgh, or to teachers of established reputation. With regard to the last query, the examiners, it was said, were all specially appointed, and that that office did not devolve on members by rotation. In conclusion, the College wished it to be known that the possession of a diploma did not constitute the person a member of the College— an honour only obtained after four several examinations. It was thought necessary to add this, as it was believed in this respect the constitution of the Edinburgh College differed from that of the College of Surgeons of London. This explanation evidently proved satisfactory, for in due time intimation was received by the College that their diploma would be accepted as a qualification for regimental commissions in that branch of the profession. The Board said that it must be distinctly understood that Army candidates would have to give proof of competent acquirements in the other branches of the profession and also of their general education, for "we are bound to state," continued the Commissioners, "that several gentlemen have appeared with the Edinburgh diploma who were very young and were indifferently qualified, being so destitute of a due degree of preliminary education as to be unable to translate the pharmacopœia or to read the Latin directions to prescriptions." This led to a proposal by the College that no candidate should receive a diploma until he had entered his twentieth year, and that he should be able to translate with accuracy a part of a medical Latin author which should be presented to him for that purpose at the time of his examination.

Dr Charles Kerr, Physician to the Army, Mr John Weir, late Director-General of the Army Medical Board, and Dr William Franklin, one of the Principal Directors of the Army Medical Board, under whose names most of the foregoing correspondence had been carried on, were soon afterwards elected Honorary Fellows of the College.

Before passing from this subject it is worthy of note that, in 1819, similar privileges to those conferred upon the College were claimed by the Faculty of Physicians and Surgeons of Glasgow. A letter from Dr Corkindale, on behalf of that ancient Institution, suggests that the framers of the Act making it obligatory that every vessel carrying more than a certain number of passengers should have on board a surgeon holding a diploma from one of the Royal Colleges of Surgeons in London, Edinburgh, or Dublin, must have been ignorant of the rights and customs of the body he represented. Otherwise they would not have proposed an enactment which, by conferring privileges on certain Corporations, passed over another similarly situated, and so sanctioned injustice. The letter, after detailing the Charters and ratifications, declared that in ten years they had licensed nearly four hundred surgeons who were then in practice in various parts of the world. It also complained that the exclusion of their diploma cast a reproach on their public character and had the effect of degrading the licensing authority with which the Legislation had invested them.

Previous to this some courtesies had passed between the College and the Faculty. In 1810, two candidates received the College diploma gratis in consideration of their being members of the Faculty of Physicians and Surgeons of Glasgow to which the College wished to pay "every respect," and at the same time it was resolved to recognise the lectures of members of the Faculty as qualifying for the College diploma. The Faculty again came under the notice of the College in 1817, when the former made application to be erected a Royal College. On this occasion the Lord Advocate, to whom the petition was referred, notified the College that it would have an opportunity of considering whether the Charter, if granted, would interfere with their privileges as a Royal College, and to lay any statement they might wish to make before him, previous to his making his report to the Prince Regent.

When the "Passengers Bill" was about to come before Parliament in 1822, a deputation of the Faculty went to London to endeavour to get their body included amongst those entitled to grant licences to surgeons of passenger ships, and there stated that they were convinced that no objection to such a provision would be made by the College of Surgeons of Edinburgh. This was notified to the College in the usual way, so that no proceedings in Parliament could be adopted which might affect the interests of another body without their being made aware of it. In acknowledging the courtesy, the College remarked they had reason for believing that, besides the Faculty, the University of Glasgow had also applied to be included in the Bill—a claim, they suggested, which ought to be determined according to the chartered rights of the respective bodies. In the opinion of the College, the Faculty appeared to have the preferable title to be included in the Bill, but they could see no reason for conferring the privilege upon Glasgow University more than upon any other University, and that, if that University was admitted as having a right to grant diplomas in surgery, the other Universities in Scotland would probably claim the same privilege. In conclusion, it was submitted that the three Royal Colleges of Surgeons in London, Dublin, and Edinburgh, along with the Faculty of Glasgow, were the only bodies in the United Kingdom having a right to grant such diplomas, and that if the claim of Glasgow University was allowed it would materially affect the rights of all the surgical colleges.

Nominations to Navy and Army.—In 1846, the privilege was granted to the College of nominating a student once every three years for the appointment of assistant-surgeon in the Navy, and in the following year the medical department of the Army agreed to a similar arrangement every second year. The candidates for Army appointments evidently gave great satisfaction, for in 1853, Dr Smith, the Director-General of the Medical Department of the Army, complimented the College on the general good qualifications of their licentiates who appeared before the Medical Board, contrasted with those of some other schools, and stated that two appointments would be given to any licentiates of the College whom they might think fit to recommend for them. The interest of the College in this branch of the service is also revealed in some correspondence which took place with Dr Smith about the year 1855, with regard to the scarcity of medical men in the Crimea. In notifying this fact, Dr Smith asked the assistance of the College in procuring suitable men, and added that "acting assistant-surgeons get ten shillings and sixpence per day and forty pounds in aid of their outfit." In acknowledging the receipt of the letter the College stated plainly that in their opinion the inducements offered to medical men to join the Army in the East did not provide an adequate remuneration for the trouble and risk attending that service; and some time later, at the instance of Mr Syme, resolutions were sent by the College to the Secretary for War and to the Army Medical Department deprecating the action of the Government in appointing, as assistant-surgeons in the Army, men not possessed of a surgical diploma, and who had merely passed through the rudiments of medical education. This was calculated to compromise the interests of the sick and wounded committed to their charge and to lower the character of the Medical Department of the Army. On the termination of the war Dr Smith was elected an Honorary Fellow of the College. In asking him to accept this honour, the College said that it was one which was rarely bestowed, and then only for high professional acquirements or distinguished public service. Called upon at short notice at the end of a long peace to provide for the supply of men and material for the medical service of a large army acting at a distance, Dr Smith had been surrounded by difficulties almost, if not altogether, unparalleled. Exposed to much unmerited obloquy, maligned by a portion of the public press, he was not discouraged much less dismayed, but continued firmly, perseveringly, and efficiently to discharge the duties of his high office in such a manner as to promote the health of the troops and to alleviate their unavoidable sufferings on the field of battle, in the hospital, and in the camp. Such an administration of the Medical Department entitled him, they said, to the gratitude of his country, and so the College, anxious that he should receive honour at the hands of those best qualified to judge, viz., his professional brethren, elected him one of their Honorary Fellows.

In 1849, the College petitioned the House of Commons in respect to certain grievances suffered by assistant-surgeons in the Navy. Their complaint seems to have originated in their being excluded from the "Ward Rooms" or general officers' mess, whereby they were compelled to mess and associate with midshipmen and naval cadets who were much junior to them ; they also complained of the want of opportunity for further study. To such causes the College attributed the unpopularity of the Naval Medical Service, a condition then most obvious, for in spite of the extensive publicity of their authority and intention to recommend a candidate for that appointment, no one applied in the first year and only one came forward in the second year. The representation of the College had the desired effect, for in 1855, by order of the Admiralty, assistant-surgeons in the Navy were admitted to the rank of Ward Room officers and were allowed a separate cabin whenever this was practicable.

Revision of Laws regarding Diplomas.—In 1806, the College considered it necessary to revise the Laws relative to the examination of candidates for diplomas and certificates. This, they said, was owing to the ignorance of pharmaceutical and chemical knowledge displayed by a large proportion of the candidates who presented themselves for examination, and was attributed to the general neglect of that practical education which could only be obtained by serving an apprenticeship to a regular practitioner. It was, therefore, enacted that a candidate for a surgeon's diploma, having served an apprentice-ship of three or more years, must also have attended lectures and demonstrations on anatomy and surgery, and lectures on the practice of medicine and chemistry in any University of reputation for two or more years, or lectures and demonstrations on these subjects by any teacher of reputation who was a member of the College of Physicians of London, Dublin, Edinburgh, or other reputable College.

From this it will be seen that the lectures recognised by the surgeons were those given only by *members* of the different colleges. As the College of Surgeons of Edinburgh was composed entirely of members or Fellows, when the regulation was made it no doubt never intended to accept the lectures of any but those of the same status in the other colleges. The constitution of the latter, however, was somewhat different to the Edinburgh College, and amongst their number they reckoned their licentiates who, probably, in general terms were sometimes alluded to as *members* of their body. Owing to this confusion, it is quite possible that the lectures of licentiates may sometimes have been recognised by the College. To prevent mistakes in future, it passed another Act, in 1816, that all candidates for diplomas must have followed their studies in some University of reputation, or under teachers who were resident Fellows of the Colleges of Physicians or Surgeons in London, Dublin, Edinburgh, or of the Faculty of Physicians and Surgeons of Glasgow.

Recognition of Lectures by Licentiates.—This was no sooner made known than a misunderstanding arose between the College and a licentiate of the College of Physicians of Edinburgh who lectured on midwifery. In consequence of Dr Thatcher, the lecturer in question, advertising his lectures on midwifery, as entitling those who attended them to appear before the College for a diploma, the President intimated to Dr Thatcher that he did not admit that lectures given by a licentiate of the College of Physicians could confer such a privilege. The President pointed out that the Laws of the College of Surgeons did not admit any lectures to qualify a candidate for their diploma, save such as were given by a member of one of the Colleges. He also stated that they had not hitherto recognised as a member of the College of Physicians any but Fellows of that body. Dr Thatcher in reply, said that the College of Physicians, in an official letter, had corroborated the statement he had made, that he was a member of that body and this led him to consider that tickets of gentlemen attending his class would be accepted at Surgeons' Hall. He further notified his intention of entering the College of Surgeons as soon as his various professional duties would permit him doing so, and requested to be informed definitely whether his tickets would be received.

Owing to the particular circumstances of the case, the College agreed, as a special favour, to accept his cards for the course he was then about to commence, but at the same time it was intimated to him that he was not entitled to the right which he claimed.

This was followed by another case which took a more serious aspect, the College being summoned at the instance of a Dr Sanders for having refused to receive his tickets, which summons concluded with the statement that the College was bound to receive them in future or be liable to him in £1000 of damages.

In order to ascertain their position, the College took opinion of Counsel on the following points :—

(1) Were the memorialists entitled to make regulations as to the course of study to be observed by those who come before them as candidates for their diploma?

(*Answer*) Yes : but subject to the control of the Court of Session, in so far as these regulations may be improper in themselves or injurious to the candidates or third parties.

(2) Were they entitled or not to change these regulations from time to time as they might think fit, proper and expedient, or in doing so could they be made liable in damages by any person who, like Dr Sanders, conceived that he was aggrieved by such alteration?

(*Answer*) The regulations might be changed subject to the same control, but the College would be liable in damages to any person who could show that he was injured by the alteration.

(3) Is a licentiate of the College of Physicians of Edinburgh to be considered a member of that body?

(*Answer*) Although Counsel was not clear upon this point, he thought that if in common speech a licentiate of the College of Physicians was styled a member of the College—and in particular if he was so styled by the College itself—the term licentiate must be taken in that acceptation. If the memorialists themselves, continued Counsel, have provided

M

upon the principle that licentiates of the College of Physicians in London and Dublin are to be considered as members of these Colleges in the sense of the regulations of 1804, and allowed to the students of those licentiates the privileges conferred by the regulations, I think it is clear that the licentiates of the College of Physicians of Edinburgh must be held to have been placed upon the same footing. For the terms of the regulations are general, and the College will not be suffered to plead that in adopting these terms they intended to make a distinction between the licentiates of London and Dublin on the one hand and Edinburgh on the other.

(4) Are they liable in damages to Dr Sanders for refusing his tickets, those tickets never having been received by them at any former period?

(*Answer*) I am inclined to think that Dr Sanders will be found entitled to damages. The regulations of 1816, if construed in the sense in which they are taken by the memorialists, would seem to make an unwarrantable distinction to the prejudice of the College of Physicians of Edinburgh and its licentiates. On the other hand, if the regulations are construed in the sense in which they are taken by Dr Sanders, he and his students have been injured by the refusal to receive his tickets as their qualification to be taken upon trial.

Upon considering the whole matter, however, the College resolved not to yield to Dr Sanders' demand without a judgment of the Court of Session.

Without following the case there, we find Dr Sanders, in 1819, requesting the indulgence formerly granted to Dr Thatcher—that they would allow his tickets to pass *speciali gratia quasi ;* in the meantime he undertook to submit to the proper forms of becoming a Fellow of the College during the summer of 1820, and also to adopt measures for an amicable termination of all differences between them.

Duration of Qualifying Courses.—Another question of the same kind, but bearing more on the duration of the surgical courses delivered in Edinburgh compared with the same courses held in London, was raised by Robert Liston, who had recently joined the College and was about to commence a course of lectures on surgery.

The points on which he desired information were :—

(1) Do the College of Surgeons of Edinburgh receive as sufficient qualification in that branch, the certificates of attendance on the surgical lectures of Mr Astley Cooper or Mr Abernethy of London?

(2) Could the College of Surgeons of Edinburgh refuse to take certificates of attendance on the same number of surgical lectures (as given by these gentlemen) delivered by me to the pupils of my class of anatomy?

(3) If the College of Surgeons of Edinburgh refuse to consider such a course delivered in this City as sufficient, can they blame me in acquainting the Master and Court of Assistants of the London College with their determination?

The College in considering these questions thought the last paragraph was expressed in terms rather disrespectful to them. Dr Gairdner, however, stated that he had at first entertained that impression, but on mentioning the matter to Mr Liston, the latter had disavowed any intention of the least disrespect towards the College, and asked him to state this to the meeting.

The following answers were then returned to Mr Liston's questions :—

(1) The Royal College of Surgeons of Edinburgh receive as a sufficient qualification in that branch the certificates of attendance on the surgical lectures of Mr Astley Cooper and Mr Abernethy of London.

(2) The College do not take upon themselves to institute any comparison between the advantages of a London and an Edinburgh course of surgery, as to the length or otherwise, neither have they ever fixed what are the fewest possible lectures delivered in London or elsewhere out of Edinburgh, attendance on which they will receive as a proper surgical course. They receive the certificates of Mr Cooper and Mr Abernethy, these being according to the practice of the School where these gentlemen reside ; but according to the practice of the Edinburgh Medical School a proper course of lectures on any subject in medicine (midwifery and clinical surgery excepted) is understood by the College to be a course of six months' duration, and if the course proposed to be given here

by you is shorter than that period, they could not think themselves justified in recognising it as sufficient.

(3) The College has no objection to your communicating their determination to the Master and Assistants of the College of Surgeons of London, as their regulations in this respect have long been made public.

This communication brought a second letter from Liston, who stated that as he had no wish to involve himself or the College in trouble, he begged to intimate that he intended to advertise his intention of giving a course of surgery of the same number of lectures as Dr Monro had been in the habit of delivering, and somewhat on the same plan. He entered the College, he said, "on the faith of having his lectures set on the same footing as those of any other member or any professor in a public University, and therefore no after-law could possibly affect him. The Royal College, he continued, must be well aware that surgery cannot be taught so well as in connection with anatomy, but that point, he added, was of no consequence to the present question.

The President was advised to give "a very short answer" to this letter, stating to Mr Liston that he was already informed of the determination of the College.

The College, however, were determined that surgery, from its importance and extent, should no longer be taught in conjunction with any other subject, and ordained that in future the course of lectures on surgery should be equal in extent and duration to those on the other branches of medicine in the Schools at which they are delivered. It was further, agreed that the resolution should be transmitted in a respectful letter to Dr Monro.

A few months later (December 1820), the President, Mr William Wood, stated at a meeting of the College that he then held in his hand a ticket for a course of surgery delivered by Dr Monro, at the bottom of which was printed the following notice—"These lectures will qualify for Surgeons' Hall"; and as he was of opinion that Dr Monro's course did not conform to the requirements of the College—he only giving two lectures a week—he thought it proper for the College not to pass over a notice of this kind, made in defiance of their express regulations.

ROBERT LISTON
SEPTEMBER 29ᵗʰ 1818.

[To face page 180.

A committee was then appointed to write to Dr Monro requesting to be informed as to how many lectures he had already delivered, and how many more he intended to deliver before he completed the course. To this Monro replied that he intended to give, during the winter session, 115 lectures on surgery. In consideration of this it appeared unnecessary for the College to take any further steps, but Mr Wood intimated his intention to bring it under their consideration at a future period, if he should see occasion to do so.

During the time of his trifling dissension with the College, Liston was engaged in a more serious dispute with the Managers of the Royal Infirmary, which led to his being excluded from attending that institution on the charge of improper interference with the patients. On this being made known to him, Liston at once laid the whole matter before the College, on the grounds that their privileges were being encroached upon. In stating his case he called attention to the original agreement between the College and the Infirmary, and enquired if they intended tamely to submit to the invasion of their privileges and the violation of their agreement, or to resist it in the general interests of the College.

He then declared himself innocent of any improper interference with the patients of the Infirmary, and that he was ignorant of a single act of his on which the Managers had founded their "vague and indefinite charge." "At any rate," he said, "the enquiry to which the Managers had alluded in their resolution was altogether private." He had never been informed of their intention to hold such an enquiry; he had never been told of any charge made against him or called upon in the course of that enquiry for any defence or explanation. In short, the Managers of the Infirmary, he declared, "had resolved to deprive a member of the College of Surgeons of his privileges, not only without legal evidence, but without even hearing him or his defence—a proceeding "which rather bears a resemblance to the act of a set of Inquisitors."

The resolution of the Managers referred to, is as follows :—

"The Managers have made such enquiries as satisfy them that Mr Liston has frequently been guilty of interfering improperly in the Surgical department of the House and with the patients, they therefore consider it to be their bounden duty to take such measures as may prevent Mr Liston, and deter others, from pursuing similar conduct in future, and therefore resolve that Mr Liston be prohibited from entering the wards and operation room of the Royal Infirmary at any time, and on any pretence whatever."

A committee of six members of the College was then formed to consider Mr Liston's letter, and to enquire what were the privileges of the surgeons in regard to the right of attending the Infirmary and walking through its wards. Acting on the report of this committee, the College unanimously resolved that it was unnecessary to take any steps in the matter.

Liston then sent a copy of his reply to the Managers of the Infirmary to the College, with the request that it might be read at the next meeting, but as it seemed to contain reflections injurious both to the moral and professional character of some of the most respectable members of the College, it was ordered, on the suggestion of Mr William Wood, to be sent back to him.

A year or two later, while Mr Wood occupied the Presidential Chair, an incident occurred which again brought these two gentlemen into opposition. It occurred through a candidate for the Fellowship in his essay upon Uterine Hæmorrhage, remarking: " It is now well known that to this last cause the death of the Princess Charlotte is to be ascribed — an event which no human foresight could have anticipated — an event which is not more to be deplored from the national calamity it inflicted, than from the disgraceful feelings it produced in the minds of some accoucheurs, which led them into an unjust persecution of the amiable and distinguished individual who had the principal charge on that interesting occasion—a persecution which has not even ceased with the life of him who fell a victim to its virulency—a persecution which I shall never cease to hold up as scandalous and infamous, because it was gratuitous as well as unjust, and unworthy of a liberal profession." Further on he adds : " Some accoucheurs, I am well aware, object to the simple manner of operating, because they will object to anything which strips this part of the profession of any of its mummery, or which will enable a general practitioner, who happens to know little of the practice of midwifery, to act as effectually as the most experienced accoucheur."

These remarks were objected to and the candidate, Dr Mackintosh, was asked if he would withdraw them without the interference of the College. This he declined to do, and he was informed that unless the passages above quoted were cancelled he could proceed no further with his examination. This led to a motion being made, which was seconded by Mr Liston, that "in future it shall not be competent for the College to discuss the merits of any essay until the candidate shall have been examined thereon." Some discussion then took place on the formality of the motion, and while the President was stating his opinion he was interrupted by Mr Liston, who enquired by what right he, the President, delivered his opinion on the matter after a motion had been regularly made and seconded, and was proceeding to address the College when he was called to order by Mr Wood, who appealed to the College to know whether he had exceeded his duty. Further discussion ensued, at the end of which Mr Liston enquired of the President whether there was any public body which allowed their President to deliver his opinion and to originate motions. The President immediately stated to the College that as that was the second time in the course of the day that the propriety of his conduct in the Chair had been called into question, he must insist on the College giving a distinct opinion on the subject, that he might know how to regulate his conduct in future, and said he should leave the Chair till this was done.

The Chair having been taken by the senior past-President, Mr Wood stated, in substance, to the meeting his opinion that the President was bound to attend to the proper administration of the Laws, and that it was his special duty to point out anything that appeared to him to be irregularly brought forward. Further, the right of originating motions was clearly proved by there being a Law stating that the business which the President may have to propose should have precedence over all other Laws, and that it had invariably been the custom for the President to originate motions in all cases where he thought anything could be brought forward useful to the College. Mr Wood then left the room. It was then moved that the conduct of the President in the Chair had been such as to deserve the entire approbation and thanks of the College.

The motion, on being seconded by Mr Lizars, was agreed to unanimously, Mr Liston observing that he had only put the question "for the sake of obtaining information."

Class Certificates of Attendance.—Before a candidate for a College diploma was admitted to examination, he had to produce, as he does now, a certificate of having attended the different courses of lectures laid down in the College regulations. These certificates were then presented to the President, who gave the necessary instructions for the examination to take place. In the year 1836, some slight misunderstanding arose between the lecturers and the College in regard to the attendance of pupils under the following circumstances. The President, it appears, occasionally had presented to him by students certificates from professors or lecturers, stating they had attended their lectures "*but not regularly.*" He therefore, asked the College what ought to be done in such cases, and whether such certificates should qualify for examination or not.

The opinion of the College was to the effect that as they had recognised the general principle that candidates should have actually attended the classes, it was most desirable that a plan should be adopted for ascertaining whether the attendance had been regular or not. It was therefore resolved that every private lecturer at their school should ascertain at least twenty times in a six months' course, and ten times in a three months' course, the actual attendances given by his pupils. This was to be done by calling the roll once every week, the students of course being kept ignorant of the particular day on which it was to be done. The roll-book was to be at all time accessible to the President and Treasurer of the College, on both of whom it was incumbent to examine the roll of each class sometime during every session. The certificates granted to pupils were in future to state how many times the roll was called, and how many times the pupil was present on these occasions. If absent more than eight times, the student was not to be admitted to examination until he had attended another course of lectures in every such department of study, etc.

As soon as these new Laws came into operation, it came to the knowledge of the College that some of their members who were private lecturers, had used expressions in their class-rooms calculated to produce a feeling of hostility and opposition on the part of the students towards the College. The President, in expressing the strong disapprobation of the College of such a course on the part of these gentlemen, said that the regulations having been adopted after mature deliberation and after using every means to meet the views of the lecturers, the College were firmly resolved not to be driven aside from their purpose by any such means as those complained of, and would not hesitate to exercise their authority in the most decided and effectual manner in enforcing compliance with the enactments.   One particular objection to the new rules seemed to have been that, as they were not applicable to other medical schools, their adoption was to place the Edinburgh School at a disadvantage.   To obviate this objection as far as possible, the College endeavoured to prevail on the University professors to adopt similar measures, and suggested a conference with the members of the Medical Faculty for the purpose of explaining the anxiety which they entertained on the subject.   In answer to the proposals, however, the Dean of the Medical Faculty replied that he had laid the letter before the professors, who expressed their satisfaction that the subject had been taken up by the College of Surgeons, and that in regard to the resolutions of the College, the professors expressed their hope of profiting by them on the final arrangement of the matter.   Some of the members were of opinion that the Dean's letter was not satisfactory, but upon deliberation, it was agreed simply to address a letter to him regretting that the Medical Faculty should have declined the conference, and that the matter be allowed to rest there for the present.

The College enforced their regulations, however, in spite of all opposition, and also announced their intention " to withdraw their recognition from any lecturer who neglected to observe them."   In this connection, Dr Robert Knox got into trouble, in 1847, owing to some irregularity in granting certificates to a student, the facts of which had been publicly called in question; in consequence of the unsatisfactory nature of his replies when called upon to justify them, the College, after taking opinion of Counsel, refused to acknowledge his lectures as qualifying for their diploma until the matter had been cleared up.

In 1853, in consequence of Knox's name appearing as a

lecturer in the Free Medical School of London, the College enquired of the London College whether they recognised Knox's lectures or not. A negative reply was returned.

The Title Licentiate.—Until the year 1817, no particular designation had been assigned to the diplomates of the College, they being simply referred to as "those holding diplomas of the College." In the year in question, however, in consequence of a Bill before Parliament limiting the eligibility to the charge of certain hospitals to "members" of the three Colleges of London, Dublin, and Edinburgh, it was apparent that something would have to be done to bring the diplomates of the Edinburgh College in line with the diplomates, or "members" as they were called, of other bodies. The Act referred to was meant, of course, to include all who held the licence of any of the Colleges, and although an understanding was come to by all concerned, it raised the question of adopting a title for those holding diplomas of the College. The decision was that in future those who held the diploma of the College should be known as Licentiates.

Fraudulent Diplomas. — In 1806, the attention of the College was directed to a forgery of their diploma by a student who had been rejected a few months before. It appears that an engraver, a writing master, and another student were also implicated in the transaction and that all of them were brought before the magistrates. From the confession of the principal offender—who was said to be of weak intellect and seemed unconscious of having done anything wrong—it appeared that he and the other student had forged the names of eight members of the College to the diploma. When the charge was made against him, he acknowledged with candour that he had committed the forgery and explained the manner in which it was done. He readily produced the diploma when requested to do so, and upon being asked his motive for committing so gross a crime, replied that it was done to please his father. Out of compassion the College decided not to prosecute the students, and recommended the magistrates to discharge the engraver who had made ample apology, but in order to prevent a similar occurrence in the future, they ordered an advertisement to be inserted in the newspapers to the following effect:—

"That an attempt having lately been made to forge their diploma, but which was discovered in time to prevent the forgery being made use of, and taking into consideration the flagrant and heinous nature of a crime of this description which may be productive of worse consequences than any other species of forgery, and which is held by the laws of this country a capital crime, they have come to the determination to expose and prosecute with the utmost rigour all who may be guilty of any such attempt in future."

A personation and fraud were practised upon the College in 1844 and only brought to light some six years later. A young man, an assistant to a medical practitioner in Northumberland, it appears, underwent an examination in the name of his employer and obtained a diploma for him in the usual form. He was convicted and sentenced to a term of imprisonment, but the College, in answer to a prayer from the prisoner's father, petitioned the Home Secretary for a mitigation of the sentence.

Revision of Regulations for Examinations.—In consequence of many alterations having been made in its domestic arrangements, principally by the introduction of several new departments and offices, and by constant changes in the examinations, the College, in 1816, thoroughly revised its Laws and brought them up to date. A few years previously (1803), at the instance of Mr Benjamin Bell, it was agreed that the examiners should receive an allowance of ten shillings each for every examination sederunt they attended. The entry fees for the Fellowship were also increased—for sons of Fellows, £8, 6s. 8d.; for sons-in-law, £16, 13s. 4d.; and for apprentices who had served a regular apprenticeship of five years to a Fellow, £100. The entrance fee of all others was fixed at £250 stg., one-half of which went to the Widows' Fund, and the other half to the ordinary funds of the College.

Examiners Assaulted and Threatened. — In December 1818, one of the examiners of the College reported an extraordinary assault which had been made upon him in his own house in consequence of his having done his duty as an examiner. The examiner in question, Dr John Gairdner, who later became a distinguished President and historian of the College, said that a young man called upon him between eight and nine o'clock on the previous evening, and on his going into a room with him alone, this person produced a whip and told him that he had come to give him a little chastisement for having rejected him at an examination at Surgeons' Hall. He then attacked him with the whip. After some struggling, Dr Gairdner got to the door, and ordered the police to be called, when the young man was given into custody. It was afterwards found that the offender had been handed over, not to the police, but to the charge of two porters or chairmen, who happened to be about at the time, and they, not considering themselves entitled to detain him, had let him escape. Dr Gairdner concluded by saying that he put the matter entirely into the hands of the College to do as they thought fit, and that he entertained no resentment or desire of revenge against the man, whoever he might be. Eventually the offender, the son of a minister in Ayrshire, was taken into custody and examined by the Sheriff, who remanded him to trial before the High Court of Justiciary for assault and hamesucken [beating a person within his own house].

A petition apologising to Dr Gairdner and to the College for the violence of his son's conduct, and expressing his sincere grief for what had happened, was then submitted by the prisoner's father, who begged the College to use its influence not to bring his son to a public trial, or, if that could not be avoided, that any punishment inflicted by the High Court might be as lenient as possible. The petition was sent to the Lord Advocate, accompanied by a representation on the part of the College that it was their sincere wish that the measures to be taken against the unhappy young man should be as lenient as was consistent with the ends of public justice, and that, if those ends could be accomplished without bringing the matter to a public trial, it would be more agreeable to the College. Finally the prisoner was found guilty on his own confession on both counts, and the libel having been restricted to an arbitrary punishment, he was sentenced to seven years' "transportation beyond the seas." As the dignity of the College had been sufficiently vindicated by the trial, and as the young man had already been severely punished by the ruin of his professional prospects, it was thought to be unnecessary to carry the sentence into execution. The College therefore resolved to petition the Prince Regent to grant the prisoner a full pardon.

Something of the same kind happened in 1826, when letters of a threatening character were sent to an examiner. Placards were also pasted upon the walls and sheds near the College and upon the lecture rooms, calling a meeting of the medical students for the purpose of expressing their opinion of the said examiner's methods of conducting the examination. The examiner, in laying the matter before the College, stated that upon receiving the first letter he had been advised by several of his friends to disregard it, and had accordingly put it in the fire, but as the system of intimidation was still continued, he felt it his duty to bring the matter before the President and his Council. He then produced two letters, one of which was as follows :—

" This is to inform you that a determined band of medical students, exasperated at the frequent rejections at Surgeons' Hall which they say you have invariably been the occasion of, have agreed to punish you most severely, in what manner I do not as yet know ; yet this I know, that should you be found off your guard, any advantage will be taken. They, it seems, lay the death of the unfortunate young man who, after rejection a few days ago, put a period to his existence on Arthur's Seat to your charge. This has roused their angry feelings, and they have sworn to have revenge. You will not despise this caution from— A FRIEND."

The second letter, signed " Ben Resper," was more alarming :—

" From the report now in circulation it would appear that your sole aim is to blight the prospects of certain young men, who unfortunately do not rank so high in your estimation as a few others who have already experienced the *good effects* of a *personal* and *particular* acquaintance with so distinguished an individual as yourself . . .

" Among the number of candidates are many who having gone through the usual routine of study . . . what a disappointment it must be to them as well as to their friends, should this rejection be occasioned by one man who, wishful of showing off the little know-ledge he may possess, puts such questions as may tend to bewilder minds already agitated and confused . . . It is in our opinion altogether impossible that out of eleven, nine should be found unqualified; such a circumstance as this never occurred in the days of individuals ranking much higher in the medical profession than Dr ——, a name which has never yet been seen in the pages of medical literature . . . Mark, however, we will all have satisfaction and ample revenge."

The examiner mentioned, in addition, that lately he had been repeatedly insulted in the course of attending his duty in the Infirmary, and that on several occasions on his entering the dissection room a hiss had arisen among the students who happened to be collected. As he was not aware that any other part of his conduct could have given rise to such a feeling of hostility against himself, he imagined that these insults were also connected with the subject of the letters and the performance of his duty as an office-bearer of the College.

The opinion of the Council was that the College could not interfere with anything that passed in the Infirmary, the proper course being to apply for redress to the Managers. With regard to the letters, it was thought that to offer a large reward for the author of them was not likely to be attended with any good effect, but, on the contrary, would evince too much of a vindictive spirit and excite in the minds of the students feelings which had better be suppressed. The most dignified course for the College to pursue would be to publish a notice to the students contradicting the reports, to express their fullest approbation of Dr ——'s conduct as an examiner, and also to declare the determination of the College to support and protect their examiners in the upright and conscientious discharge of their duty. Finally, it was decided to draw up an address and to request the different professors and lecturers to read it from their Chairs, in which way it would be made known to the students without making it so public in the town.

CHAPTER XII

THE COLLEGE AND THE TEACHING OF ANATOMY [1]

Anatomy—James Borthwick—Gift of Bodies by the Town Council—Public
Dissections—First Teachers of Anatomy—Body Snatching—John
Monro—Alexander Monro *primus*—Surgeons' Hall nearly Wrecked—
Practical Anatomy—Memorial to the Secretary of State—The Anatomy
Bill—Dr Knox—His Report.

As the early Minutes of the College refer more to its domestic
affairs than to its professional character, but little information
can be gained as to the use the surgeons made of the "one
body a year" which was granted to them by the Town
Council in 1505 for anatomical purposes. For the same reason
it is impossible to describe the features of the examination
mentioned in the Seal of Cause or to form an estimate of its
worth. In 1647, however, the subjects of examination were
clearly defined by an Act which explained that "as no constant
course had hitherto been kept or preserved at the trial of
Intrants, the examination shall in future be conducted as
follows :— On the first day, the candidate shall begin with the
introduction to surgery . . . and make a general discourse of
the whole of anatomy without any demonstrations." On the
second day, "he is to demonstrate by ocular inspection more
particular on some parts of the anatomy which shall be
appointed to him by the deacon and masters, and to answer
the demands of his examination and masters thereupon."
Thirdly, he is to show some operation on the foresaid subjects
as the deacon and masters shall think fit, and "for facilitating
the Intrant his examination and trial they do allow him to
have at his own pleasure a conductor and accordingly, if the
deacon and masters find him qualified or unqualified, they may
admit or reject him or otherwise continue his examination in
the first subject—aye and until they find him qualifit."

[1] Reprinted from *The Edinburgh Medical Journal*, February 1914.

In all probability this orderly system was due to the exertions of James Borthwick, who had become a member of the Incorporation in 1645, and whose admission entry contains the important declaration that he took the oath to conform to the Seal of Cause, "especially to the point of dissecting of anatomy for the further instruction of apprentices and servants." It may be claimed for James Borthwick, therefore, that he was an advanced anatomist, and perhaps the first to introduce the dissection of the human body into Scotland, for this clearly proves that practical anatomy was taught, and also formed at the very early period of 1647 a subject of examination.

From that time no particular attention seems to have been given to anatomy until the advent of Alexander Monteith, who obtained from the Town Council a promise, for dissecting purposes, of the bodies of prisoners who died in gaol. This was closely followed by an application of a similar nature by the Incorporation itself, as it was apparent there were other bodies at the Council's disposal besides those allotted to Monteith. The Act of the Town Council, including the surgeons' petition and the conditions of their gift, is dated 2nd November 1694, and is as follows :—

"Anent a petition given in by the Incorporation of the Chirurgeons of Edinburgh, showing, The Petitioners understanding that the Council for encouragement of so necessary a work as the improving of anatomy has been pleased upon a Bill given unto them by Alexander Monteith, one of their own number to grant him a gift of their bodies that die in their Correction House, and the bodies of foundlings that die upon the breast, and to allow him a convenient house for dissection, and the use of the College Kirk Yard for the burial, And the Petitioners that the improvement of Anatomy is of so necessary import that the same desire to be very much encouraged, and that the ground of their appearance against Mr Monteith's gift was only upon the supposition that he had enhanced and monopolised the whole subjects of anatomical dissections. But finding that besides these subjects that the Council had been pleased to give him were yet other subjects that might fall in the Council's power to give the petitioners, viz. :—The dead bodies of foundlings after they are off the breast, and the bodies of such as may be found dead upon the streets, and such as die violent deaths, all which who shall have nobody to own them, upon which subjects the petitioners might make anatomical dissections for the further improvement of anatomy, and being confident that the

Council's forwardness to encourage so necessary a work . . . Which being considered by the Council they (notwithstanding the above mentioned act in favour of Alexander Monteith and without prejudice thereto) allow to the petitioners the dead bodies of foundlings who die betwixt the time they are weaned and their being put to schools or trades, while they remain upon the charges of the Kirk, unless the friends of those concerned reimburse the Kirk Treasurer whatever they have cost the town.   As also they allow the dead bodies of children stifled in the birth which are expired, and have none to own them, as also the dead bodies of such as are *felo de se*, when it is found unquestionable self-murder and have none to own them.   Which includes what former pretentions of that kind the petitioners have, the petitioners always burying the dead bodies within ten free labouring days upon their own charges in what place that shall be appointed by the Council.   And that these presents shall take effect in the winter session only which in this case is reckoned to be from one equinox to the other.   And it is hereby declared these presents are only granted expressly upon conditions that the petitioners shall before the term of Michaelmass 1697 years build, repair and have in readiness an anatomical theatre where they shall once a year (a subject offering) have a public anatomical dissection as much as can be shown upon one body, and if they fail these presents to be void and null."

More than two years elapsed before the surgeons decided whether they would accept these conditions or lose the benefit of the Act, but upon its being put to the vote, they unanimously agreed to erect a new hall in which a suitable place for the dissections should be provided.

At a meeting of the Calling on 17th December 1697, the theatre was reported to be finished, and a committee was then formed to consider the methods of carrying out the dissections and to appoint the operators.

Five years later—January 1703—the deacon represented to the Calling that the dissections and demonstrations of the several parts of the body obtained from the Town Council of Edinburgh on 29th November past were performed by the several members chosen by them for that purpose; he, therefore, desired their opinion upon the same, and whether it ought to be recorded in their books.   The operators were then desired to leave the room, and the Calling having considered, gave their opinion by a vote as follows: " For the first day, a general discourse on anatomy.   The common teguments and

N

muscles of the abdomen, performed by James Hamilton, deacon. It being put to the vote whether they were satisfied with it or not, they all declared they were well satisfied, and having called him in, gave him their thanks. For the second day, the peritoneum, omentum, stomach, intestines, mesentery and pancreas, performed by John Baillie. On the third day, the liver, spleen, kidneys, ureters, bladder and parts of genera- tion, performed by Alex. Monteith. Fourth day, the brain and its membranes, with a discourse of the animal spirits by David Fyfe. Fifth day, the muscles of the extremities by Hugh Paterson. Sixth day, the skeleton in general, with the head, by Robert Clerk. Seventh day, the articulations and the rest of the skeleton, by James Auchinleck. Eighth day, the epilogue, performed by Dr Pitcairn." After all the operators had been called in and thanked, a vote was carried that the same be inserted in their books, there to remain "*ad futuram re memoriam.*"

This is the first public dissection mentioned in the Surgeons' records; another was performed in April of the following year, and carried out in much the same way. The Treasurer's account of incidental charges, disbursed by him in November 1702, contains some significant items which no doubt were incurred in connection with the first demonstration :—

27th November.	To the officers and trone men for carrying David Mylles corps [1] . . .	£1	8	6
12th December.	To the two Sentinells for six days attendance . .		4	7	0
,, ,,	For Weights for weighing the body . . .		0	9	6
,, ,,	To the Suttimen for carrying the body from the gibbet to the church . .		0	17	6

After two public lectures had been carried out in this manner, a new system was adopted whereby the entire demonstration was given by one man. The alteration was brought about in consequence of several members of the

[1] On referring to Hume's *Commentaries on Crimes* we find that David Mylles was executed for incest with his sister Margaret, and that the latter was also executed for the murder of her incestuous issue.

Calling having been informed that a person then in Edinburgh was about to apply to the Incorporation for the privilege of teaching anatomy both in public and private, and if the Calling would give him access to the bodies they were entitled to, and the use of the theatre, he would give their apprentices and servants gratis the benefit of the yearly dissection.   On hearing of these proposals, Robert Eliot, who became a master-surgeon in 1696, petitioned the Calling that he humbly judged it would no less tend to the credit of the Incorporation to appoint one of their own number who would make the same offer, "especially seeing they had already begun it in their own persons"; for that end he offered his services, and hoped the Calling would favourably consider his offer, and at the same time impute it to a desire of preventing extraneous hands meddling in their matters, than to any prospect he might have in view.   The Calling granted his request, gave him the use of the theatre, and promised that none of their apprentices or servants should be taught by any person who was not a member of their Society.

In this way Eliot became teacher of anatomy to the Incorporation, and some few months later (29th August 1705) received an appointment in the Town's College or University, at a salary of £15 stg. per annum.   Although not appointed Professor of Anatomy in as many words, he is, as such, subsequently referred to in the Burgh Records, and as the magistrates are the best interpreters of their own Acts, to Eliot belongs the distinction of being the first Professor of Anatomy in the University of Edinburgh.   In 1708, Eliot applied to the Incorporation to have Adam Drummond conjoined with him in teaching, "he having already obtained an Act from the Town Council for that effect."

A great impetus was now given to the teaching of anatomy, and although the Town Council had disposed of all unclaimed bodies in favour of the anatomist, the supply was unequal to the demand.   The zeal of the student was unbounded, and when body-snatching was resorted to in 1711, it was only natural that suspicion should rest with those most interested in the dissecting rooms.   Whenever these desecrations took place, therefore, the surgeons were strongly suspected, and in order to free themselves from such imputations they passed the following Memorial Act, which was sent to the magistrates in Council:—

"The Incorporation taking into their consideration that of late there has been a violation of the sepulchres in the Greyfriars Church-yard by some who most unchristianly have been stealing, or at least attempting to carry away bodies of the dead out of their graves; a practice to be abhorred by all good christians, and which by the law of all nations is severely punishable; But that which affects them most is a scandalous report, most maliciously spread about the town, that some of their members were accessory thereto, which they cannot allow themselves to think, considering that the Magistrates of Edinburgh have been always ready and willing to allow them what dead bodies that fell under their gift, and thereby plentifully supplied their theatre for many years past, which would considerably aggravate their crime if any of their number should be guilty thereof. They do therefore declare their abhorrence of all such unnatural and unchristian practices, earnestly intreating the Magistrates to exert their utmost power they are capable in law for the discovery of such atrocious and wicked crimes, that the authors, actors and abettors thereof may be brought to condign punishment. The Deacon, Masters and Brethren on their part and for the vindication of their Board have this day enacted that if any of their number be found accessory to the violation of the sepulchres in the Greyfriars Church Yard, or in any burial place whatsoever, or shall be convicted of having taken, or been accessory to the taking of any dead bodies out of their graves, they shall be expelled their Society, their names razed out of their books, their acts of admission torn and shall forfeit all the freedom and privilege they enjoyed by being freemen of their Incorporation, and if any Apprentice or Servant belonging to their number shall be found guilty of the foresaid crimes his name shall be expunged out of their books, he shall forfeit the benefit of his Indentures, and shall be expelled his Master's service with disgrace."

On the death of Eliot, John M'Gill, in 1717, became associated with Drummond as Joint-Professor of Anatomy. The Minute recorded in the Surgeons' books is quoted as showing that M'Gill appears to have received his Professorship at the hands of the surgeons.

"The Calling, considering that through the death of Robert Eliot, one of their number, Professor of Anatomy in conjunction with Adam Drummond, they wanted a professor, Therefor they nominated and appointed Mr John M'Gill, present Deacon, to

be their professor in conjunction with the said Adam
Drummond "

The partnership of Drummond and M'Gill was, however,
of short duration, for they both resigned their positions—"as
the state of their health and business were such that they could
not duly attend the said professorships"—in favour of Alexander
Monro, then a young man of twenty-two and a member of the
Calling of but three months' standing.

The history of the Monros is too well known to require
repetition here. A few brief remarks concerning John Monro,
the father of the first Alexander, may perhaps not be out of
place. He is first mentioned in a Minute of the 9th January
1689, when the Calling, "taking into their consideration the
good offices and service done and performed to them by
Alexander Monro of Bearscroft, Commissar of Stirling, and
in hopes of and the farther to engage him to continue his
kindness, the Deacon, Masters, and Brethren have ratified and
approven the booking of John Monro, son of the said Commissar Monro (who was bound prentice to William Borthwick
at a time when he was not in a capacity to book the said John,
three years not having elapsed since the booking of his late
Apprentice) as prentice to Dr Christopher Irvine, but in respect
that the Doctor does not keep a public shop whereby the said
John Monro may get insight and knowledge into the art of
Chirurgie, he is allowed to stay in service with William
Borthwick, his former master, during the remainder of his
time."

John Monro became a freeman of the Craft in 1703, Treasurer
in 1708, and occupied the Deacon's Chair some five years later.
With him originated the idea of establishing a medical school in
Edinburgh for the uniform teaching of the different branches of
medicine and surgery, and to his son Alexander lies the credit
for so efficiently carrying his father's cherished plan into effect.
His son, known to us in these days as Alexander Monro *primus*,
was admitted into the Incorporation on 20th November 1719.
His first and second examinations were upon surgery and
anatomy in general, and the containing and contained parts
of the thorax with the circulation of the blood; his third
included fistulas in general, with the operation of fistula
lachrymalis; and his fourth and final was upon the bandages

of the face and head. A month usually intervened between each examination, but this was dispensed with on Monro representing at his third lesson that he was ready instantly to be tried, and that it was highly inconvenient for him to be delayed, "because he was resolved suddenly to go abroad." Two months later the surgeons unanimously recommended him to the Lord Provost and Town Council to be Professor of Anatomy within the City.

In 1718, before his admission, he presented to the surgeons "some anatomical pieces done by himself," for which they ordered their thanks to be given to him, and that his father should be desired to acquaint him with it. Monro's gift, in the shape of an incomplete articulated skeleton, is still in the Surgeons' Museum. A narrow mahogany case contains the specimens referred to, and an inscription informs the reader that "These Anatomical Preparations were gifted to the Incorporation of the Chirurgeon Apothecaries of Edinburgh by Alex. Monro, 1718."

Amongst the papers of the College is a receipted account for thirty-three pounds Scots which contains some curious items, but whether these appear together by mere coincidence or whether a connection exists between them must always be left in doubt. It bears the same date with which Monro's gifts were announced :—

To Walter M'Ardle for gilding and painting case with Mr Monro's son's preparations .	.	£4 16	0
To Charles Hay for a Chicken Pye .	.	7 13	0
To Ale, Brandy and Cheese .	. .	3 15	0
To the Bibliothecarius for Spirits to Mr Monro's son's preparations .	. . .	0 12	0

In less than a year after his admission Monro was elected "Library Keeper," a position he held until 1728. During this time many important changes took place. The number of books in the library had been considerably augmented in 1709, by a gift of the library belonging to Thomas Kincaid, containing nearly two hundred volumes. As for curiosities three scorpions and a chameleon were presented by Lord Royston, and the Calling ordered the Treasurer "to pay the man a crown for showing them two live tortoises"—an incident that will not cause so much surprise after reading in the *Edinburgh Herald* that on a dromedary and camel being exhibited in Edinburgh in 1759, crowds flocked to see them, and doubts were expressed whether there were other "two such animals in the whole island of Great Britain."

Monro was for many years closely identified with the Incorporation, and regularly gave his lectures in their theatre. This continued until 1725, when, his anatomical preparations being in danger as the result of a public demonstration against body-snatching, he was forced to seek safety within the gates of the University.

In this way the Chair of Anatomy was transferred from the Incorporation to the Town's College, where Monro *primus* carried on his arduous duties for many long years. The last time we hear of him in the Surgeons' books is in 1756, when, on joining the College of Physicians, he took leave of the Incorporation in a letter bearing that as he had lately engaged in a business which was thought inconsistent with the exercise of surgery and pharmacy, both of which he was about to relinquish, it could not be expected that he would attend the meetings of the Incorporation or be employed in any of the offices connected with it, and therefore thought they would not think it necessary to continue his name on their roll.

He, however, "in taking leave did himself the justice to assure them that as he was gratefully sensible of the honour his father and he had in being members of their Society, so it should always be his endeavour to promote the honour and interest of the Surgeons of Edinburgh all that was in the power of their Most and Obed." etc.

On the occasion of the riot just referred to, the Surgeons' Hall was in peril of being wrecked by a furious mob whose anger against the surgeons had been aroused again, in consequence of the violation of graves for the purpose of dissection. But whatever steps they took to deny their participation in this gruesome work, suspicion naturally pointed to them as the offenders. In 1721, a clause had been inserted in all their indentures for discouraging and preventing the raising of the dead from their graves, and later, in consequence of this disturbance, the Calling had the following notice printed and distributed throughout the town :—

"Act of the Incorporation of Chirurgeon Apothecaries of Edinburgh, April 17th, 1725.

"Considering that several malicious and evil-disposed persons have industriously raised and spread calumnious reports importing that the bodies of the dead have been by them or their apprentices, raised from their graves to be dissected at the Theatre in their Hall; which reports have met with great credit among credulous and unthinking people, insomuch that they have created great uneasiness in their minds, and of late, have been artfully improven by factious designing men into tumults and disturbances in this city. Therefore, the Incorporation to show their just abhorrence of this monstrous crime, upon the very first rumour of such practices, did, by their Act, dated 27th Jan. 1722, enact, that each apprentice who should be convicted of raising or attempting to raise the dead from their graves, should forfeit their freedom and all privileges competent to them by their Indentures, and be extruded from their Master's service. And for further vindication of the honour of the Incorporation, and removing effectually all groundless suspicions, they have this day enacted that no human body, or any other subject shall be taken for dissection into their theatre, or any other part of their Hall, but such only as shall be allowed by the Magistrates for public dissections, according to Acts of the Town Council for that purpose. And further, the Incorporation oblige themselves and their successors to pay Five pounds stg. to any who shall discover the person or persons accessory to the raising, or attempting to raise the dead from their graves.

"As also, the Incorporation understanding that country people and servants in town are frightened by a villanous report that they are in danger of being attacked and seized by Chirurgeons' apprentices in order to be dissected; and although this report will appear ridiculous and incredible to any thinking person, yet the Incorporation, for finding out the foundation and rife thereof, do promise a reward of Five Pounds stg., for discovering such as have given just ground for this report, whether they be Chirurgeons' apprentices or others personating them in their rambles or using this cover for executing their other villanous designs."

Body-snatching, nevertheless, continued more or less throughout the century, and frequently led to rioting by the populace. In 1724, we read of a scuffle between some surgeon apprentices and the friends of a woman supposed to have been executed, for possession of the body. Luckily the latter were successful, when to their great surprise they found that life had not yet departed. The woman, afterwards known as " Half-hangit Maggie Dickson," soon recovered, and lived for many years. The records of the Tolbooth also contain an account of two women being executed for stealing a child and selling its body to the Chirurgeons for dissection.

We now pass to the years between 1824 and 1830, which saw great changes in the Medical School of Edinburgh, and particularly in the teaching of anatomy. The introduction into the College curriculum of a three-months' course of dissection or practical anatomy, whilst adding to the popularity of the Anatomical School, soon made it apparent that considerable difficulty would be experienced in obtaining a supply of bodies, without which it would be impossible to carry the new law into effect. Even before this, a motion had been made by Mr Lizars to inquire how far the difficulties of prosecuting the study of anatomy in the city were injurious to the interests of the College and of surgery, but nothing seems to have come of it. Another four years passed, and then the surgeons, thoroughly roused, called a special meeting of the College to consider the propriety of petitioning Parliament to amend the laws which affected the procuring of dead bodies for the medical schools. Under the existing law, it was said, the supply of these subjects had become in a high degree both inadequate and precarious, while those bodies that could be obtained were not only exorbitantly high in price but so disgustingly putrid as to render them to a great extent useless. Mr Lizars, in deploring the situation, stated that there could be but one opinion on the subject, and urged the necessity of something being done to remove the obstruction which existed to the study of anatomical science in the country.

The President stated that he was well aware of the importance of the object, but doubted if it would be best promoted by a public discussion in Parliament. The difficulties, he said, which stood in the way of getting subjects did not arise solely from the state of the law, but principally, if not entirely, from the state of public opinion which prevailed, perhaps more in Scotland than in any other country, against the measures which were necessary for procuring dead bodies. He therefore thought that the most prudent course for the College to pursue would be to approach Mr Peel, whose attention had been already directed to the subject.

The President's advice was adopted, and a Memorial sent to Mr Peel, who replied that as he was presenting petitions to Parliament from other bodies he would gladly present one from the College. At the same time he requested the College to furnish him with some details concerning the practice of anatomy in Edinburgh, the present number of schools and students, and the price at which subjects for dissection could be obtained. "I apprehend," he added, "the public feeling against dissection is stronger in Scotland than it is in this country or in Ireland, and that it is much more difficult from local circumstances to find the means of supplying subjects than in almost any other part of the Empire."

Petitions were then sent to both Houses, stating that it was almost impossible, for the reasons stated above, to obtain the necessary opportunities of studying or teaching anatomy without being directly or indirectly engaged in the commission of crime. In the meantime a committee was appointed by the College to draw up a report in answer to Mr Peel's inquiry, Dated 4th May 1828, this report contains an interesting description of the conditions under which anatomy was taught at the period in question.

Forty years ago in Edinburgh, it runs, there was no teacher of anatomy except the Professor of Anatomy at the University. There was no class of practical anatomy, and it was believed that no bodies were dissected except those used by Dr Monro for his demonstrations. Soon after this period the study of practical anatomy was introduced and rapidly advanced in progress. This seems to have arisen from the desire of the students to attain knowledge in this department, and through the zeal of individuals who established schools of private anatomy in promoting its study, and, more recently, because the College of Surgeons had rendered it indispensable that all those who apply for the diploma of surgeon shall have attended a course of practical anatomy; from the Senatus Academicus having introduced it as a branch of study required from those who were examined for medical degrees, and from the public boards requiring it of candidates for the medical offices in the public service.

At the date of the report four Fellows of the College in addition to the Professor of Anatomy were lecturing on the practical part of the subject in Edinburgh, and the total number of students studying medicine was estimated at about 900, of whom 380 were calculated to have attended the extra-mural classes. The number of subjects used in the previous winter was said to have been 150, and, on an average, cost the lecturers nine or ten pounds each. They were supplied to the students, however, at about eight pounds each. From the statement, continued the report, it was obvious that since the cultivation of practical anatomy the supply of bodies for dissection had not increased in proportion to the demand, and was insufficient; the teachers, in fact, had submitted to a considerable pecuniary sacrifice in order to place the means of prosecuting their anatomical studies within reach of the students.

The committee, therefore, were of opinion that of 900 students annually resorting to the town, 300 would necessarily require to attend courses of practical anatomy, and that the supply of subjects should be at the rate of, at least, one body to each student. If this supply could be procured at about five pounds each, it was thought that every purpose desired would be served. When the study of practical anatomy was followed by students only to a limited extent, the small number of subjects required was procured in Edinburgh and its vicinity, and the price was three or four guineas. As the school of anatomy extended and a greater number of bodies was required, the violation of churchyards was more frequently detected, and the feelings of the populace were often irritated by the audacity and recklessness of the degraded class of men who were necessarily employed in the occupation of procuring bodies, and whose numbers were considerably increased. For some time afterwards a very considerable supply was obtained from London, though at an increased cost. There was reason to believe that this had the effect of diminishing in some degree the supply of the anatomical teachers in London. It diminished also to a certain extent the work of the body-snatchers, and contentions arose between the teachers and the body-snatchers and among the body-snatchers themselves. The difficulties of procuring subjects in London were by this time much increased, and, at last, from various causes, the supply almost entirely ceased. After this, bodies were secured chiefly from a distance, and a considerable number were obtained from Ireland, where it seems they could be obtained more easily and with less outrage to the public feelings.

The committee acknowledged their difficulty in finding a remedy which could have an immediate effect upon the evils complained of, but they thought that if the bodies of persons who died friendless and without anyone to care for them (which numbered between 400 and 500 annually) could be procured for anatomical purposes, a full supply for all useful ends would be obtained. If this were done, it was thought that the public at large would soon understand that the greater the facility that was given for procuring the bodies of the worthless and of those who died without friends, the less would the feelings of the respectable part of the community be outraged.

Strange to say, during the very time these negotiations were being carried on, those notorious miscreants Burke and Hare were, all unsuspected, carrying on their loathsome trade in the West Port.

In March 1829, the Anatomy Bill was introduced by Mr Warburton, but on account of its unsatisfactory details and unpopularity with the public it was thought expedient to withdraw it. The principal objection the College had against it was, that while it did not at all insure that teachers of anatomy could obtain a supply of bodies from the sources which it rendered legally available, it would at once effectually prevent them from obtaining the necessary supply from any other source; but when the College heard that the Bill had passed the Commons and had been carried to the Lords, they decided to petition that House against it.

In the meantime a letter had been received from Mr Warburton, who had framed the Bill, deprecating any objection to it on the part of the College that might have the effect either to throw it out or to provoke discussion, the consequences of which, he said, might be the introduction of still stricter and more objectionable clauses. This produced such a change in the sentiments of the teachers and various members who took an interest in the subject, that it was at once agreed that it would be better for the Bill to pass as it then stood than that any objections should be made which would lead to its being thrown out altogether.

The Bill, however, was withdrawn, but only to be re-introduced a couple of years later, in a slightly modified form, in consequence of an attempt having been made in London to imitate the doings of Burke and Hare in Edinburgh.   This time it was more successful, and was ultimately passed into law, and so with it disappeared most of the difficulties of the anatomists.

The information contained in the College report to Mr Peel was gathered from all the lecturers on anatomy in the town, with the exception of Dr Monro, who sent his report direct. It seems possible that Dr Knox may also have had some independent communication with Mr Peel, for amongst the College papers is a letter addressed to the Secretary of State and signed by Dr Knox, in which the latter gives his own views on the question, and relates some of the difficulties which he had encountered in his endeavours to obtain anatomical subjects for the use of his students.   In commenting upon the obstacles which obstructed the anatomist in his work, he first blamed the local authorities, including the magistrates, police officers, and officers of Excise and Customs; in proof of which he submitted the following statement :—

"A short time ago I was anxious to import anatomical subjects viâ Liverpool—they were in the best possible condition, having been selected by one of my assistants sent to Ireland for that express purpose; they were most carefully packed, and indeed deceived all those connected with the shipment and transport, until their arrival in the Brunswick Dock of Liverpool.   There the packages were broke into by an officer of the Customs and Excise, the contents by some means or other got into the hands of the local police, and were after-wards, as I have been assured, interred at the public expense; finally, that nothing might be wanting to render the exposure as complete as possible, an account of it found its way into the Liverpool journals, and the police even endeavoured to trace the names of the shippers of these subjects, with what view I cannot pretend to say.   Some few days ago some packages were seized at Greenock, and an exposure made which has alarmed this part of the country. At Carlisle, last winter, the authorities broke open, on mere suspicion, a package passing through the town by coach; this package was done up with the greatest care. They knew by the way-bill that it must have travelled a hundred miles before it fell into their hands, and was on its very way to Edinburgh; yet, regardless of these circumstances, with which they were well acquainted, they seized the package, summoned a jury, whose verdict was 'that they had found a dead body in a box, but how it came there they knew not.'

"There is one subject in particular," continues the letter, "on which I beg most respectfully your attention. Anatomists generally are most anxious to avoid public scenes such as these, and for this purpose they are careful to select subjects which are claimed by no relative or friend, and thus often avoid the painful necessity of violating the burial grounds and by so doing inflicting a shock on the most sacred feelings of human nature. Now, when anatomical subjects procured under such circumstances are nevertheless seized on their way to the schools, very alarming reprisals are made in the burying grounds of the place where the seizure has been made, often without the smallest regard to risk or circumstances. Clear proof of this can easily be submitted to you should it be required."

In the second place, Dr Knox considered that the conduct of the teachers of anatomy towards each other had at times been disgraceful, and still continued so. "During the course of last summer," he said, "two cases containing anatomical subjects were shipped on board a steam packet in Dublin Harbour. A few hours previous to the sailing of the vessel, one of the lecturers in Dublin, who had probably received information of the shipment, sent his assistant on board, who, suspecting the boxes to contain subjects, procured a warrant, had them broken open, and their contents left exposed on the quay for, as I am informed, the space of two days, apparently for the purpose of irritating the populace and preventing the supply of the schools; and this at a time when subjects abounded so much in Dublin that, to use a mercantile phrase, the article was in no demand whatever. Permit me most respectfully to remark to you, that I have ever been an advocate for the making these matters as little public as possible, but now that the anatomical enquiry is patent to all, I therefore thought it my duty to state to you the obstacles which impede the progress of anatomy in Great Britain."

How the letter came into the hands of the College is immaterial. It bears date 3rd November 1828 (Monday), but the fact that Burke was arrested on Saturday night, 1st November, and Hare early next morning, may have had something to do with its never being sent to the Secretary of State.

CHAPTER XIII

THE EARLY ASSOCIATION OF THE INCORPORATION OF SURGEONS WITH THE ROYAL INFIRMARY [1]

The Royal Infirmary—Its Origin—The Incorporation's Offer Refused—
And afterwards Accepted—The Surgeons' Hospital—Proposals for
Coalition—Modification of the Infirmary Laws—Mr Russell and Mr
Flanagan — Description of the Royal Infirmary in 1800 — The
Surgeons and General Practitioners—The Allocation of Beds to the
Professor of Surgery.

IN the short accounts of the College which have already
appeared, all references to their early connection with the
Royal Infirmary have been of the briefest description, while
the events which led to their establishing an hospital of
their own have also been but imperfectly related. The
object of this chapter is to supply that deficiency, and at
the same time to explain an erroneous report which gained
credence at the time, and which has since been repeated by
contemporary writers, viz., that the Infirmary did not at first
receive the support and assistance of the surgeons as an
Incorporation. Such a statement, unless accompanied by an
explanation of all the facts connected with it, is misleading,
and might easily give rise to the supposition that the surgeons
were not in sympathy with the undertaking. True, it was not
until 1738, or nine years after the doors of the Infirmary had
been thrown open, that the surgeons as a body became
associated with it, but this was due to an offer of service made
by them, in 1729, having been rejected by the Managers. In
consequence, however, of the Infirmary, or Physicians' Hospital
as it was then called, being unequal to the demands made upon
it, the surgeons, anxious, no doubt, to participate in the
charitable work of the city, decided to erect a hospital for
the treatment of surgical cases alone. This hospital was

[1] Reprinted from the *Edinburgh Medical Journal*, October 1913.

opened in July 1736, but after being in active operation for only a couple of years, it was found expedient to merge the two institutions into one. In this way the Surgeons' Hospital became part of the Royal Infirmary, and the surgeons part of the Infirmary staff, for by one of the articles of the Union— and a very important one it turned out to be—*All members of the Incorporation of Surgeons were to serve in rotation under such rules and regulations as the Managers of the Infirmary might from time to time make.* For many years all went well, the Managers modifying their rules according to circumstances and for the benefit of the institution, until in 1800 they introduced a plan limiting the number of surgeons who were to act to six, and appointing them for a period of two years. This gave great offence to the large majority of the Incorporation, and particularly to its younger members, who hitherto had had the privilege of attending, though only for a few weeks at a time. In it they saw an infringement of their rights and a breach of the agreement of 1738. At last, after all efforts to come to an understanding had failed, the surgeons applied to the Court of Session for interdict to prevent the Managers putting their proposals into execution. This was granted, but almost immediately recalled, and both parties were ordered to state their case in memorials for the information of the Court. It is from these memorials and other sources that the following details have been elicited.

The origin of the Royal Infirmary may be traced to the members of the Royal College of Physicians, and to them is due the credit, not only of collecting a large sum of money for its erection, but also, when this had been accomplished, of undertaking to give their services and attendance without any prospect of reward. Previous to the erection of the Infirmary the sick poor of the city were attended by the physicians in their own hall. The inconvenience attached to this arrangement, and probably a growing demand for clinical study, first led them to think of providing a place where a more extended treatment of patients could be carried out. This was begun about the year 1729 on a very limited scale in a small house[1] near the University, with accommodation perhaps for ten or

[1] Said to have been situated at the head of Robertson's Close.

O

twelve beds. It then became necessary to appoint a surgeon, and in response to an invitation by the Managers two proposals were made, one by the *Incorporation* of Surgeons offering to furnish medicines and operations gratis to the sick and wounded in the Infirmary for two years; the other by Mr Alexander Monro and five other surgeons, who offered to undertake the duty of the hospital in the following manner :—

" 1st. The year being equally divided amongst us, we shall in our turn regularly attend the hospital as ordinary (the time to be fixed as soon as the Managers shall accept our proposal), acting as surgeons, and dispensing out of our own shop as we do to other patients the medicines, whether external or internal, prescribed by the physicians for the sick poor, and that gratis, renouncing all claim of payment of accounts or of fee.

" 2nd. In all extraordinary chirurgical cases, he who in his turn is ordinary shall call a consultation of us all, who shall meet and assist him with our advice or service.

" 3rd. When the time of attendance is finished, he of us who is to succeed shall have from his predecessor an exact detail of all the chirurgical cases then in the hospital, and of the method of cure he has followed, together with a copy of all receipts ordered by the physicians for the different sick during his attendance.

" 4th. On the necessary avocations of the ordinary, he shall acquaint any other of our number who shall attend, but send to the ordinary's shop to be dispensed.

" 5th. This our service shall continue till the number of sick exceeds ten, or as the committee pleases to restrict it."

The Managers approved of this latter proposal, and the six gentlemen arranged the order of their attendance amongst themselves. The proposal therefore given in by the Incorporation of Surgeons was virtually rejected by the adoption of that of Mr Monro. In this way the service in the hospital was performed by the attendance of the whole College of Physicians if they chose to do so, and by the six surgeons appointed in the manner above mentioned.

The advantages of such an institution, the surgeons said, were soon felt, and under the patriotic exertions of Provost Drummond it became an object of public attention. That the plan might be more effectually executed, an application was made to the Sovereign to erect the contributors by a Royal

Charter into a legally recognised corporation. Accordingly a Charter was granted in 1736, bearing :—

"That several well-disposed persons had by subscription raised a considerable sum, the interest whereof by an agreement of the subscribers and donors is to be applied for erecting a house in Edinburgh wherein poor sick, properly recommended from any part of the country, who are not absolutely incurable, are to be entertained and taken care of by the Royal College of Physicians of Edinburgh and some of the most skilful surgeons ; that under the direction of the Managers chosen by the contributors a house has been hired, and so far as the interest of the fund could go poor persons have been received into it, and have been so well taken care of that many under the blessing of God have thereby been restored to their health ; that this charity is so apparently of universal benefit that it is hoped the fund may be considerably increased by the donations of charitable persons, if authorised by our Royal permission, and if the undertaking shall be brought and kept under good management and regulations."

The Charter then

"Erects, creates, and incorporates all and every the said contributors who have already contributed to the said charitable design, and all such persons as shall hereafter contribute thereto, into one body corporate and politic, by the name of the Royal Infirmary of Edinburgh, under which name they shall have perpetual succession, and a common seal ; and they and their successors, under the same name, shall be legally entitled and capable to purchase and enjoy lands, tenements, and any other heritage in Scotland, not exceeding the yearly value of £1000 sterling; and to lend such sum or sums of money to any person or persons, and upon such security as they shall think fit ; and to sue and be sued ; and to make such by-laws, rules, and orders, consistent with the laws of our realm, as may best conduce to the charitable end and purpose above mentioned ; and generally all other matters and things tending to the pious design aforesaid to do and execute as fully and amply, in every respect, as any body corporate lawfully may do, and as if the said matters and things were herein set down."

A system of management then follows, concluding with an arrangement for an annual meeting of the whole contributors above £5 sterling each, who were to be called a General Court, and they, or a majority of them so assembled, were to have full power and authority to make and constitute such by-laws, ordinances and regulations for the management and government of the affairs of the Corporation as they should think fit, providing such by-laws were not contrary to the true intent and meaning of the above, nor repugnant to the laws of the realm.

In virtue of the powers thus conferred upon the contributors, various regulations were made by the Managers, not only for directing the internal economy of the hospital, so far as regards the sick—the immediate object of the institution—but also for cherishing the School of Medicine, as far as the hospital could serve that purpose. And foreseeing that its interest would soon be interwoven with that of the University, the Managers resolved to adopt every measure that could tend to facilitate medical education and to render it complete.

It has already been mentioned that when the College of Physicians established their hospital, an offer was made on the part of the Incorporation of Surgeons to take the management of the surgical department; this offer, however, was not accepted, as the Managers of the Infirmary were of opinion that a general Corporation Act would not answer the purpose, in regard that no such Act, though agreed to by a majority of the Incorporation, could bind any particular member to a deed and service of charity, and that the service of the hospital ought not to be left on that footing. They therefore considered that the service would be best undertaken by such of the members of the Surgeons' Incorporation who were willing to contribute to the service of the hospital, and would sign a paper to that effect. Six members of the Incorporation, including Monro, then offered their services on the terms above stated, and on their offers being accepted they were appointed by the Managers surgeons to the Infirmary.

From this it is quite clear that the surgeons were not only willing but anxious to serve the Infirmary from the commencement. It is also equally plain that the Managers were determined not to permit them to do so as an incorporated body. It then occurred to them to erect another Infirmary under the name of the Surgeons' Hospital, and, in 1736, they passed an Act to that effect. Their object, they said, was to alleviate the deplorable condition of the many indigent and diseased poor who languish under various diseases, and are ready to perish for want of that timely assistance which they might find in a hospital erected for their entertainment, and although the Royal Infirmary, in a great measure, answered that valuable purpose, yet they thought there were still many well-disposed persons willing to extend their charity to such a laudable object.

Previous to passing this Act the Incorporation communicated their intention to the Managers of the Infirmary by letter, which concluded with a suggestion for coalition of the two hospitals, on the grounds that by the curtailment of expenditure which would ensue, a more extensive service could be prosecuted and a more general opportunity for improvement would be given to students.   As an inducement to the Managers to accept their plan the surgeons made the following offers :—

" 1st. We undertake to give our attendance in common with the gentlemen surgeons who have hitherto served the Infirmary, and for the six following years—a time somewhat more than equal to that already elapsed since your institution—and to furnish, at our own charges, all the medicines that shall be needful, and as long afterwards, in conjunction with them, as it shall please God to spare us, and we follow our business in this place.

" 2nd. And that we shall further become donators to your hospital, by which, and the preceding article, £30 sterling yearly will be immediately saved, and much more afterwards, when you shall think fit to take in a greater number of sick persons.

" 3rd. We shall further endeavour to persuade the subscribers to our foundation to allow their donations to be transferred to your stock, by which we hope something considerable may likewise accrue for the further encouragement of so good and religious a design : That, therefore, we may be all of one mind, and with the same single aim visit the sick and diseased poor in their affliction and distress."

In consequence of this letter a committee was appointed by both sides to confer on the matter, and the surgeon-erectors having afterwards been desired to give in to the Managers of the Royal Infirmary written articles of what was proposed as the foundation of the coalition, they submitted the following proposals to their consideration :—

" 13th May 1736.—1st. That they offer, without fee or reward, to serve the Infirmary as surgeons, conjunct with the gentlemen who have hitherto acted in that capacity; and that they consent that the manner of their attendance as to numbers and time be at the direction of the Managers.

"2nd. That they undertake, for six years after their admission, to furnish, at their proper charge, all the medicines that shall be used in the hospital, exempting throughout that period the surgeons already concerned from any share of the expense.

"3rd. That after these six years are elapsed they oblige themselves during their lives, or exercise of their employment, to furnish their proportion of all the necessary medicines gratis.

"4th. That they engage to become donators to the Infirmary to the extent of two thousand merks Scots, payable the first term after their admission.

"5th. That they will use their endeavours to persuade those who already are, or yet may become, donors to their foundation, to allow their donations to be transferred to the funds of the Infirmary."

An answer was made to these proposals on the part of the Managers, in which there is the following observation :—

"As the proposers were pleased to observe, at a meeting with the Committee of Managers, that the benefit of their apprentices and students was a considerable motive to them to make the proposal for a new infirmary, or to be admitted into the old one, they may be assured that nothing is more at heart with the Managers than to answer that original design of the Infirmary of giving the students of physic and surgery all opportunities of education in their power, which the smallness of their house (that could not admit more than have hitherto had the privilege of attending there) only has prevented them from executing. But so soon as a large house can be got that inconveniency will be removed, and no time is to be lost in providing one."

At this period no further steps towards amalgamation were taken, and the surgeon-erectors, in July 1736, opened their hospital for surgical patients. In their Memorial the surgeons said it was a well-known fact that their hospital was remarkably well conducted, "and the patients, in every respect, were much better attended to than at the other hospital." Its character was every day increasing, and the applications for admission were extremely numerous. From its success the "jealousy of the Managers of the other hospital was said to be excited," and the proposal for a coalition was again renewed. Consequently a committee was appointed as before, and in May 1738 the following terms were offered by the Incorporation :—

That in order to preserve an equality among the surgeons of Edinburgh, and that their apprentices and students may have equal opportunities for their improvement by serving in the Royal Infirmary, it is proposed by the erectors of the Surgeons' Hospital—

"That every member of the Incorporation of Surgeons and their successors, in all time coming, while in the exercise of their employment, shall be permitted to serve in the Royal Infirmary as surgeons upon their application to the Managers thereof for that purpose, and that their apprentices and students be admitted to attend there without distinction or partiality; for the performance of which the Managers of the Infirmary shall give sufficient security to the Incorporation of Surgeons.

"That upon their granting such security, the erectors of the Surgeons' Hospital shall, with the consent of their donors, deliver up to the Treasurer of the said Infirmary the whole stock belonging to the said hospital, for the use and behoof of the Infirmary.

"That advantages of this coalition to the Royal Infirmary will, we hope, be so obvious to all of the Honourable Managers, that we need not make particular mention of them."

After consultation, the Managers replied that as they had nothing more at heart in carrying on the charitable work of the Infirmary than (next to the taking all possible care for the right entertainment and cure of the sick brought into the hospital) to make the Infirmary as subservient as possible to the education of the students in physic and surgery, and for raising the reputation of the practice of surgery by the members of the Incorporation of Surgeons in Edinburgh, they unanimously agreed

"That as soon as that part of the building first designed for the patients, which they have agreed to build, is finished—the work being already begun, and to be carried on with all convenient expedition—they will admit all the Masters of the Incorporation residing in the city and suburbs, and in the exercise of their employment, to be surgeons to the Infirmary, to serve in it on the same footing as the present surgeons do, to be classed, and their attendance and practice regulated by, the Managers; and they now actually agree that the members of the said Incorporation be surgeons to the Infirmary, to enter upon their attendance and services, according to the regulations to be made from time to time, after the building is finished, upon a paper being signed by such as are willing to undertake the service, within three months after this day, obliging themselves to serve upon the same footing, and to subject themselves to the performance of the conditions which the present surgeons of the Infirmary are subjected to.

"That the same privilege shall be extended to all future entrants to the said Incorporation, upon their applying to the Managers of the Infirmary, by a signed paper, desiring to be admitted in the terms foresaid, within three months after their being received by the said Incorporation.

"That all the young gentlemen attending the study of physic or surgery in Edinburgh, either as apprentices or students, shall be privileged to attend the patients in the Infirmary, in such order, and under such regulations, as shall from time to time be adjusted and fixed by the Managers, upon each of them paying such an annual premium to the Treasurer of the Infirmary as the Managers shall think fit to determine, and appoint to be applied towards defraying the expenses of the house and patients, until such time as the Managers of the Infirmary shall think fit to admit them gratis, upon the revenues becoming sufficient to defray the whole charges of the Infirmary.

"That during the time of building that part of the house now designed the gentlemen erectors of the Surgeons' Hospital may, if they think fit, entertain patients in the house presently possessed by them for the benefit of their apprentices until the building is finished."

On this being communicated to the Incorporation they agreed to accept the invitation, provided the Managers gave security for the continuing the whole Incorporation in their service, and that they be admitted thereto with all convenient speed. At the same time the erectors declared that upon such securities being given they were willing to give up their hospital and transfer their stock, amounting to £500 sterling, to the Royal Infirmary.

At this stage of the transaction the surgeons took legal opinion as to the manner of carrying the matter effectually into execution, and thereafter passed the following Act:—

"The Corporation taking to their consideration an Act of the Royal Infirmary, dated 19th May 1738, inviting all the members of the Corporation to serve as surgeons in the said Infirmary, and reflecting with sensible pleasure on the many advantages that will arise from the invitation if complied with, such as, that the Royal College of

Physicians and this Corporation jointly concurring for carrying on this charitable work of the Infirmary by serving it in their several professions, the erection will prove a national benefit for the relief of sick poor, and a great advantage to all students in physic and surgery ; that the Royal Infirmary will be secured in the service of plenty of able surgeons in all time coming ; that if our brethren, the erectors of the Surgeons' Hospital, shall agree to make over the stock contributed thereto to the Royal Infirmary, it will be a considerable benefit, and augment the funds of the Infirmary, and thereby all emulation betwixt the Surgeons' Hospital and the Royal Infirmary about procuring donations, subscriptions, and contributions, etc., which has hitherto been attended with many inconveniences, hurtful to the charitable work, will happily cease, and all after-rivalship be prevented by the coalition of the two houses hereby recommended; and, lastly, the public will be infinitely pleased to see physicians and surgeons, and everyone concerning themselves in this good work, animated with sincere Christian zeal, and cordially joining hand in hand to promote this most useful piece of charity, wherein piety and policy jointly concur, the one to relieve sick and distressed poor, and the other to breed up able physicians and surgeons for the honour and service of the country, and thereby saving money to the nation by completing their education at home " ;

to which Act the approbation of the erectors of the Surgeons' Hospital was subjoined.

Nothing now remained to finish the business but a confirmation on the part of the Managers, and this was obtained on 19th July 1738, when, at a meeting held by them, it was agreed that William Mitchell, Adam Drummond, John Kennedy, William Wood, George Young, Francis Russell, William Wardrobe, George Langlands, George Murray, Thomas Glen, Gilbert Laurie, Joseph Gibson, Robert Smith, John Kirkwood, Charles Ramsay, John Wallace, Harry Osburn, George Lauder, and Martin Eccles, with the six surgeons then serving in the Infirmary, and such other members of the Incorporation as shall oblige themselves to serve the Royal Infirmary in terms of the Act of the Managers, or who shall hereafter subscribe such an obligation within three months after being received into the Incorporation of Surgeons, shall be surgeons to the Royal Infirmary so soon as that part of the house now about to be built shall be fit to take in patients, under such regulations as shall be appointed by the Managers.   It was also arranged that until the new building was completed the Surgeons' Hospital should be considered a part of the Royal Infirmary, and it was earnestly hoped that the Managers would regulate and settle the attendance of the six present surgeons of the Infirmary and of the surgeons formerly attending in the Surgeons' Hospital in such manner as would tend to unity and harmony, and the welfare of the whole.

The erectors of the Surgeons' Hospital then conveyed their funds, amounting to £500 sterling, and the whole effects of their hospital, to the Managers of the Infirmary.

At the same time all members of the Incorporation were assumed as surgeons to the hospital in the same manner as the original six.

The surgeons claim that the measure here adopted was no hasty one, and that the Managers, when they appointed the Incorporation in general to be surgeons to the Infirmary, did so "under such regulations as should be appointed by them," or, as it is more fully expressed above, "to serve on the same footing as the present six surgeons do, to be classed, and their attendance regulated by, the Managers from time to time."

In this way the Incorporation came to give their attendance to the Royal Infirmary, and continued to do so while the regulations were conformable to the agreement that had been made, and were not in violation of the right which the Incorporation had obtained.

Soon after this agreement the Managers proceeded to class and regulate the order of attendance of the surgeons, and ordained "That four surgeons do attend the Infirmary *per vices* for the space of a month, being two surgeons for each ward or 'floor monthly,' and the members of the Incorporation were further divided into seven classes of four each."

When this Act of the Managers was brought before a meeting of the Incorporation it was objected to by John Kennedy, a past deacon, who gave in the letter underwritten :—

"Deacon,—Having seriously considered the Act and order of the Royal Infirmary laid before this Incorporation, I am of opinion that their classing and appointing the surgeons to serve and attend there without consulting them in it is using them more like hired servants than useful members and benefactors to it, seeing they are to give their medicines and attendance to the diseased in it gratis.   This, I think, a very masterly procedure, and derogatory to the honour and credit of this Society and to every member thereof, and as the Managers have begun in this disagreeable manner, I have good reason to suspect they will proceed in it.   Therefore, for my part, I am resolved not to submit to such arbitrary government, and do refuse to serve or attend on it for the future."

This declinature was adhered to by David Aitkenhead, William Wood, and three others.

Nevertheless, this order of attendance continued until May 1748, when some further alterations were made, but as they were unanimously agreed to by the surgeons, there is no need to detail them.

So matters went on till July 1766, when the Managers, after pointing out that there were several defects and inconveniences regarding the attendance of the surgeons, ordained :—

"That all the members of the Incorporation of Surgeons shall attend monthly by turns, as at present, each surgeon, during his own month of attendance, performing the operations which shall occur, and advising the chirurgical cases in the Infirmary, but shall not have the power of substituting any other in his place, either for advising or operating ; and in order to ascertain the stated and regular attendance of surgeons in the house, agreeably to the plan pursued so successfully with respect to the physicians, they hereby nominate and appoint four surgeons, viz., Messrs James Rae, Peter Adie, John Balfour, and Alexander Wood, and declare them to be ordinary surgeons of the Royal Infirmary, ordaining them, besides attendance those months which shall fall to them by rotation, to attend together with the surgeon whose turn it shall be to wait on the Infirmary, and in his absence to advise the chirurgical cases and perform the operations that shall occur ; and they hereby authorise and appoint their Treasurer to pay annually to each of the said surgeons the sum of £10 sterling in name of salary ; and it is hereby declared that their offices, as ordinary surgeons, shall commence from the first day of August 1767."

The appointment of these substitute surgeons was objected to by the Incorporation as being invidious, and as making a "distinction incompatible with the terms of their junction with the Infirmary."

They therefore presented a memorial to the Managers, pointing out the grievance.   The arrangement, however, was continued, the ordinary surgeons still acting by rotation.

In 1768, another memorial upon the subject was presented, upon which the opinion of Counsel had been taken, and the matter at last having been deliberately considered by the Managers, they resolved:—

"1st. That they will change one of their four ordinary surgeons annually, and will add another member of the Incorporation in his place.

"2nd. That they will make this annual change and election according to seniority, and in the order in which the gentlemen above mentioned willing to act as ordinaries stand in the list above inserted. [This referred to a list given in of gentlemen who wished to serve as ordinaries.]

"And 3rd. That this shall continue until altered by the Managers, in case that at any time hereafter they shall see cause to do so."

The establishment of the four substitutes continued till 1785, when the Managers resolved to abolish the arrangement of substitute surgeons and the salaries attached to it. In place of this, the Managers ruled that in future when a surgeon entered upon his term he should have entire charge for two months instead of one as hitherto. At the end of the two months he was to be succeeded by the next in rotation, and so on. The Managers considered this would be for the benefit of the patients in the hospital as every surgeon in turn, by having the chief charge for two months together, would have it in his power to prosecute many cures, which a monthly rotation often prevented his having time for. Some minor details were also laid down for the succeeding surgeon.

From this time onwards until the year 1800, the attendance of the members of the College had been in conformity to these regulations. Whatever alterations were made were agreeable to the principles laid down in the agreement of 1738, and no deviation from that was in any respect made. On 1st September 1800, however, in consequence of a memorial having been laid before the Managers by one of their number (Dr Gregory), they transmitted to the College a Minute stating their opinion "That the manner in which the surgical department is at present conducted is not so much for the advantage of the public as the Managers wish, or might be the case if some new regulations were adopted, and that it is their duty as guardians of the public charity to make such alterations as may from time to time appear to be for the advantage of the institution.   But before proceeding to consider any new regulations for that purpose they are desirous to have the sentiments of the Royal College of Surgeons on the subject," etc.

The Incorporation, or College, as they had now become, promised to consider this letter, and soon afterwards submitted a plan to the Managers, obviating all the theoretical objections they had made.   The latter, however, returned a letter disapproving of it, together with a plan prepared by themselves.   By it the duty of the hospital was to be done by six surgeons, to be elected by the Managers, two of whom were to go out every two years, but who were to be entitled again to re-election after four years.   Thus the surgical staff of the hospital was to consist of six surgeons, to be elected by the Managers, two always doing the permanent duty for a period of two years at a time, *and all the other members of the College of Surgeons were to be excluded.*

This plan appeared to be entirely adverse to the agreement of 1738, and in the opinion of the College quite unnecessary, as the grievances complained of might easily have been adjusted without adopting so strong a measure.   They therefore, from a consideration of duty to their successors, resolved to oppose it with all their energy.   Upon the disapprobation of the College being communicated to the Managers, it was suggested that a committee should be appointed for adjusting their differences but, after some further negotiations, the Managers' declared their intention not to depart in the main from their plan of election, and declined any conference on the head as totally unnecessary.

They then elected the following six surgeons, viz., James Russell, Andrew Wardrope, James Law, Andrew Inglis, William Brown, and John Thomson, to take charge of the surgical department of the hospital in terms of the foregoing regulations. The College, in consideration of what they called the " precipitate action " of the Managers, then applied to the Court of Session for an interdict to prevent the Managers from carrying into execution the new plans which they had adopted.   This was granted by the Lord Ordinary, but upon a petition being presented by the Managers to the succeeding Lord Ordinary the interdict was recalled, and both parties were ordered to state their case in memorials for the information of the Court.

On the interdict being removed, the Managers at once put the newly-elected surgeons in possession of the hospital, and here occurred an unfortunate incident which, it was said, pointed to the Managers being desirous of excluding from the Infirmary every member of the College except those whom they had recently appointed.

It had always been the custom, it appears, for members of the College to meet, about the visiting hour, in the consulting-room, and, in pursuance of this old habit, when a number had assembled as usual on the morning of the introduction of the new rules, they received the following message: " The Managers, hearing that several of the College of Surgeons are now in the consulting-room, request those surgeons to withdraw, and leave the room for the use of the acting surgeons for whom it is intended, as, according to the regulations now established, no person has access to the consulting-room but the attending physicians and surgeons."

In consequence of this, Dr George Wood and Dr Harkness, two members of the College who were present at the time, waited upon the Managers, and intimated their intention of not again entering the room alluded to ; they also requested to be informed if members of the College were now prohibited from walking the wards. In reply to this inquiry the Managers signified that they had no objection to their doing so at the usual hours, but insisted that they and other members of the College should behave with proper respect and decorum to the attending surgeons, and should not, on any occasion, make any remarks on their practice or conduct, or in any way interfere with them in the discharge of their duty.

This apparent act of discourtesy on the part of the Managers was not, however, so gross as at first appears. The circumstances that led up to it are these: When Mr Russell, one of the newly-elected surgeons, took charge of the surgical department at the time appointed by the Managers, Mr Flanagan, the retiring surgeon, was not there to hand over his patients. After waiting half an hour Mr Russell commenced his duties, but no sooner had he begun than Mr Flanagan came in, and in angry tones said, in presence of the students and nurses, that after the handsome manner in which he had behaved to Mr Russell he did not expect that he would have taken charge of the patients without waiting for him, and that if he had been a younger man than he was he would have spoken to him in a different way.   Mr Russell replied that he had waited some time, and that he was acting by the authority of the Managers, but that if Mr Flanagan had behaved in a civil manner he would have requested his opinion and assistance in regard to those patients on whom operations had been lately performed, but owing to Mr Flanagan's temper this was impossible.

Mr Flanagan was accompanied by Mr John Bell and his brother Charles (afterwards Sir Charles), both of whom were said to be similarly excited.

In consequence of Mr Flanagan's conduct, which the Managers described as highly improper and reprehensible, they resolved that if any member of the Royal College of Surgeons should hereafter be guilty of such unwarrantable conduct, he should be deprived of the privilege of access to the hospital. At this moment, while the Managers were expressing their sentiments, they were informed that a large number of surgeons and an unusual number of students had assembled in the consulting-room.   They then sent the message complained of.

In summing up the case in their memorial, the surgeons claimed that since they legally acquired a right to be considered surgeons to the Royal Infirmary, and had been in actual possession, they ought to have been maintained in it until the question had been more deliberately considered. They also submitted that, in virtue of the agreement of 1738, they could not be excluded from the Infirmary, their attendance, of course, always being regulated by the Managers agreeable to the good faith of their contract and the common principles of justice to all concerned.

The memorial of the Managers, to a great extent, covers the same ground as the one submitted by the surgeons, and need not be repeated at length.   A few extracts from it, however, will be necessary to show their object in taking such a drastic step, and their reason for their belief that the patients in the Infirmary would benefit by it.

At the beginning, they state that as soon as the question

as to the method of regulating the surgical department was agitated, the Managers were conscious of the disadvantage of treating with the surgeons as a body in regard to attendance. They foresaw that the individual members would not consider themselves bound by an Act of the College unless it suited their own interest. By this it was meant that the Managers had no security that the more skilful and experienced surgeons would not neglect the hospital as their private practice increased, and leave it entirely in the hands of the younger surgeons, who, although having more time at their disposal, would necessarily bring with them less professional skill and experience.

It was also pointed out that the Surgeons' Hospital was not erected and maintained at the expense of the College, but by a public subscription from all parts of the country—just as the Infirmary was. Consequently when it was handed over to the Managers of the original Infirmary the surgeons were not making over their own monies except to the extent of the 2000 merks which they contributed amongst themselves.

The Managers said they did not wish the College of Surgeons to suppose that the late regulations were adopted merely in consequence of some sudden and instantaneous impression as to the evils attending the former system of indiscriminate rotation, neither could they pay Dr Gregory the compliment of admitting that their conviction upon this subject was produced by his memorial, although, no doubt, their opinion was much strengthened by it. On the contrary it was well known, they said, that the numerous disadvantages attending the system of indiscriminate rotation was a constant subject of regret, and that many deliberations were held with a view to altering it. Nothing would have prevented this being done long ago save the opposition which former experience taught them to expect from the College of Surgeons, and the difficulty of making a new arrangement, which would be beneficial to the hospital, equally beneficial to the School of Surgery, and, if possible, also agreeable to the College of Surgeons, whom it certainly was the wish of the Managers to please. Dr Gregory's memorial, therefore, whatever its intrinsic merit, had no other effect, with reference to the conduct of the Managers upon this occasion, than perhaps to bring matters to a crisis, and to accelerate the abolition of a system which the Royal College of Surgeons themselves would now hardly venture to defend.

On referring to the arrangements made in 1738, the Managers pointed out that some individual surgeons bound themselves personally to attend the hospital, but the Incorporation itself came under no obligation which could be binding upon it, or upon its individual members for the time ; it merely recommended to its members to accept the invitation of the Managers, leaving it, however, perfectly open to them to refuse.   In point of fact four or five of the members of the Incorporation paid no attention to this recommendation till nearly two years afterwards, which demonstrated that the proceedings on the part of the College were not considered as creating a solemn obligation, either on the part of the College or the individual members of it.

If there was any contract at all binding the members of the Incorporation to attend by rotation, it was certainly a mutual contract ; and, if the Infirmary was bound to admit of the attendance of the surgeons by an unalterable rotation, the surgeons, on the other hand, were certainly committed to give their attendance according to the same rotation ; in fact if the Managers of the Infirmary, in the course of this rotation, became bound to submit their patients to all the ignorance, rashness, inhumanity, and awkwardness which might at any time exist among the members of the College of Surgeons, certainly the College was bound in its turn to furnish to the Managers all the skill, dexterity, experience, attention, and humanity which, to the honour of the College of Surgeons, is the more distinguishing character of its members.   It was then declared that as the College of Surgeons had conducted this rotation, they kept every advantage which attended the system to their own members, and threw the whole disadvantages of it upon the Managers of the Infirmary and their patients, for out of twenty-three senior surgeons on the list, it was shown that only four took their turn of duty at the last rotation.   The Managers, however, did not mean by this to cast a reflection on these gentlemen, as they knew that some of them gave up attending on account of the very disagreeable circumstances occasioned by this very system of rotation.

The College was finally charged with having converted the

P

Infirmary almost *entirely into a school,* in which their young members might acquire dexterity and experience at the expense of the patients, instead of a noble and honourable theatre, where their more skilful and experienced members could display their talents.

The result of the memorials was adverse to the surgeons, the judgment of the Court being : "the Lords refuse the desire of the petition, and remit to the Lord Ordinary to refuse the Bill, without prejudice to the suspenders again laying their case before the Court in a reclaiming petition, to be presented and put into the boxes on or before the 16th day of April next" (1801).

A reclaiming note in name of the College was accordingly presented, but the Lords adhered to their former decision by a majority of 6 to 4.

In consideration, however, of the fact that certain of their Lordships were favourable to the claims of the College, although these were highly disapproved of by the Lord President, who insisted that without a Declaratory Action they were not entitled to be heard, the College took advice of Counsel, viz., Henry Erskine, Mathew Ross, and David Williamson, as to whether it would be prudent and advisable to appeal against the judgment now pronounced. In consequence of their united opinion that it was not, the College on 16th November 1802 resolved, by a majority of 23 to 1, that no further proceedings be carried on between them and the Royal Infirmary of Edinburgh.

Thus ended one of the most serious questions the College had engaged in since its separation from the barbers in 1722.

So far, the dispute has been narrated as between the surgeons and the Infirmary only. As a matter of fact it led to a division among the members of the College, which was attended with the most lamentable results.

Although a few of the older Fellows had no particular objection to the change, and conscientiously believed the College had but a doubtful right to oppose it, it raised such a feeling of resentment in the minds of the others, particularly the younger members, who, by it, had all to lose and nothing to gain, that for two years the most bitter feelings existed. John Bell was the chosen leader of the juniors, and so vigorously did he attack Gregory's memorial that he was voted the thanks of the College.

James Law, Andrew Wood, and Benjamin Bell were all in favour of a long-service system—the last submitting a plan for the approval of the College, suggesting a term of five, ten, or even fifteen years' continuous service, but when put to the vote not a single member supported it.   Schemes were also drawn up by John Thomson and others, but to no purpose. One, however, addressed to the Managers by Robert Jackson, M.D., Inspector of Military Hospitals, is deserving of more than passing mention, as it contains an interesting description of the Infirmary in the year 1800.

Dr Jackson begins by remarking, that as Dr Gregory, in a memorial, had painted with a profusion of colours the improper management of the surgical department of the institution, he took the liberty of bringing to view some defects in the construction, arrangement, and equipment of the hospital, which experience had taught him was a matter of more consequence to the good of the sick than the medical prescriptions of the physician or the manual dexterity of the surgeons.   The wards he describes as not exceeding eleven or twelve feet in height, the width much narrowed by the projection of closets, and the area broken and interrupted by posts and partitions which seemed to have been intended to mark divisions between the beds.   Continuing, he said that the position of the hospital was disadvantageously situated for ventilation ; confined on one side by a wall, on another by lofty houses, the air in it could only be preserved sweet and wholesome by the operation of strong causes acting within.   The windows of the wards were not large and were badly constructed for the admission of air. The grates were small, and the fireplaces so fenced in by partitions that heat, or the circulation of air occasioned by heat, did not extend to the middle of the apartment.   After pointing out how these defects might be remedied, Dr Jackson proceeds : The frames of the bedsteads are made of iron—a material durable and little liable to contain the contagion of disease ; the bottom part, however, is formed of thick and spongy rope, disposed to receive and to retain every kind of contagious mischief.   The bed is, moreover, a palliasse filled with straw, a flock mattress, and bolster or pillow, which, if not actually noxious in themselves, are in many cases so offensive to the eye that the Inspector of a Military Hospital would consider it his duty to condemn them to the flames. The sheets are often dirty or ill washed, the blankets and coverlets small and beggarly, and the appearance of the bed altogether most uninviting. The patients are also allowed to retain their own clothing, though its condition be not always proper, a custom which admits the introduction of contagion into the house, while no sure means are placed in the hands of the physician or surgeon of stopping its progress when thus introduced. As the Royal Infirmary, Dr Jackson concludes, is considered as an appendage of the Medical School of the City —a place to which young men resort to see diseases and to learn to treat them successfully—it becomes a duty incumbent upon the Managers to give effect to such arrangements as may permit pupils to approach the sick, and to examine minutely the circumstances of disease without danger to their own lives.

In returning from this short digression we find that for some time the College meetings had been attended with considerable confusion. At one of these the "most scandalous scenes that ever a gentleman was obliged to witness" are said to have been enacted, while on another occasion—the majority being against the Chair—a vote of censure was actually passed on the President.

Of the principal actors who took part in the foregoing proceedings, John Bell is said never to have quite recovered his exclusion from the Infirmary; Lewis Flanagan, whose encounter with James Russell will not be forgotten, soon afterwards announced his intention of going abroad, and begged the College to furnish him with a letter of introduction to the medical colleges in Berlin and Vienna which he intended to visit. On the other hand, when the Chair of Clinical Surgery was founded in 1802, Mr Russell was the first to occupy it, an arrangement which met with general satisfaction. The College, however, in consideration that the appointment had been made without reference to them in any way, resolved to record their opinion —that, as a public body vested with the sole and exclusive privilege of teaching as well as practising surgery in the city, they were in justice and equity entitled to some share in the recommendation or patronage of a Chair which must be filled from their body, and which, without presumption, they considered themselves to be the best, if not the only competent, judges.

The reader, with all the facts before him, will now understand how it came about that the Incorporation of Surgeons did not at first serve the Royal Infirmary. He will also be entitled to form an opinion as to whether the reasons adduced by the Managers for rejecting the surgeons' offer were as *bona fide* as they appear to be.

The surgeons, in 1800, had some doubts about this, and called attention to the terms of the Charter (p. 211), which arranged for the sick in the hospital being attended by the *whole College of Physicians* and *some* of the *most skilful surgeons*. If, in 1729, their offer had been accepted instead of Mr Monro's, they most reasonably claimed that the Charter would have included the *Incorporation* of Surgeons in the same manner as it did the Physicians. Such at least was the surgeons' opinion, and in debating the point they made a most interesting statement, which illustrates the *rôle* of the surgeon in the medical profession at the beginning of the eighteenth century. "Everyone knows," they said, "that the business of a surgeon in this country is not merely confined to surgical practice, or to the giving out of medicines as apothecaries, but they are employed as physicians-in-ordinary. Hence the surgeons of this country have always been held in a superior rank to what they are in other places. It is only at extraordinary times that the assistance of the regular physician is required, and even that is very much confined to the higher and superior classes. Hence it has always happened that in this place, and indeed over Scotland, the great bulk of the practice is confined to the surgeons. And, therefore, if practice is so very essential to perfection in this profession, the chance of obtaining more skilful men was infinitely greater from the College of Surgeons than from the College of Physicians. And if the Managers had been weighing with that accuracy which it is now contended they ought to have done, viz., the true end and design of their institution, they ought just to have reversed the matter, and to have taken the Charter to the *whole College of Surgeons and to some of the most skilful physicians.*"

Where the Surgeons' Hospital was situated, or the extent of its accommodation, there is nothing to show. It is, however, recorded that a Captain Sutherland in 1737 presented the College with "a strange creature called ourang outang," and that it was sent to the Surgeons' Hospital until a room could be prepared for it in their own house.

Incidentally, the attention of the reader may be directed to the frequent passages which crop up accidentally, as it were, in reference to the Incorporation and the Edinburgh Medical School. The charge made against the surgeons of turning the Infirmary *almost entirely into a school* is the greatest compliment the Managers could have paid them. On another occasion, when addressing the Managers, the surgeons made use of the following remarkable sentence: "And lastly, the public will be pleased to see *physicians* and *surgeons*, and everyone concerning themselves with this good work, animated with sincere Christian zeal . . . *the one to relieve sick and distressed poor, and the other to breed up able physicians and surgeons for the honour and service of the country.*"

Before concluding this chapter it may be mentioned that upon the Managers, in 1756, resolving to fit up a ward for the reception of women suffering from venereal diseases, the surgeons, in order that the ordinary funds of the Institution might not be thereby impaired, agreed to raise by voluntary subscription a sum of money sufficient to defray its expenses, and a committee was appointed to meet with the Managers to devise the most proper methods of carrying the design into execution.

The Allocation of Beds to the Professor of Surgery.—In 1852, in consequence of the Managers of the Royal Infirmary resolving to confer the appointment of permanent surgeon upon the Professor of Surgery in the University, it was suggested that the College should use their influence to protect their fellows from the injury which they were likely to sustain from such a regulation. This led the College to express to the Managers of the Infirmary their disapproval of the scheme, which, they declared, was not only detrimental to the interests of the profession, but also to the extra-mural school of medicine, the welfare of which the Infirmary had hitherto carefully considered. The appointment was made, however, and the only notice taken of the College's communication was a simple acknowledgment of its receipt.

Mr James Miller was Professor of Surgery at the time, and in virtue of his new position a certain number of beds were allotted to him.

The action of the Managers was adversely criticised by Mr Syme, who saw in it an encroachment upon his own domain, and considered that his Chair would be injuriously affected by the granting to the Professor of Systematic Surgery the advantages now conceded to him.   Mr Syme also pointed out, in terms of strong disapproval, the conduct of the majority of the Managers in making the concession in opposition to the minority, which embraced, with one exception, the whole of the medical Managers.   He therefore proposed that a committee be appointed by the College to consider how the harmful consequences anticipated by the change might be averted.

Professor Miller then entered into a long vindication of his own conduct and that of the Managers of the Infirmary, with a view to showing that he had proceeded entirely upon public grounds; further, if he had omitted the opportunity that had recently occurred in the extension of the hospital wards, of obtaining increased facility for illustrating his lectures, he would have considered himself justly open to reflection in having neglected his duty to the Chair which he had the honour to hold.   He explained further that as the Professor of Surgery in the University possessed no permanent position in the hospital, he laboured under a grievous disadvantage in comparison with the ordinary surgeons, one or more of whom, during their term of office, were almost certain to turn to account the advantages thus arising in the teaching of an extra-academical class of surgery.   Mr Miller then concluded by moving as an amendment that " the question of the allotment of beds to the Professor of Surgery in the University having been, after mature deliberation, determined in favour of the Chair by the Managers of the Royal Infirmary, this College do not feel it incumbent upon them to oppose that settlement."

On the College dividing, Mr Syme's motion was carried by eleven to four, whereupon the College drew up a memorial for presentation to the Managers, which contained, amongst other statements, the following:—

"That the first instance of a permanent appointment as acting Surgeon to the Royal Infirmary took place in 1833, when the present

Professor of Clinical Surgery succeeded Mr Russell, who possessed no such position, and lectured merely on the cases treated by his colleagues. That the lectures thus delivered, though more of a systematic than a clinical nature, were much valued from there being no separate Professor of Surgery in the University. That, in 1831, a Chair of Systematic Surgery having been established in the University there was no longer any occasion for systematic instruction being delivered by the Professor of Clinical Surgery, while the importance which that department of Education, in its proper sense, had assumed in the Continental Schools of Medicine rendered it very desirable that instruction of the same kind should be afforded in Edinburgh.

"That the College, therefore, have not objected to the present Professor of Clinical Surgery having a permanent field of practice in the hospital, especially as in all the arrangements for this purpose the interests of the ordinary Surgeons had been recognised and treated with respect by the Managers, and as they believed that the peculiar circumstances of the case would prevent it from being ever regarded as a precedent for extending the system of permanent appointment.

"That the recent arrangement for giving the Professor of Systematic Surgery an allowance of beds in the hospital is a complete departure from the long established compact between the Managers and the College of Surgeons, and could not be justified upon the ground of regard for clinical instruction, since Mr Miller was precluded from trenching on the province of his colleague, and had indeed pledged himself to the Managers to abstain entirely from any sort of clinical instruction whatever.

"That the effect of this arrangement would be to withdraw two wards, or twelve beds, from the proposed department of the Clinical Professor, and one ward from that of the Senior ordinary Surgeon, thus rendering the cases to this extent of no use for clinical instruction.

"That the University has no claim upon the Managers except for the means of conducting clinical courses.

"That Mr Miller had founded his claim upon untenable grounds by instituting comparison between his own position and that of the ordinary Surgeons, which are no wise warranted by their respective circumstances, and by producing opinions in his favour from the teachers of schools which did not possess a Professor of Clinical Surgery, and where, consequently, clinical instruction, if given at all, must be given by the systematic lecturers."

The College, in conclusion, earnestly entreated the Managers to reconsider their resolution, and thereby prevent the disunion now threatened between two bodies which had so long co-operated for the public advantage.

The memorial was vigorously supported by Mr Syme, Mr Spence, Dr Andrew Wood, and Dr Gairdner, while, against it, it was urged that the granting of twenty-one beds to the Professor of Systematic Surgery to illustrate his course of lectures was indispensable to enable him to discharge efficiently the important duties of his Chair. If the Chair of Systematic Surgery was to be kept up, such a measure was calculated to promote the interests of the University and the medical school without injuring those of the extra-academical teachers. At the same time, it did not interfere either with the course of lectures or the operative department of the Professor of Clinical Surgery, who had assigned to him as many as sixty-four beds, a number more than was necessary for clinical instruction, and far beyond the reach of the personal superintendence of one surgeon.

It was held therefore that, in place of occasioning injurious competition, the resolution of the Managers, by preventing a monopoly of teaching or operating within the walls of the Infirmary, would tend equally to promote the cause of surgical science and the general and progressive reputation of the University and the extra-academical school. This view, however, had no supporters, and consequently the memorial was duly forwarded to the Managers, who at considerable length detailed the whole history of the connection between the College and their institution from the beginning It concluded by stating that they had been unable to find any clauses in the agreement made between them, or any record as to the subsequent practice of the Infirmary, as to indicate that it was a step beyond the power of the Managers to appoint Mr Miller, a Fellow of the Royal College of Surgeons, to the extra charge of a small number of beds for a limited period.

Although the College agreed to discuss the Managers' reply at some future date, it never seems to have been brought forward again. Dr Richard Mackenzie, who first introduced the question in the College, died soon after of cholera in the Crimea consequent upon the great fatigue he had undergone in attending upon the wounded at the Battle of the Alma.

CHAPTER XIV

THE PROFESSORS OF SURGERY OF THE ROYAL COLLEGE OF SURGEONS OF EDINBURGH [1]

James Rae — Alexander Monro — James Russell — John Thomson—Professorship of Military Surgery — J. W. Turner — Sir George Ballingall — John Lizars — James Syme — Proposed Professorship of Lithotomy.

ALTHOUGH Mr James Russell was the first Professor of Clinical Surgery, the idea of clinical teaching did not originate with him. The credit of applying this method of study to surgery perhaps belongs to Mr James Rae, who also had some reputation as a dentist. Mr Rae appears to have taught surgery some years previous to 1772, for in that year, in reply to an application from him, the College agreed to recognise his lectures, and ordered the following notice to be inserted in the public press :—

"The College of Surgeons being desireous to promote every usefull undertaking towards the advancement of the knowledge of Surgery, have taken into their Consideration A PLAN of Lectures on the whole Art of Surgery; Also practical discourses on the Cases of Importance as they occur in the Royal Infirmary, given for several years past at their Hall by James Rae, Surgeon in Edinburgh and one of the members of the Society. As this course is founded on the practice of the Hospital and delivered by a person who has been in the habit of Constant Observation, they recommend it as usefull and necessary to the Students of Physic and Surgery, and to render this course more extensively usefull the Society are resolved to Communicate to him such cases of Importance as may occur in their practice."

Mr Rae's endeavours seem to have been successful, and four years later he again applied to the College for assistance. On this occasion, however, it was a proposal that they should make application to the King for establishing a Chair of Surgery in the University. In his letter to the College Mr Rae, after com-

[1] Reprinted from the *Edinburgh Medical Journal*, June 1914.

menting upon the close connection which existed between the Infirmary and the surgeons, and the early care bestowed upon it by the latter " when it had scarcely any friends," goes on to say that the students, sensible of the advantages which they reaped from clinical lectures, which were originally set on foot by Professor John Rutherford on medical cases, had solicited him (Mr Rae) several years ago to undertake on the same principle practical lectures on the surgical patients. He then laid the matter before the College, which not only approved of the suggestion, but at once made application to the Managers of the Infirmary, with the result that Mr Rae's request was readily granted.

Mr Rae shortly after this begged the College to frame a memorial to the magistrates asking them to adopt the measures necessary to found a Professorship of Surgery on the practical system established in the College of Edinburgh. He further observed that Dr Monro, on hearing that an application to that effect was likely to be made, had taken some alarm, apprehending that it might be detrimental to him as Professor of Anatomy, and that he had got his brethren of the University at a Faculty meeting to give their opinion as to the utility of such a post, as he taught all that students could learn from it. In conclusion, Mr Rae submitted to the College whether it was not proper for them to take the matter into their consideration, and if they were of opinion that it had no direct interference with Dr Monro, and would be of advantage to students in matters which the latter did not teach or profess, they would make their opinion known to the magistrates and Council.

A committee was now appointed to consider Mr Rae's proposal. In due course they reported that they considered they would be wanting in their duty to the community, as well as in their obligation to support the interest and credit of the College, if they did not embrace every opportunity of promoting the culture and advancement of the particular branch of medicine which they professed. Therefore, if they were so fortunate as to obtain the Royal sanction for the appointment of a Professor of Surgery from amongst their number, it would not fail to be attended with the best effects towards the improvement of surgery in general, to the University of Edinburgh as well as to the Society of which they were members. It was also pointed out that as the Professors of Anatomy and Midwifery had connected themselves with the College, it behoved the members to qualify themselves to fill future vacancies in these branches, which seemed naturally to arise from their College, and which would always be to their credit either as a body or as individuals. One thing, however, appeared to them to bar the way towards making application for the proposed Chair. The present Professor of Anatomy, who, they said, had filled that Chair with so much success, seemed to consider the teaching of surgery to be connected with his province, and thought that any new appointment of that kind would be prejudicial to him and injurious to his property. For this reason the committee declined to take upon themselves the judgment of such a delicate question, and thought it best to refer to the College how far Dr Monro's rights and interest might be affected by such a measure. But if the College should view the matter as in no way prejudicial to Dr Monro, they were of opinion that their application should be made at once, "as it must be obvious to every unprejudiced person that two such extensive and important branches as anatomy and surgery must be more completely taught by two persons properly qualified for each branch than that both should be taught by one." "And we flatter ourselves," concluded the report, "that a truth so clear and perspicuous, fraught with a prospect of advancing so material a branch of physic, will have full weight with Dr Monro and the other professors, as well as with every person of liberal sentiments, as we dare not allow ourselves to think that private interest would overbalance their known attention to public emolument."

The College, on arriving at the conclusion that the proposed Chair would not interfere with the Professor of Anatomy, proceeded to frame the petition, which included the following extract: "The Society of Surgeons having already been so sensible of the want of a professor of this Art in Edinburgh, that for ten years past they have authorised Mr James Rae, one of their number, annually to read public lectures on practical surgery more particularly from the Cases which occur in the Royal Infirmary. . . ." It also contained a clause that the nomination should always be in favour of a member of the College of Surgeons of Edinburgh. Sir Lawrence Dundas, as representing the City in Parliament, was requested to present the petition to the King, and the Lord Advocate was asked to support it.

The former, in undertaking the duty, explained that he had written to Lord Suffolk, the Secretary of State, through whom the petition would go to the King, desiring his Lordship to appoint an hour when he might wait upon him. In answer to this Lord Suffolk, acquainted Sir Lawrence that he would be glad to see him in Duke Street the next day at twelve o'clock. A second letter arrived, however, with information that the gout had made such advances upon his Lordship the night before that he was quite unable to keep the appointment.

An answer was also received from the Lord Advocate, in which he regretted his inability to serve the College on this occasion, as he had many months before received a letter from the Principal and Medical Professors of the University request-ing that if an application should be made for the erection of a Chair of Surgery in Edinburgh he would represent to his Majesty's Ministers that in the opinion of the University, and particularly of the medical part of it, the erection of such a Professorship was useless and would be very improper. But as the subject of the letter was one upon which he was totally incapable to judge, he had simply transmitted the representation to Lords North and Suffolk, and had forwarded their reply to the University. His Lordship, however, observed that he did not think the petition was calculated to present a favourable view of the application, for, when an application was made to the Crown founded upon public consideration, it was not usual to limit his Majesty with regard to the mode of election. If the application was to be successful, he thought there would be little doubt that the appointment would be made from amongst the surgeons in Edinburgh. If it was made part of their application, and if they even went so far as to exclude his Majesty's personal recommendation, they would agree with him that any person hostile to the application would be apt to urge that it was founded rather upon partiality to an individual than upon any urgent necessity of the public. The letter is dated May 1777.

A couple of months later, in consequence of Monro having made a similar petition to the Town Council in favour of himself, the College strongly protested against the appointment. They, however, were told by the Lord Provost, in reply, that he was at a loss to know what they meant—that the magistrates were the patrons of the University, and whatever compliments they might pay to the recommendation of any set of men, they were to be directed in their choice of a professor only by merit, and when they found a man properly qualified they would appoint him and would not confine themselves to any body of men or to any place — not even to the City of Edinburgh. It was well known, they had at one time brought a medical professor from Glasgow and also from Aberdeen, and as it was not even necessary for a medical professor to be a member of the College of Physicians, how could the Incorporation of Surgeons expect that because several professors were once members of their body, the magistrates were in future to confine their choice of a Professor of Surgery to their Society. But, continued the Lord Provost, although the Incorporation had disregarded the power of the magistrates, and had not waited for a refusal from them before secretly applying to the Crown for a nomination, the magistrates, to show their impartiality, offered to suspend all proceedings in respect of Dr Monro till they saw if the surgeons could show from their Charters that they had power, as a College, to elect professors in the surgical department of the University, as they seemed to suggest they had.

This insinuation was denied by the College, who, in acknowledging the authority of the magistrates said that as the Charter of King William and Queen Mary gave them an exclusive privilege of operating both upon living and upon dead bodies, they expected that any nomination of a Professor of Surgery should be made from their Society. They also expressed the opinion that the appointment of Dr Monro would bring no credit to the University, as it was impossible to suppose that he could teach both anatomy and surgery in the time employed in a course; before the latter branch could be effectually taught, a practical surgeon would have to be nominated who would have an opportunity of operating upon living bodies, by which the students would be better instructed than from simply witnessing the operations on the dead body.

A fortnight later, when the magistrates met to reconsider the question, the Deacon of the Surgeons craved a further delay, but, as this was refused, he entered a formal protest against Monro being appointed until the Incorporation had had full time to be heard. All this was to no purpose, and eventually Monro received a new commission appointing him Professor of Medicine and "particularly of Anatomy and Surgery." Thus the scheme for appointing James Rae as Professor of Surgery failed. As Monro *secundus* was not a member of the Surgeons' Incorporation, it is easy to conceive their disappointment at his selection to fill the Chair, to which they might with some reason be excused for considering they had some claim. The chagrin at being passed over in favour of an outsider must have been keenly felt, but the surgeons had the satisfaction of knowing that it was entirely due to their efforts that the Chair was established, and that their failure to create for it a separate existence, free from that of anatomy, was only brought about after every means had been taken to prevent it.

The Chair of Clinical Surgery, certainly, had an easier birth and was raised without opposition in 1802. Mr James Russell, a distinguished member of the Incorporation who had taught clinical surgery for some considerable time, was the first to occupy it. Although the appointment seems to have given general satisfaction, the College, notwithstanding that it had been made without any reference to them, said they took the opportunity of expressing their cordial approbation of the foundation of a Chair that had for its object the illustration of the principles of surgery by actual observation and practice. At the same time they were unanimously of opinion that as a public body vested with the sole and exclusive privilege of teaching as well as practising surgery within the City, they were in justice and equity entitled to some share in the recommendation or patronage of a Chair which must be filled from their body, and of which, without presumption, they considered themselves to be the best if not the only competent judges. Ultimately it was agreed to petition his Majesty upon the subject, but before doing so the College thought it advisable to acquaint the Lord Chief Baron, son-in-law to Mr Dundas, of their intentions. His Lordship also thought there would be little chance of obtaining their object by petition, but suggested their leaving a copy of it with him to transmit to Lord Pelham, not as an official paper, but merely to show the views of the College.

The advent of the year 1804 saw the College more alive than ever to its responsibilities in the teaching of surgery and firmly determined, at all costs, to advance its progress to the utmost of their ability. In comparison with other branches of medical education, surgery had received but little attention, and, with the exception of Mr Russell's course of clinical lectures, had been taught simply as an appendage to the courses of anatomy. In consideration of these facts, the members of the College were fully persuaded that it would be more to their interest and more conducive to the improvement of their art, if surgery were taught under the immediate direction and patronage of the College by one of its own members, rather than by those who had never practised it, and who, not being members of the College, could not be expected to feel any interest in its reputation. Accordingly, it was proposed that a lectureship in surgery be instituted by the College, and that a course of lectures on the principles and practice of surgery should be annually delivered by their lecturer. It was also proposed and eventually agreed to that Mr John Thomson be elected to the new office, with the title of Professor of Surgery of the Royal College of Surgeons. The appointment, however, was not made without some misgivings as to their right of creating such a post, and Mr Bennet, the late Deacon, formally protested against it for the following reasons : First, because he had doubts whether the College possessed the right of making the election ; second, because of the undue superiority and advantage such an election would give to the member so elected to the prejudice of those members giving private lessons in surgery, and thirdly, because he was tired of lawsuits, in which the College had been lately too much engaged. He therefore protested that if any litigation arose over the act, the funds of the College should not be employed in carrying it on. In allaying these fears and in vindication of their right in designating their lecturer Professor of Surgery, the College claimed they were fully warranted to do so by the practice of other Colleges in similar circumstances, and pointed out that the College of Surgeons in Dublin had recently elected a Professor of Anatomy, and that, according to their information, the College of Surgeons in London had two professors of its own and of its own election. But independently of this the College considered that, as the appointment bore no relation to its political connection with the City of Edinburgh, but related only to a privilege which it enjoyed with any other body of men, it had a perfect right to make the designation without fear of opposition from the Town Council. Other conclusions arrived at by the College in connection with the appointment were: That none but members of the College shall be eligible for the post; that the professor shall deliver a course of lectures of the same duration as those given by the Professors of Medicine in the University or longer if deemed necessary; that he shall not lecture on anatomy unless it be for the express purpose of illustrating his surgical operations; that officers of the medical staff of the Army and surgeons and surgeons' mates in the Navy may attend the lectures gratis; that it would greatly facilitate the teaching of surgery and prove useful as well as creditable to the College to form a *museum* of morbid preparations, casts, and drawings of diseases, and that all members of the College should be requested to give their assistance in promoting this very necessary part of the plan by supporting it with all such articles of this kind as may be in their power. It was also agreed to furnish the professor with a gown at the expense of the College.

The College were wrong, apparently, in their prediction about the Town Council, for as soon as the intentions of the former became known, a strong remonstrance was made by the Principal of the University to the magistrates, complaining that this appointment would necessarily interfere with one of the classes taught in the University, and craved that measures might be taken to prevent the lectures from being delivered in Edinburgh. The Town Council, of course, were in duty bound to inquire into the case, and so demanded from the surgeons an explanation of their conduct. The surgeons, in reply, after expressing their surprise and sorrow that some members of the University had taken umbrage at their action, submitted that in appointing a practical surgeon, and one of their own body, to teach surgery, the College conceived they were exercising a right vested in them not only as one of the Incorporated Trades of Edinburgh, but also as a Royal College

Q

empowered by Charter to teach the art they profess. In exercising this right, they had not the inclination, neither did they conceive they had the power, to injure any of the professors of the University.

In supporting the opinion that the right of teaching their own trade was invested in themselves, a point, they said, which it was obvious could not be given up without relinquishing their most valuable right, it was represented that, in the Charter of King James constituting the magistrates patrons of the University of Edinburgh, no mention whatever was made of surgery in the enumeration of the different branches of education to be taught in that institution. For this omission, they were of opinion, there were several reasons—first, the craft or mystery of an incorporated trade could not be taught as one of the branches of education in the University without an infringement of the privileges of that trade; and secondly, that surgery was and still is the peculiar profession of one of the incorporated trades, all of which by their constitution possess the exclusive right of teaching as well as practising their own craft. In the circumstances, the surgeons said it was scarcely necessary for them to add that the appointment by the magistrates, in 1777, of Dr Monro to be Professor of Surgery in the University was in direct opposition to the various grants made in favour of the College, and a point upon which—outside the University—there was never any difference of opinion.

The surgeons then appealed to the Town Council to protect them against the unfounded claims of a public body, which on a former but similar occasion, in order to defeat the desire of the College to have their own art taught in the University by a practical surgeon, did not scruple to declare in a representation sent to the then Lord Advocate, to be by him transmitted to his Majesty's Ministers, " that in the opinion of the University, and particularly the medical part of it, the erection of such a Professorship in the University of Edinburgh was useless, and would be very improper." This declaration, they were sorry to state, was made at a time when the Senatus were not ignorant of the fact that Dr Monro was using every means in his power to be appointed Professor of Surgery in that very University by the magistrates and Town Council of Edinburgh. In conclusion, the College stated that it would have been more agreeable to them to have had the concurrence of the Town Council, but recollecting the opposition that was made on a former occasion, and fearing that some members of the Senatus might still be actuated by that spirit of monopoly which had so long obstructed the public good, they were unwilling that their intentions in regard to the institution of a Professorship of Surgery should again be misrepresented to the magistrates. They felt themselves reduced to the necessity either of abandoning a measure which had long been a favourite one with them, or of performing an act which, however disagreeable it might be to some of the members of the Senatus Academicus, the College could not but regard as meritorious; and one which they humbly hoped would meet with the protection of the magistrates, the support of the incorporated trades, and the approbation of the public.

Taken unawares by the daring tactics of the College, and prompted to action by the Senatus, whose patrons they were, the Town Council intimated to this refractory Craft that, having seen an advertisement in the public papers that the College had instituted a Professorship of Surgery and had appointed one of their own body professor of that science, they had reason to believe that this act was an encroachment on the rights of the University, and such a one as the College of Surgeons was not authorised to make. The Council, therefore, thought it proper to put the College upon their guard in relation to their late resolution, and declared their intention to investigate the subject with the most scrupulous attention, in order to ascertain their own rights as head of the community, as well as the rights of the College, and then to determine what steps to pursue. At the same time, they wished it to be understood that their present forbearance should not be interpreted as an acquiescence on their part to any supposed right of the College.

Without pursuing the subject further, as neither the University nor the magistrates attempted any serious measures to deprive Mr Thomson of his professorship, we may reasonably assume the College was well within its right in making the appointment. If there had been any chance of upsetting it, there is little doubt but that this would have been done.

For two years Mr Thomson occupied the Chair unmolested,

when, just at the time the University was preparing a memorial for his deposition, he was appointed by the Crown to the Professorship of Military Surgery in the University. In making this announcement to the College, Mr Thomson said he would now have occasion to treat of wounds at great length in his lectures, and he asked permission of the College to omit in future the more full and minute consideration of that subject in the course of lectures which he was still to deliver under the immediate patronage of the College. He therefore continued to act in the dual capacity of Professor of Surgery of the College of Surgeons and Professor of Military Surgery in the University.

In spite of the objection of the Monros, who again protested against the latter appointment, the arrangement seemed to work well, and nothing happened to mar the cordial relations which then existed until, in 1816, Mr Thomson, in order to come to a proper understanding regarding the regulations under which his successor would have to act, objected to the rules which enacted that medical officers of the Navy and Army might attend the lectures gratis. This proposal, he explained, originated with him, and was not a condition made by the College in conferring upon him the Professorship. The opposition to the scheme rendered it at the time an object of importance to gain the approbation of the Army Medical Board. In order to assist in obtaining that approbation he was willing, he said, to forego any pecuniary advantage which might arise from the attendance upon his lectures of the medical officers of the Navy and Army. As this was his own free offer, there was no reason why it should pass into a regulation and so bind his successor. The recent appointment which he had received from H.R.H. the Commander-in-Chief, while it remunerated him in some degree for the sacrifices he had made, made him feel it to be his duty to continue his lectures without fee to the officers mentioned. He could not but protest, however, against the burden voluntarily undertaken on his part being imposed upon those who might succeed him, and who might not be so fortunate as to reap from their gratuitous services the same advantages which he had done.

The College took an opposite view of the affair, and refused to alter the regulations governing the appointment.

In 1819, Professor Thomson requested the College to allow his friend Mr Turner to assist him in conducting the operative part of his course. This was objected to by Mr R. Allan, who said he feared it would be a step towards the succession and, in a great measure, close the door against other candidates for that Chair when it might become vacant. For this reason Mr Allan was of opinion that the professor should be left to choose his own assistants, but that they should not be recognised by the College. If, however, continued Mr Allan, the College should determine otherwise, " I now in justice to myself respectfully beg to offer my services on this occasion." This brought a second letter from Mr Thomson, who stated that his reason for asking aid was that, after having had the private assistance of the late Dr Gordon, he felt the operative part of the course particularly oppressive and often injurious to his health from the fatigue which necessarily attended it. His request was then granted.

In April 1821, Mr Thomson, who at the time of his death had the reputation of being the most learned physician in Scotland, resigned his College appointment and became a candidate for the Chair of Physic, then vacant by the death of Dr Gregory. The College, in accepting his resignation after seventeen years' service as their professor, expressed their regret at being deprived of his services in a situation in which by his labours in teaching, his writings, and his reputation, he had contributed in so great a degree to promote the study and improvement of the science of surgery and to maintain the character of the Medical School of Edinburgh. The College then proceeded to elect his successor, and as two candidates offered themselves for the vacant Chair, viz., Robert Allan and J. W. Turner, it had to be determined by vote which of these gentlemen should be appointed. On the vote being taken, nineteen were found to be in favour of Mr Turner— a majority of three over his opponent—whereupon Mr Allan resigned his position as an examiner, and requested the College to erase his name from all the lists of office-bearers and to substitute the name of some other member in its place.

Previous to the election, a law was enacted by the College " that if the Professor of Surgery to the Royal College of Surgeons shall join the College of Physicians or shall accept a professorship in the University he shall *ipso facto* vacate his situation as professor, but that his doing so shall not operate as a disqualification to prevent him from being re-elected." (Thomson became a licentiate of the College of Physicians in 1815.)

When John Thomson resigned the Chair of Military Surgery, the College lost no time in reminding the Secretary of State of its claims to have his successor selected from amongst its members. Dr David Maclagan and Dr George Ballingall were the candidates nominated by the College, and in submitting these names to the Lord Clerk Register, Member of Parliament for the Burgh, that they might be forwarded to the proper quarter, the College trusted that their services and talents would not be overlooked. A reply was immediately returned that his Lordship had no objection to transmit to Mr Peel their letter and testimonials in favour of Dr Maclagan, but that his constituents had desired him to support the application of Dr Borthwick (who was not a Fellow of the College). Evidently his Lordship had overlooked the testimonials of Dr Ballingall, but this accidental omission was put right by the President, who also took the opportunity of correcting another error into which his Lordship had fallen. The constituents of the Lord Register as Member of Parliament were the Town Council, and the President of the College being a member of that body knew that no public resolution to support Dr Borthwick had been made. The President, however, ascertained from the Lord Provost himself that he and Mr Kinnear, a member of the Council and brother-in-law to Dr Borthwick, had taken it upon themselves to solicit the interest of the Lord Register, but they did so, of course, as private individuals and not as representing the Council. This the Lord Provost undertook to explain, and did so in the most explicit terms.

When Dr Ballingall got the appointment some fortnight later—November 1822—he at once acknowledged the part played by the College, without whose recommendation, he said, his own exertions to obtain the Chair would probably have proved unsuccessful.

Defeated in his efforts to obtain the Chair of Physic, Mr Thomson devoted himself to pathology, and when, in 1831, a Chair of Pathology was created by the Crown, he was the first to occupy it. The same year saw the accomplishment of what the surgeons had laboured so earnestly for in 1777, viz., the erection of a Chair of Surgery separate from that of Anatomy. Monro *tertius* protested against it on very much the same lines as his father had done before him, but in spite of him and of the opposition of the Senatus, the Government not only founded the Chair but nominated John William Turner, the surgeons' Professor of Surgery, to occupy it. As soon as the surgeons got to know of what was about to happen, they were at once on the alert to secure the appointment for one of themselves. Their first step was to represent to the Government the injury that might result to the Medical School of Edinburgh by the hasty appointment of a professor, and without affording candidates for the office an opportunity of making known their claims. Their fears, however, were soon dispelled by an intimation from Mr Turner that the Chair had been offered him, and that he had accepted it. In making this communication he told the College that he valued no event in his life more highly that that of having been appointed the Professor of Surgery to the College, and that he should always retain a most grateful remembrance of the kindness and indulgence he had experienced from them during the time he had held that office.

In terms of the Laws the College Professorship was now again vacant, and the first to intimate a desire to fill it was James Syme. The President, however, explained that the Professorship of the College was instituted in 1804, in order to secure that the principles and practice of surgery, which were at that time taught merely as an appendage to courses of anatomy, should be fully and efficiently treated of by a practical surgeon in a separate and distinct course of lectures. That as these ends had now been attained by the establishment of numerous courses of lectures on surgery by Fellows of the College, and also by the institution in the University of a Professorship of Surgery separate from that of Anatomy, and by the appointment of a Fellow of the College to that important post, he (the President) considered it unnecessary and inexpedient to fill up the vacancy. This led to a long discussion in which considerable warmth was displayed, and after opinion of Counsel had been taken as to whether a two-thirds majority was necessary to carry the point, it was decided that the College should at once proceed to the election of Mr Turner's successor. In the meantime Mr Lizars made it known that in the event of the College deciding to fill up the vacancy, he too would offer himself as a candidate for it, and promised that, if elected, no exertion on his part should be wanting to sustain the respectability and celebrity of the Royal College of Surgeons and the School of Surgery in Edinburgh. In the vote which ensued, twenty-three members voted for Mr Lizars and twenty-two for Mr Syme, fourteen declining to vote. In returning thanks for his election, Mr Lizars followed the example of his predecessors by presenting his collection of specimens to the museum, subject only to the condition that he should have uncontrolled freedom of it during his lifetime. The College in accepting the gift, took into consideration a motion made by one of its members that in the event of any calamity befalling Mr Lizars which might prematurely deprive those dependent upon him of the benefit of his exertions, it would be the duty of the College to take care that these individuals should not suffer by Mr Lizars having presented his museum to the College. It was therefore proposed to insure Mr Lizars' life so that his heirs would receive one thousand pounds if he died within seven years, while if his demise should happen between seven and fourteen years they should receive five hundred pounds. The annual premium required would be about thirty pounds for about the first seven years, and a half of that sum during the second seven years. It was also suggested that the insurance might be effected in such a way that the insured would have the option of continuing it at his own will. On further consideration, however, it was agreed that, although the College continued to appreciate the importance of Mr Lizars' gift, it was inexpedient for them to be under an obligation of that nature and magnitude to one of their office-bearers. The collection was therefore returned.

In 1839 an unfortunate incident occurred in which Lizars and Syme were the principal parties. Lizars, it appears, presented to the College a copy of the second part of his work on *Practical Surgery*, but as it was understood to contain a bitter attack on Mr Syme's professional ability, in regard to which a lawsuit was then pending, its acceptance was held over until the legal proceedings terminated. The book was then declined in consequence of the jury having found it to contain "a false and calumnious charge" against one of the Fellows of the College. At the following meeting of the College, Lizars made a statement protesting against the rejection of his book on account of its containing an objectionable passage, but as, in the course of his remarks, it appeared to the College that he went into the discussion of matters which they were not competent to judge, it was irrelevant for them to listen to it, and Lizars was requested to confine himself to the subject of the motion of which he had given notice. He accordingly moved "that that part of the business of last meeting relative to his work on *Surgery* be rescinded, it being illegal, incorrect, and unjust." On this being seconded it was allowed to lie over to the next meeting. Lizars then explained that at the time he was interrupted he had no intention to impugn the judgment of the Court, but that he intended to explain away what appeared offensive in his book, and to state that the passage which had been objected to was expunged and the leaf which contained it cancelled. It had been his intention, he added, to request leave to withdraw the copy of his work which had been sent to the College, and to present an amended copy in its stead; he had been prevented doing so, however, because the report of the Library Committee had been approved of without any communication being made to him on the subject.

The College, having ascertained that the passage referred to had been deleted, then intimated their willingness to accept the volume, and at the same time expressed their regret that previous to their last meeting, they were not made aware that the offensive paragraph had been cancelled, otherwise they would have signified their cordial acceptance of the work. This was followed by the President reading a letter from Professor Lizars to Mr Syme (now Professor of Clinical Surgery in the University) retracting the charges made against him in a printed work, and also verbally in the College. The President then congratulated the College on the amicable termination of such an unpleasant matter, and hoped that nothing of the kind would occur again. At the same meeting Lizars notified his intention of resigning his appointment of Professor of Surgery to the College after the winter session. This the College unanimously agreed to accept, and as it had been arranged some four years previously to abolish the Professor-ship as soon as it should become vacant, the office then ceased to exist.

James Syme.—The introduction into these pages of the name of such a distinguished surgeon as James Syme may furnish an excuse for referring to his connection with the College of Surgeons, in so far as it can be traced in its records.

James Syme, it appears, entered the College in 1823, and first attracted attention as one of its members some six years later by signifying his intention to establish a surgical hospital in opposition to the Royal Infirmary, in which institution he had just failed to obtain an appointment for which he had applied. His object in communicating with the College was to solicit their approval of his tickets of attendance as a qualifica-tion for their licentiates. In describing the facilities of his proposed hospital Mr Syme said it had long been a matter of general surprise that Edinburgh, the capital of Scotland, and seat of the greatest medical school in Europe, should possess only one surgical hospital. Attempts, he said, had been repeatedly made to establish a second hospital, but from various causes had hitherto failed. A private individual, he continued, who was able to institute a new establishment on a respectable scale, had at length determined to carry this important measure into effect by his own exertions, and trusted, when the people recognised its advantage to the suffering poor, that they would contribute so as to render it still more useful. Minto House, which Syme had taken, he describes as being a large and commodious building situated in a quiet and healthy part of the City and in the immediate vicinity of the University. It was, he said, surrounded by extensive private grounds, and the apartments were large and airy and provided with every convenience. He proposed commencing with twenty beds and increasing their number according to the means which might be derived from public support. Some of the rooms were to be reserved for patients able to pay for their maintenance. By contributing a guinea per week they might have the comfort of a private lodging and the satisfaction of agreeably reflecting that they were not objects of charity.

After some discussion the College decided that attendance

JAMES SYME.
24th June 1823.

upon a purely surgical hospital containing twenty beds, though connected with an establishment for out-door patients, should not be considered sufficient hospital attendance for qualifying students for being taken upon trial for a surgical diploma. A certificate of attendance, however, upon a regular course of clinical surgical lectures of the usual extent and duration delivered in the hospital should be a sufficient testimony of attendance upon clinical surgery, provided that the hospital should contain not less than twenty beds, and that the number of students attending at one time should not exceed the number of forty.

A year later (1830), as the College required its candidates to attend for eighteen months a public general hospital containing at least eighty beds, or such a hospital for twelve months and a medical and surgical hospital recognised by them for six months, they agreed to recognise Mr Syme's hospital as conforming to the latter class. They made the condition that attendance at his hospital by each candidate or student should take place either previously or subsequently to the period of attendance at a public general hospital, it being positively required that the period should not be less than eighteen months altogether.

Mr Syme could scarcely have got his hospital into working order before he was appointed by the Crown to the Chair of Clinical Surgery, which had recently become vacant by the retirement of Professor Russell, then in his eighty-first year, and who had held the post for thirty years. In spite of his good fortune, however, Syme was ever a College man, entering largely into its debates and taking a lively interest in all things connected with its welfare, besides fulfilling the onerous duties of curator of the museum.

In 1838, in compliance with a request made by the College to state his views relative to the improvement of clinical instruction, Syme offered the following suggestions. After describing the objects of hospital attendance and clinical instruction, he pointed to the many advantages possessed by the Infirmary as a clinical school, in containing a large number of patients coming from all parts of the country and exhibiting every variety of disease. But there was unfortunately, he stated, a defect which prevented the establishment from working efficiently as a source of instruction, and that was the want of discipline among the

students who attended it.   Beyond the porter issuing the tickets
of admission and receiving the subscriptions of those who
wished to get certificates of attendance, no control whatever
was exercised over the students, who might follow any one of
five physicians and three surgeons they chose, or, if they pleased,
might stay away altogether.   Many of them, he thought, never
attended the hospital, or, at all events, did not remain unless
there was to be an operation, when those who did attend, with
few exceptions, crowded together, not for instruction, but merely
for the gratification of their curiosity.   Hence it happened that
the medical wards, which ought to have been attended by one-
half of the students, were nearly deserted, while the surgical
wards were thronged to such an extent that rendered it
impossible either to teach or to learn.   Syme then proposed
certain plans to obviate these irregularities, which, if they met
with the approval of the College, he hoped the Managers of the
Infirmary might be induced to sanction.   The advantages which
this new system of teaching seemed to promise were : first,
affording all the students a certainty of seeing a great deal of
what was interesting and instructive ; second, of enabling the
professor to extend his instruction ; third, of ascertaining the
regularity of attendance ; and fourth, of exciting energy among
the students, not only while attending the hospital, but also in
cultivating the various branches of their education, by holding
out a prospect of situations valuable in themselves as sources of
information, and, when conferred for the reward of merit, likely
to exert no small influence in promoting their professional
success.

Finally, it was arranged that the College should transmit
Professor Syme's propositions, after some slight alterations had
been made, to the proper quarter, accompanied by a respectful
communication suggesting their adoption.

Professor Russell, who made way for Syme in 1833, lived
but a short time to enjoy his retirement.   In 1836, his death
was announced to the College by the President.

"Professor Russell," he said, "had been for forty-nine years a
Fellow of the College, and was for a considerable time its senior
Fellow.   He had filled the office of President and many of its other
offices with much ability, and had occupied for a long period an
important Chair in the University.   But it was no less to his personal

qualities than to his official services that the attention of the College would be naturally turned. He had during a long series of years been a successful teacher of clinical surgery, and had by his own exertions secured for it its rightful place in the curriculum of surgical study. He had taken an active and zealous part in the business of the College, and especially in promoting the interests of the museum; and at a period of life when other men might have retired from the fulfilment of active duties he offered an instructive example to the younger members of the profession, not only by the regularity of his attendance at meetings, but by the zeal which he manifested in scientific researches and his anxious desire for the prosperity of the profession to which he belonged."

Russell was held in high esteem by the members of the College, and seems to have steered clear of the jealousies and painful rivalries to which many of his contemporaries fell a victim. In appearance he was, according to one who knew him in his later days, "a tall thin gentleman of the old school, who wore a red wig, was always dressed in black with a white neckcloth . . . and indulged in a broad frill on his shirt breast. His tailed coat was then the ordinary morning coat—so that was not conspicuous, but he considered it essential to maintain the style of knee-breeches and silk stockings and shoes, though the muscular development of his lower limbs, at that time, hardly warranted its continuance." Such were the peculiarities of James Russell, Fellow of the Royal College of Surgeons of Edinburgh, who through his own exertions is credited with having secured for clinical surgery its rightful place in the medical curriculum.

Proposed Professorship of Lithotomy.—A further addition to the number of Professorships that owe their origin to the surgeons might have been made, had it not been that the opinion of the Calling was divided as to its utility. The proposed Chair was one of Lithotomy, and Dr Thomas Glen was the candidate for the honour of filling it. The subject was first introduced at a meeting of the Incorporation in 1741, when it was claimed that great advantages would accrue from having a Professor of Lithotomy in the City, whereby not only many poor people afflicted with that dreadful distemper the stone might be relieved, but students in surgery could be instructed in that difficult and useful operation. As Dr Thomas Glen had for several years successfully practised the operation of lithotomy or "cutting for the stone," and as his abilities in that line were well known to all the members of the Society, they judged it incumbent upon them to recommend the deacon to use his utmost endeavours with the Lord Provost and Council to appoint him Professor of Lithotomy. Having regard to the fact that the doctor had signified his resolution to serve the town's poor gratis, they further recommended him to be declared the Town Lithotomist.

Although this was agreed to by a majority of the Incorporation, it was represented by several members who were absent from the meeting that they also were qualified and resolved to practise lithotomy, and that as the appointing of a professor might in some measure prejudice them in their views, they moved that the Town Council be requested not to make the appointment. This raised a protest to which several members adhered, but at the next meeting a vote was again taken whether Dr Glen should be recommended or not. The result was in the affirmative, but only by the deacon's casting vote.

Another protest was then made on the grounds that the whole affair had been brought about in a most irregular manner; and that as no other professor of that subject existed, the creating of one was quite unnecessary, especially as Mr Monro had declared it to be a branch of his profession, and one which he had always taught along with any other part of anatomy. It was also pointed out that by distinguishing Dr Glen in this way a reflection was cast on the merits of several other members who were well qualified to perform the same operation. And, as it appeared that Glen had taken most unjustifiable methods to suppress and prevent others from practising the operation, it was to be feared his appointment might be attended with very bad consequences to the public. It put it in his power, they said, to monopolise the practice, and to deter others from undertaking an operation so universally useful.

This is the last we hear of the attempt to establish a Chair of Lithotomy; if the surgeons had been anything like unanimous in their opinion, it would probably have succeeded.

Before quitting this subject it may be of interest to refer to the case of a certain Duncan Campbell, a Glasgow chirurgeon, who, according to the *Edinburgh Gazette* for July 1702, performed some surprising operations for stone in the West Bow, he having "cutted nine score persons without the death of any, except five."

The following case was reported before Lord Fountainhall in 1709: "Duncan Campbell, of Ashfield, giving himself out to be the best lithotomist and cutter for the stone, pursues Mungo Campbell of Netherplace, that he being under the insupportable agony of the gravel, and was kept down in his bed by two servants, sent for the said Duncan to cure him, who, leaving the great employment he had, waited on him for several weeks, and by an emaciating diet fitted him for the operation, then cut him and brought away a big stone of five ounces weight, and since that time he has enjoyed better health, for which extraordinary cure all he got in hand was seventeen guineas; whereas, by his attendance and diversion from other patients, and his *lucrum assans*, he has lost more than fifty pounds sterling, and craves that sum as his fee and the recompense of his damage." The Court, however, in consideration that the work had been done unskilfully and the patient put to much pain, found that the sum already paid was sufficient.

CHAPTER XV

THE ASSOCIATION OF THE COLLEGE WITH THE TOWN COUNCIL

Granting of Seal of Cause (1505)—Disputes with Town Council regarding election of Deacon (1720-1774)—Assistance in City Improvements—Closing of Drug Shops on Sunday—Separation from Town Council.

Granting of Seal of Cause.—From its earliest days the College had been intimately associated with the Town Council, indeed it was the Council that granted the Seal of Cause (p. 2). Although from time to time differences of opinion arose between the two bodies, the relationship had on the whole been amicable.

Disputes with Town Council regarding election of Deacon.—About the year 1720, friction arose between the Incorporation and the Town Council on the subject of the election of the deacon, the procedure then in vogue giving the Council considerable power of limiting the choice of the Craft in the election of their representative.

A few examples will make these misunderstandings more clear, and permit their being viewed from different points.

In 1720, after the surgeons had elected their deacon in the usual manner, it became known that the Council designed making him one of the *extraordinary* deacons. As the councillors of this class had only occasional duties to perform, the Calling considered this treatment of their representative to be an affront and indignity to the senior Craft of the City, and requested their late deacon to use his endeavours with the Council to make some other arrangement. He, however, refused, saying that using the deacon so was "quite within the Council's rights." As a consequence, at the next meeting of the College, Mr Lauder, the late deacon, was censured for his "disregardful behaviour" to the Society and deposed from his position on the Deacon's Council.

At the election in the following year (1721), John M'Gill and George Cunningham were charged with having acted and behaved contrary to the intents of the Incorporation; Cunningham being a councillor, in having absented himself from the Council on the day of the election, and M'Gill as proxy for him in having voted contrary to a statute of Magdalen's Chapel, an act and behaviour at once prejudicial to the honour and interest of the Incorporation. To make matters worse, M'Gill, instead of paying deference to their wishes, told them he had "no regard for the Chapel." As a punishment, both were declared incapable of any public charge or trust in the Incorporation again, and their names were ordered to be inserted last on the roll—Cunningham's last but one and M'Gill's "the very last." At the expiry of twelve months, the censure upon them was removed, and both were placed in *statu quo*.

So unsatisfactory was this election that, at the next meeting of the Incorporation, it was informed by one of its members, that several persons, who had formerly held office in the town, were resolved to call in question many undue practices and illegal steps that were taken in order to secure the government of the City and the administration of its revenues in the hands of certain persons. This was done, he said, by electing tacksmen of the town's revenues, by inducing those members of the Incorporations who had votes to absent themselves, and by confining the lists to persons well known to be devoted to the interests of those particular men. He therefore proposed that the Incorporation should concur in any process that might be raised for declaring the last election of magistrates and councillors void, and for restoring the freedom of the burgesses. This the Incorporation agreed to do.

A Minute of a Sederunt of the Calling, in 1728, contains full details of the method followed at the election of the deacon, and shows to what extent the election could be influenced by the magistrates making use of a practice which they frequently employed. In September 1728, the Incorporation met for the purpose of drawing up a long leet, out of which their deacon for the ensuing year was to be chosen. This was, as usual, submitted to the Town Council, who should have deleted all but three names and then sent it back to the Incorporation to

R

settle which of the remaining three should preside over them. The leet, however, did not seem to please the magistrates, for on its return two names were found upon it which were not formerly there. The deacon, in deprecating this action of the Town Council, declared it was not in their power to return any other names than those submitted to them, and, as they had, by such proceedings, imposed upon the Calling's privileges, it was lawful for the latter to proceed with the election without in any way referring to the magistrates' list.

The same thing happened again in 1774. This time the magistrates sent back a short leet of three fresh names. A protest against this was at once lodged by Mr Alexander Hamilton. When it was put to the meeting whether, in consequence of Mr Hamilton's protest the case should be appealed to the Court of Session, it should be at the expense of the parties, and that no part of the funds of the College should be applied for carrying on the process, the Incorporation quietly submitted to the magistrates and elected one out of the list.

The Trades were now fairly roused, and delegates from each Incorporation formed a committee to consider what steps should be taken to free themselves from the arbitrary actions of the Council. Ultimately, it was decided to petition the Annual Convention of the Royal Burghs to abolish that part of the Sett or Laws which dealt with the shortening of the leets, but as this could only be done with the concurrence of the Town Council, some difficulty was expected. The Council, however, by a majority of eighteen to twelve, agreed to the proposition, but before it could take effect the twelve who had opposed the measure obtained a Bill of Suspension and upset the whole affair. As these men were said to be the friends and dependents of Sir Lawrence Dundas, the member for the City, the blame for the whole opposition to the Trades was attributed to him.

The committee in its first report, after dealing with the above question, called attention to the many insults the Trades had lately received at the hands of those who managed the metropolis, especially in "depriving Mr Brodie, a respectable worthy citizen, from being a councillor, merely because he offered his services to be Convener of the Trades, contrary to the views of those who opposed him. Also in electing a bankrupt to be a Council Deacon, who at the time had taken sanctuary in the Abbey, and in electing another bankrupt to the same position, who was apprehended when entering the Council Room to take his seat at the table."

In order to prevent the same abuses occurring in the future, which, it was said, brought nothing but reproach and disgrace upon their Incorporations, the following resolution was agreed to :—

"That in order to carry the object they have in view, and to defeat the Opposition made to it by the friends of Sir Lawrence Dundas, the Incorporations of Edinburgh ought, with firmness and unanimity, in choosing persons into the long leets of their respective Corporations, to consider those who have most at heart the freedom and independence of the Trades, and who are of good respectable characters, persons who have not, by folly and extravagance, brought themselves into difficulties and straits."

This seems to have had some effect, for at the next meeting of the delegates, held in " Mary's Chapel " on 20th September 1777, they congratulated the Incorporations on the choice they had made of their representatives.

As so many difficulties hindered the Trades as a whole from effecting their purpose—viz., freeing themselves from the arbitrary actions of the magistrates— the surgeons, when their new Charter was granted in 1778, made an effort to do so by themselves. The grounds upon which they based their desire were, that from experience they had found that their connection with the City politics had been a source of much dissension in their Society, and that it had long been the earnest wish of most of the members to free themselves from the Town Council.

Opinion of Counsel was then taken, but none of the measures suggested seemed practicable, inasmuch as by the Sett of the City of Edinburgh, and also by long usage, the Incorporation was a part of the body politic of the City, and should be represented in the Town Council by the deacon. The only way of separating themselves effectually from that body was by an Act of Parliament, as, since the Union, no other way would be recognised as a sufficient authority for such an alteration. It was in their corporate capacity they were erected into a Royal College, and even under that denomination they must act accordingly.

Another way out of the difficulty, which appealed to them, was to institute literary meetings, and elect a President annually to preside over them, thereby hoping to escape the now very apparent anomaly of being classified as tradesmen. All these artifices, however, were of no avail, and the surgeons, much against their will, remained craftsmen for many years to come.

Once, in 1746, the Trades were authorised to appoint their own deacon, but, as the date implies, it happened under exceptional circumstances and was due to the rebel army being in possession of the City, at the time the previous election of the Provost and Magistrates should have taken place.

Assistance in City Improvements.—Although the entrance to Writer's Close is still extant, many of the old closes in its vicinity were demolished to make room for the extensive altera- tions which were made in the City between 1750 and 1780.

A plan of these improvements was submitted to the Incorporations by the Town Council, in which it was proposed to erect "a handsome Exchange or Public Forum" on the north side of the street opposite the Cross. A building was also to be put up on "the ruins to the south of the Parliament Close"—where the Burgh Room and Council Chamber formerly stood—to contain a great room for the Convention of the Royal Burghs, a Council Room for the magistrates, a Robing Room for the Lords of Session, and a handsome Library for the Faculty of Advocates, etc. It was also con- sidered desirable that easy access be made to the High Street, both from the south and north sides of the City, and that the North Loch should be made an ornament instead of a public nuisance.

As the City revenue was not sufficient to meet so great an expense, the Incorporations were invited to contribute towards a work, which, it was pointed out, would be to the great advantage of the nation as well as being beneficial to the capital City of this part of the United Kingdom. The surgeons, with their usual liberality on all questions concerning the welfare of the Town, voted the sum of £105 stg.

When the Bill for erecting the South Bridge was submitted to them, the College unanimously approved of it and thanked the magistrates for their endeavours to make proper roads to the different parts of the City and neighbourhood; they also signified their approbation of the public spirit which had been shown in attempting to bring about an equal taxation over all the inhabitants of the ancient and newly extended Royalty. They thought, however, that the trustees should not have it in their power to call for more than 10 per cent. upon one year's valuation in case of a deficiency.   Further, unless there be a deficiency, it should not be in their power to feu out or otherwise dispose of the ground on the west side of the South Bridge lying between the south wall of College Street and the Town Wall, in order to keep it free for the building of a University.   On 11th November 1789, five days before the foundation stone of the new University was laid, the College agreed to subscribe one hundred guineas from their funds towards carrying on the work.   This they did as being particularly called upon to give every aid in their power to a work of such general utility.   They also agreed to subscribe liberally as individuals.

In 1781, they were appealed to by the Lord Provost for an opinion as to how far it might affect the health of the inhabitants of the City by continuing the slaughter-houses where they then stood.   A reply was returned to his Lordship that they had no difficulty in declaring that all nuisances must be in some measure pernicious to health and that the slaughter-houses in particular, from their tendency to corrupt the different kinds of meat hanging in them, were noxious not only to those in the neighbourhood but to all the inhabitants in the City.

In 1756, in consequence of a threatened famine, the Incorporation subscribed £20 to a fund raised by the Town Council for alleviating the distress of the poor.   In soliciting support for so charitable an object, the magistrates explained that as the price of meal was so high at the mercat, it bore very hard upon the poor who lived mostly upon it.   As it was known how the price of meal in their mercat influenced all the other mercats in Scotland, they were considering the best means to prevent the unhappy effect which would attend any further rise.   It was therefore arranged to purchase and sell meal to such families as were judged unable to pay the mercat price for it, as much below that price as should be thought proper.

To indemnify the City of the charge of executing this

scheme, and to encourage the Town Council to proceed with so salutary a measure with spirit, the Incorporation not only contributed the sum mentioned, but promised further assistance if required.

In a Minute of the same date, the surgeons complained to the magistrates of the exorbitant charges made by "Chaise hirers" when they were called upon to convey them to the country in a hurry. The chaise hirers, it was said, frequently refused to give their chaises at all during the night, and never gave them at any time save under extravagant prices. The Town Council was asked to regulate the fares, and to oblige the "hirers" to get their chaises ready whenever called upon.

A brief account of the Incorporation is to be found in Maitland's *History of Edinburgh*, published in 1753. Maitland's application for particulars concerning the Calling is found engrossed in the Minutes. As he had, he said, in his *History of the City of London*, given an account of the several Incorporations or Trades in that City, he proposed, for the honour of the Incorporations of the City of Edinburgh, to give an ample account of their respective Companies, and therefore begged the surgeons would give him a note of all their rights and privileges. To this request, in explaining their ancient constitution, the surgeons said, that as the arts of surgery and pharmacy were indispensably necessary for the preservation of the life of man, it was the interest of every nation to improve these professions: and that nothing seemed better calculated for promoting these arts than by erecting the professors of them into Corporations, Societies, and Colleges.

Closing of Drug Shops on Sunday.—In 1839, a memorial was addressed to the College by the druggists' assistants, proposing that the hour of closing their shops should be 9 P.M., and during divine service on Sundays. To this the College replied that, while they appreciated their motives, it was their opinion that serious evils might arise to the public if such a practice became general. They therefore recommended the assistants to endeavour to make some arrangements with their masters whereby a proportion of their number might be relieved from attendance at times, when the duty was not too great. The apothecaries, however, resolved to shut their shops during divine service on Sundays, with the result that the College intimated their disapproval of such an action and hoped that a modification of the measure would be adopted so as to obviate the difficulties which they apprehended, if the arrangement continued on its present footing. The druggists then proposed a conference in order that an arrangement might be entered into satisfactory to the College, and combining at the same time relief to the assistants. To this reasonable request the surgeons demurred, alleging they had already given a deliberate negative to such a proposal. The College further stated they would cordially receive any proposal that might emanate from the apothecaries for promoting the sanctity of the Lord's day, and which would likewise procure to the medical profession and to the community at large the facility of obtaining such secondary agents as were requisite for the mitigation of acute suffering or of unforeseen attacks of severe disease occurring during divine service, the relief or care of which could only be hoped for, under God's blessing, in the prompt administration of the appropriate remedies. The question took a wider turn when Sir Andrew Agnew, the well-known promoter of Sabbatarian legislation, espoused the druggists' cause and called a general meeting of practitioners in Edinburgh and Leith, when, Dr Abercrombie having taken the Chair, a number of resolutions were passed in favour of the movement. These were produced at the next College meeting, but before discussing them, Mr Syme called attention to a printed letter bearing the signature of another Fellow, containing some expressions which he (Mr Syme) conceived referred to him, and which might lead, he thought, to the inference that he had accused the promoters of the measure of hypocrisy, a meaning which he never intended to convey. Mr Brown, the writer of the letter, then expressed his regret for having unintentionally injured the feelings of any of his fellow-members, but for the subject-matter of the letter he had no apology to make, as it consisted of reasonings which had not been controverted and to which he still adhered. The druggists' resolutions were then discussed and counter resolutions moved by the College, one being "that it seemed highly expedient that the practice should be abandoned of the druggists trading on Sunday in articles not strictly medicinal." The result, evidently, was not in favour of the druggists, for we find the surgeons congratulating themselves upon having secured access to the drug shops on the Sabbath, and also suggesting that additional opportunity should be afforded for the procuring of remedies during the night. It was more incumbent upon them, the surgeons said, to express their opinion upon this subject, because, though originally by their Charters the authorised apothecaries of this part of the Kingdom, they had practically surrendered their rights and duties, as such, to a separate class of men. They held the conviction that such surrender was demanded in the circumstances of modern times by consideration of public advantage, and because that surrender was now so complete, that the practice of dispensing medicines to their own patients from private laboratories—a practice very general only twenty years ago—was now almost universally discontinued by the Fellows of the College, as well as by other practitioners in the City.

Separation from Town Council.—When the Incorporation became a Royal College, the opinion of Counsel was taken as to the possibility of severing its connection with the Town Council. The position seems to have been somewhat involved, because as a Royal College they were entitled to be presided over by a President, but as one of the Incorporated Trades of the City, their representative in the Town Council must necessarily be a *deacon*. In these circumstances the question was raised, in 1798, as to whether there existed a legal bar to the separation of the two offices. Eventually the matter was referred to the Solicitor-General and the Honourable Henry Erskine, who were asked to decide whether, as the members wished the College to be considered more in the character of a literary society than a trade, they could elect a President to preside over their meetings, and, at the same time, choose a deacon whose duty should be to assist at the deliberations of the Town Council according to the Sett of the Burgh. The reply in effect was that, although they were now distinguished from the general mass of incorporated craftsmen by an appropriate title more suitable to the profession they followed and the rank which they individually held in society, yet they must still consider themselves to be an incorporation in the legal sense of the word and subject to the same rules of law which governed other incorporations. Consequently, their plan of electing a President who was to supersede the deacon in the privileges he had hitherto possessed of presiding at all meetings of the College, could not legally be carried into execution by any Act or resolution of their own. As this decision did not meet with the approval of all the members, some of whom were still of opinion that it would be for the honour and advantage of the College, and would tend greatly to the improvement of their profession were they to establish themselves into a literary society, Mr John Bell moved that he be appointed to draw up a memorial on the subject. After some debate a vote was taken whether to proceed or delay, and when postponement was carried Mr Bell protested against the resolution of the meeting. The next meeting of the College proved a stormy one. It was convened for the election of the deacon, and many protests were entered on various grounds against the votes of several members. Amongst the votes challenged was that of John Bell himself. It seems that Bell, probably through an oversight, had neglected to take out his burgess ticket, but as he had sat and voted in College affairs for over thirteen years without being challenged, his surprise can be imagined when he received from Mr Andrew Wood the following letter :—

EDINBURGH, 28th January 1799.

"SIR,—As President of the Royal College of Surgeons permit me to suggest to you the necessity of your producing to the Clerk a burgess ticket previous to the next meeting, being clearly of opinion that you have no right to be present at any of the meetings of the College from your having neglected to comply with the law which positively requires every person to produce to the Clerk a burgess ticket before he is admitted a member of the Royal College of Surgeons."

After this letter had been read to the College it was moved by the deacon that, until Mr Bell became a burgess of the City, he was not entitled to sit at the Board, and upon a vote being taken it was approved of by a large majority. After protesting against the vote, Mr Bell handed in the following notice :—

"Mr Bell having had an intimation from the deacon that he is to be violently deprived of his rights and privileges, and having been so deprived suddenly and violently, and deprived by an arbitrary vote even of the right of defending himself, shall before next meeting give in printed defences."

At the next meeting the deacon withdrew his motion and also read a protest, signed by six members of the College, against the proceedings relating to Mr Bell. The Royal College of Surgeons, it said, being but a corporate body was not a Court of Justice. It might pursue to a competent Court a member as having no right to sit at its meetings, but it could not decide his privileges otherwise than by the sentence of the law. A member once acknowledged as duly qualified in his profession, sworn into the Incorporation and allowed to sit in his place and vote for years, was in fact a member until his rights were not only challenged but legally proved defective. It also recommended the deacon to remember that he was elected by the members of the Society and must return to the condition of a private member, and that he ought to guide the affairs of the College by its laws and not by his own arbitrary will. It was further pointed out that the deacon who admitted a member without due respect to the forms which the laws required must have been neglectful of his duty and was therefore liable to the members of the Society: that a deacon who offended against his appointed duties deliberately and retained a consciousness of what he had done for years— who admitted on the same day two members of the Society who were not burgesses, and, in one day, made one a burgess and protested against the vote of the other, as suited his own private purpose — certainly behaved very unworthily. The protestors declared they would admit of no compromise on the code of honour, nor acknowledge politics as an apology for wrong, for had the member been one of the worst of culprits, had he resisted the will of the College—even then he ought to have been listened to; but the President most peremptorily, and with marks of peculiar resentment, refused to hear one word from him—first, he called with vociferation and violence for a vote, forbidding the member to speak; secondly, he called for a vote to declare him incapable of a seat in the College; thirdly, he called upon him personally to speak, even after he had been thus publicly insulted and to defend those privileges of which he had been already deprived." The protest was signed by George Wood, Henry Johnston, and four others.

In reply, the College, in admitting the protest upon their records, said they had to lament the very intemperate language in which it was written.   They were obliged, however, in justification of their conduct as a public body, and with a view of preventing in future all such unwarrantable attacks on the peace and reputation of the Society, to state their disapprobation thereof in the most clear and unequivocal terms.   Mr Bell's admission into the College, they avowed, was not only contrary to the rules of the Burgh, but to the express Laws of the College.   It was therefore at all times competent for any member to object to Mr Bell's vote, and accordingly it had been challenged on repeated occasions, particularly at the two last elections of Presidents, when, it was thought, Mr Bell had good cause to know and to feel the effects of his not being duly qualified.   As Mr Bell, however, still refused to comply with the Laws, his privileges were suspended by an Act of the College, to which they were determined to adhere; and further to prevent him from resuming his seat, until he had complied with that part of their regulations or till the Supreme Court of their country should say that they were not entitled to insist on it.   Regarding the duties of the President and Treasurer, the College opinion was that it was the duty and interest of every individual member to take care that the forms of the College were duly complied with and its Laws strictly obeyed.   That an impropriety had been committed in the admission of Mr Bell was tacitly acknowledged, but the blame, it was held, did not lie solely with the President, but with every member of the College, for at the time of Mr Bell's admission it was a standing order that an entrant, before taking his seat, should produce his burgess ticket to the whole College.   It was also the opinion of the College that whatsoever omission was committed by either party at the time, it was certainly Mr Bell's duty to correct that omission the moment the circumstance was pointed out to him.   In reply to the last reason of protest, it was remarked that the action of the President in writing Mr Bell was in consequence of a vote of the College, when, out of twenty-four members present, not a single one voted in favour of Mr Bell's right, nine declined voting, and the rest were of opinion that Mr Bell had no right whatever.   Regarding the subject of the proposed Literary Society, it was absurd to think that that business or any other business of the College should be postponed until

Mr Bell should qualify himself to vote, and that its dismissal for the time was of as much importance to every member of the Society as to Mr Bell who had never been desired by the College to take charge of it.

In the meantime Mr Bell applied to the Court of Session for interdict to prevent the College carrying out their Act of Suspension, with the result that the Lord Ordinary (Lord Cullen)

"Having heard parties at great length, and having considered the writings produced, in respect the suspender in the year 1786 was admitted a member of the Royal College of Surgeons in consequence of his having been found duly qualified, and that he has continued to exercise and enjoy the rights and privileges of a member of the said College till the second February 1799, when the proceedings now under challenge in the present suspension took place,—Finds that it was irregular and unwarrantable in the Chargers in the summary manner they did to deprive him of all or any part of his said rights and privileges as a member of the Royal College of Surgeons."

On this being made known, the College agreed to be led by the opinion of Counsel as to whether to proceed further in the case or not. An appeal was evidently made against this decision, for, in February 1801, it was reported that in the question with Mr Bell depending before Lord Cullen, his Lordship had pronounced an interlocutor refusing the representations of the College and adhering to the interlocutor complained of. Mr George Wood, who had backed Mr Bell all along, then moved that as there had been repeated decisions in favour of Mr Bell on the question between the College and that gentleman, the College should acquiesce in these judgments. The motion was carried by only a bare majority.

Although in the opinion of the Court Mr Bell was entitled to all the privileges of membership of the College, events show that some few years later he was reluctantly compelled to produce his burgess ticket in order to book an apprentice. In 1807, he applied for a dispensation from attending the College meetings and also to book two apprentices—one of whom was John Lizars. Of these requests the former was refused and the latter was granted conditionally that he produced his burgess ticket. On this being intimated to Mr Bell he transmitted his burgess ticket to the Clerk along with the following note :—

"Sir,—Every token of enmity from the Royal College of Surgeons must be acceptable, as it cannot be but an honor to your most obedient   John Bell, No. 9 Queen Street."

The last mention of John Bell in the Surgeons' books occurs at the end of 1804.   At that time, as the feu-duty of his lecture room had not been paid for some years, the College directed their Treasurer to write Mr Bell that if it was not paid by Martinmas next "diligence would be done against him."   To which Mr Bell replied that upon the sale of his hall he would with pleasure pay the arrears of feu-duty upon it or any other debt due to the College.   The property was soon after disposed of to Mr Alexander Ritchie, Writer to the Signet.

In the year 1817, the College made another strenuous effort to free itself from the Town Council.   Some irregularities which had taken place at the election of the magistrates gave them an opportunity of again pressing their claims for a much-needed reform in the Constitution of the Burgh.   For this purpose a meeting of the College was called to consider the best plan of co-operating with the other Incorporations of the City in order to obtain such alteration of the Sett of the Burgh as might be judged most advantageous to the community, and particularly to enable the College to elect their own President.   After several resolutions had been made, it was finally agreed "that the Royal College of Surgeons regard that part of the Con-stitution of the Burgh as particularly objectionable which gives to the several Incorporations the semblance of a power of electing representatives in the Council while in truth the Council possess the real power of accepting or rejecting at their pleasure the persons fixed upon by the Incorporations to be their deacons."

"That as the Constitution of the College in connection with the Burgh involves the necessity of the Deacon of the Incorpora-tion being the President of the Royal College of Surgeons, they as a literary and scientific body feel it peculiarly degrading that they may at any time be prevented from having for their President the person whom they might all wish to fill that important office."

A committee was then appointed to meet with the other

public bodies to consider the proper measures for obtaining their ends, with the result that it was resolved to communicate to the Lord Provost and Council the wish of their general committee to proceed in the business entrusted to them in the most conciliatory manner, in the hope that they might be induced to co-operate with them in the measures that might be necessary for obtaining a more liberal system of Town policy than then existed. It was also learned by the committee, on the authority of Counsel, that the irregularities which had taken place at the last election of magistrates were sufficient to warrant a process being raised for its reduction with every prospect of success. It was further said that, since the meeting, it had been reported that the necessary legal steps for reducing the election had been commenced, that the Lord Provost had declined any conference with the committee, and that some Incorporations had voted contributions from their funds in furtherance of these proceedings. The committee was thanked for its report, and a motion was made that it should proceed no further with the business. This, along with a protest that no part of the College funds should be applied for that purpose was defeated, and a sum of £50 was voted to be placed at the disposal of the committee for the purpose of furthering such measures as might appear best calculated for freeing the College from the control which the Town Council possessed over the election of their President.

The next report of the committee stated that circumstances had occurred which promised to facilitate materially the advancement of the object committed to their charge—a decision having been obtained in the suit that was raised against the last election of the magistrates, sustaining one of the objections against that election finding it accordingly *null and void* and the magistrates liable in costs. The magistrates and Council had reclaimed against this decision, so that nothing more could be done until the next Session of the Court, when it was expected that the decision would be affirmed. Without following the case into Court we find the surgeons' next step to be in favour of petitioning the House of Commons on what they termed " Burgh Reform."

From the petition, which contains many important passages, it may be gathered that originally the burgesses of Scotland possessed the right of electing their magistrates and Councils, but by Acts of the Scottish Parliament in the years 1469 and 1474, the burgesses were deprived of this right and the power of election was vested in the magistrates and Council themselves. The system of self-election thus established deprived the burgesses of all control over the appointment of the Councils and also over the affairs and revenues of the Burghs, and at the same time enabled the members of the Councils, by re-electing themselves or by choosing their adherents to fill the offices in the Burghs, to perpetuate particular sets of men in possession of these offices and to place the different Burghs of Scotland under the influence of powerful individuals or of political parties. The magistrates and Councils, being independent of the burgesses for the possession of their offices, had no incitement to consult the wishes of those for whose interest they were supposed to act. Possessing full control over the funds of the Burghs and not responsible for their intromissions in them, they had in many instances suffered them to be mismanaged, the properties of the Burghs to be dilapidated and alienated, and the revenues to be lavishly spent and misapplied. Heavy debts were thus incurred which the burgesses had no share in contracting and no power of preventing, but for which, it had been stated on high legal authority, their private properties were liable. The interests of the burgesses and of the magistrates had consequently been separated and often became antagonistic, and it was a well-known fact that the latter did not enjoy either the confidence and support of their fellow-citizens, or that high respectability which they would possess were they really elected by those whom they were supposed to represent. The surgeons complained that they, along with others, suffered more or less under the grievances stated, and most forcibly drew attention to the way in which the magistrates had used their power by rejecting at their pleasure the person fixed upon by them to be their deacon, whenever that person happened to differ from the magistrates either in principles or opinions. The surgeons further disavowed that they were influenced by any consideration of party politics, and disclaimed any feelings of hostility either to the existing magistrates and Council, to the Government, or to the Constitution of the country—"to which they were sincerely and ardently attached."

After some slight opposition from Mr William Wood, who thought it inconsistent with the dignity of the College to interfere with the politics of the Burgh, it was arranged to send the petition to Lord Archibald Hamilton, M.P., with a request that he would present it to the House of Commons. In due course a reply was received from his Lordship desiring the College to send up such witnesses as they might think necessary to be examined before a Select Committee appointed by the House for the purpose of receiving evidence upon the allegations contained in their petition. Accordingly, the College prepared a statement of their own particular grievances and appointed Mr William Bell, W.S., to appear before the Select Committee as their agent. Some three months later Mr Bell, in reporting progress, informed the College that he had brought the petition frequently before the committee, by whom it had been received with much approbation, and he believed it would be acknowledged by them as having afforded important information, in addition to that which was acquired from the examination of witnesses. Unfortunately, the unsettled state of the country towards the end of the year caused the proceedings against the magistrates to be brought to an abrupt termination. The close of the year saw ominous signs of trouble brewing in the west, which later on culminated in strikes and riots among the labouring classes. In anticipation of what was to come, the Convenery hurriedly met at the Magdalen Chapel and unanimously passed the following resolution :—

"That it is the duty of every good citizen in time of difficulty and danger to come forward in support of the constituted authorities of the country. That although the Convenery are satisfied of the loyalty and good disposition of their fellow-citizens yet they learn with regret that in the neighbouring counties turbulence and disaffection prevail to such an extent as to have induced the Commander-in-Chief to remove a great part of the military force to that district in order to preserve the public peace. That under the circumstances it is desirable that those dissensions occasioned by difference of opinion in regard to the burgh policy should for the present be buried in oblivion and every aid afforded to the civil power for the preservation of the peace of the city and the security of property which the commander of the forces has left under the protection of our fellow-citizens. The meeting was therefore of opinion that it was expedient for the heads of the various

Incorporations to recommend their respective constituents to enrol themselves as special constables, volunteers, or in any other associations which the authorities may think it necessary to embody."

In consideration of the above resolutions, the College stated that they viewed with the deepest regret and sympathy the distress and privations to which a large portion of the manufacturing classes of the community were subjected.   They could not but feel horror and indignation at the attempts which had been made by wicked and infatuated men to take advantage of these distresses to alienate the lower orders of society from their duties as subjects, to disseminate among them principles subversive of the Constitution and religion of the country, and to excite them to turbulence and sedition.   The members of the College then expressed their determination and readiness to assist the civil authorities, by every means in their power, in opposing and resisting those who might be engaged in proceedings dangerous to the Constitution or injurious to the peace or safety of society.   For these reasons the Crafts resolved to suspend all action in favour of Burgh reform until a more propitious moment, which, as events proved, was still some distance off.

Some fourteen years were destined to elapse ere Lord Advocate Jeffrey introduced a measure in Parliament aiming at the destruction of the system of self-elective Town Councils. The surgeons were at once deeply interested in the Bill and saw in it the means of effecting their long-cherished desire of severing their municipal connection, and freeing themselves from the power that body had so long, and sometimes arbitrarily, used in controlling the election of their President and interfering in other ways with their proceedings.   By September 1833, the Bill for reforming the Constitution of the Royal Burghs had passed into law, and the office and title of Deacon as an official and constituent member of the Town Council was abolished. The Trades had now the unfettered election of their own office-bearers, but the College was so far connected with the town that the President still retained his seat in the Convenery, and his vote in the election of the Deacon-Convener.   Thus far the College was relieved of its civic duties, not so much by any immediate agitation of its own as by the demand of the people for constitutional reform ; it was still one of the

S

Incorporated Trades however, and remained so for nearly twenty years.

William Wood, who took such an active interest in the proceedings of the College about this time, was the grandson of William Wood who joined the College in 1716, and the son of Andrew Wood, who became a Fellow in 1769; Andrew had previously been surgeon to the North British Dragoons, but, on the death of his father, joined in partnership with his cousin Alexander Wood in Edinburgh. In such esteem was he held that on his death, in 1821, a special meeting of the College was convened and the following resolution agreed to :—

"That the Royal College of Surgeons deeply lament the loss they have sustained in the death of Mr Andrew Wood, the senior member of the College, who for fifty-two years has by the integrity and respectability of his character and by his interest in the College contributed so much to its honour and advantage, and who, by the ability and humanity of his professional conduct and by his amiable manners, had endeared himself to all who had intercourse with him in public and private life—That while condoling with his family in the affliction they have sustained and wishing to evince in the only manner in their power their respect for his virtues, the College shall offer their attendance at his funeral as a tribute to his memory."

This letter was ordered to be sent to Mr William Wood, who, in declining the honour for family reasons, said—" It is a tribute to his worth that to the last hour of our lives we must ever cherish in our most grateful remembrance." It may here be of interest to note that between the years 1805-1807 no fewer than five members of this distinguished medical family were Fellows of the College at the same time. They represented two branches of the family, but all sprang from the same stock, were closely related, and took a keen interest in the affairs of the College.

The offer to attend the funeral of a Fellow was seldom made by the College and, although it was repeated on the death of Dr Barclay, to find a former parallel we must go back to the olden days of the " mortclaith," when by an Act of the Craft every member was required to convoy the corpse of his deceased brother to the grave " under a penalty of twelve shillings scots."

The College had no sooner severed their connection with the Town Council than they took steps to withdraw from the Convenery. It was evident, however, that as one of the Incorporated Trades, and thus forming a constituent part of the Convenery, they could not separate themselves from that constitution by any act of their own. Recourse would therefore have to be made in the ordinary way to Parliament, but as such a step, particularly if it met with opposition, might lead to a greater expenditure than the College could well afford, it was decided, in order to save expense, to get a clause inserted into one of the numerous Bills then coming before Parliament, which would serve the same purpose. An opportunity soon occurred, for when, in 1838, the College informed the Convenery that they had for many years been anxious to be separated from it, in consequence of the awkward situation in which they often found themselves through holding a double status, viz., that of an Incorporated Trade and also of a Royal College, they now applied for such separation by means of a clause in the Municipal Incorporations Bill for Scotland. The College did not achieve their object through the Municipal Incorporations Bill, and the question remained in abeyance until the year 1845.

In 1834, the College were persuaded that the time had arrived to renew an application for a grant from the Government, previously made in 1825, and they prepared a memorial for the Lords of the Treasury, and solicited the Duke of Buccleuch, Lord Melville, the Earl of Haddington, and Lord Rosebery to support the application with their interest. The grounds upon which the claim was based were that, in furtherance of their endeavours to promote the advancement of medical and surgical science, they had, in 1804, formed an anatomical museum, which by the exertions of the Fellows of the College gradually rose into importance. Being anxious to extend the means of professional instruction which the museum afforded they expended a sum of £3000 on the purchase of Sir Charles Bell's collection. They had also been put to a considerable expense in providing a new hall, and a large museum to accommodate the valuable bequest of Dr Barclay. All the funds of the College had consequently been devoted to the purchase and preservation of preparations in their museum, and to the erection of a building principally for their proper reception, on which objects the College had altogether expended a sum of no less than £27,000. Their funds were now not only exhausted, but they had incurred a debt of upwards of £7000, and this the College had reason to fear would seriously embarrass their efforts to maintain their museum in a state of efficiency and usefulness. Conscious that their best efforts had been directed to the improvement of the medical profession and for the benefit of the public, they indulged the hope of receiving the gracious aid of his Majesty's Government. A return which accompanied the application showed that the museum at that time contained 7237 specimens.

After a delay of three years the College received a copy of the public estimates, which included as an item a donation of £5000 for the use of the College, and on receipt of this sum from the Exchequer the Treasurer was instructed to apply the same in paying off some of its most pressing debts. In spite of the Government grant, however, the financial state of the College was anything but satisfactory and as no improvement took place within the next few years a finance committee was appointed to investigate the whole circumstances connected with the income and expenditure of the College, and to find an expedient, if possible, whereby they might be relieved of their anxiety.

The result of their labours was reported in 1843, and is important as bearing upon the connection between the Fellows and the Widows' Fund. This connection, it was suggested, had an unfavourable effect upon the revenue of the College, on account of its injuriously limiting the number of candidates for the Fellowship in consequence of the high rate of entry money, which was £250, half of which went to the Widows' Fund. But, as no alteration could be made in the system without appealing to the Legislature, and as considerable difficulty was anticipated in making a change with due regard to the interests of all concerned, it was proposed that no steps should be taken in the matter until a thorough investigation had been made by competent persons into the whole details of the Fund. Meanwhile, as the expenditure of the College had for the past few years exceeded the income, the examiners gave up their claim to pecuniary remuneration, and the Clerk or Secretary, as he was then termed, when some question arose regarding the cutting down of his perquisites, wrote: " I shall always regard my emoluments as Secretary to the College, whatever these may be, as quite a secondary consideration to the honourable distinction which the possession of that office must confer on anyone of my profession."

It was now apparent to all that, if the College wished to keep up its membership, an end would have to be made to the Widows' Fund, which, owing to the introduction and development of insurance schemes, had now been rendered unnecessary. To carry out this plan there was no alternative but to obtain a new Charter, and as the College were still waiting an opportunity to press their claims for separation from the Convenery, a draft Charter was prepared embracing these two important objects. The proposed Charter, however, went further than this, for it contained a clause whereby the College was to be raised to the status of a National College under the title of the Royal College of Surgeons of Scotland. In return for this concession the Government proposed that both Colleges (the Physicians were to receive the same dignity) should open their doors for a limited period to licentiates in surgery and medicine, irrespective of the body they belonged to, and that during a specified time persons of character and repute should be admitted without examination, and on payment of a smaller fee than future Fellows. The whole business was to be arranged by a private Act of Parliament, but when the customary notice of the intentions of the College was made known in the Edinburgh newspapers in terms of the standing orders, the Faculty of Physicians and Surgeons of Glasgow at once lodged a Bill for the purpose, amongst other matters, of giving them the name of the Royal College of Physicians and Surgeons of Glasgow. As it appeared highly undesirable to the Edinburgh surgeons that more than one Royal College of Surgeons should exist in Scotland, they determined to this extent to oppose the Glasgow Bill. The whole scheme fell through, however, because the Faculty withdrew their claim, but only on condition that the College of Surgeons gave up their aspiration to national distinction. The Bill then passed through its different stages without opposition, and, in March 1851, the new Charter was granted.

The constitution and general administration of the affairs of the College were now entirely changed, the Widows' Fund was brought to a close and the connection of the surgeons with the Incorporated Trades, the Convenery and the Municipal Incorporation which had lasted for three hundred and fifty years, was completely severed. Mr Syme was President at the time this important event was consummated, and the thanks of the members were voted to Mr Andrew Rutherfurd, the Lord Advocate, to whose legal advice and efficient aid the College were mainly indebted for bringing to a successful conclusion their most cherished desire.

CHAPTER XVI

THE COLLEGE AND MEDICAL EDUCATION

Medical Reform—The question of Medical Reform in one form
or another exercised the professional mind both in Great
Britain and Ireland for such a considerable period, and embraced
such complex and extensive problems and side issues, that no
attempt can be made here to pursue its development further
than it affected the interests of the College of Surgeons.

The question was raised in 1806, and the surgeons of
Edinburgh were invited to express their opinions on the matter.
A meeting of the medical profession had been held in London
and a copy of the resolutions then agreed to was submitted
to the College. The aim of the Faculty in England in which
the various medical bodies in the kingdom were asked to
assist, was to devise a plan which, while it preserved inviolate
the rights and privileges of the different corporate bodies,
should offer protection to the profession against the ignorant
and unskilful, and ensure to the community well qualified
practitioners. The College, however, did not then see the
necessity for taking action and politely declined to share in
the movement. From the information they had been able to
procure, the College were inclined to believe that the practice
of medicine in Scotland, so far from being in a low and degraded
state, was at that time in all its branches on a better footing,
and its practitioners more highly educated than in any former
period. For a great number of years they had observed with
satisfaction the gradually increasing knowledge and acquire-

ments of candidates for their diploma, and although they were
by no means disposed to deny the existence of abuses in the
profession, in this as well as in other countries, they were of
opinion that the powers with which the different medical bodies
were already invested, were sufficient, if duly exercised, for the
correction of the greater part of the abuses complained of.
They therefore did not think it was necessary to enter into
any discussion or report on the merits of the plan "which the
state of medical practice in this country did not seem to
require," and which did not make better provision for the
instruction of future candidates than the regulations already
adopted by the College.

The main obstacle at that time to an amicable understanding
between the medical bodies in the kingdom, was the want of
uniformity in their curricula, the varying privileges conferred
upon the members or licentiates by the Charters and grants of
the several Corporations, and the jealous way in which these
were guarded.

Although most of the bodies recognised the necessity for
reform, the difficulty was to reduce so many conflicting interests
to one common principle, and to formulate a plan acceptable to
all. This could only be done by abolishing their individual
privileges and monopolies, and substituting a uniform course of
study and common rights, which was almost impossible without
the aid of legislation.

In 1815, the Apothecaries of London obtained an Act of
Parliament by which all persons were prohibited from practising
as apothecaries in England and Wales, unless they held the
licence of that body. As the diploma of the College of
Surgeons of Edinburgh previous to that date was admitted
as a qualification to practise surgery and pharmacy, and consequently to act as a *general practitioner* throughout the United
Kingdom, it is obvious that the position of the licentiates of
the College residing across the Border could be made very
uncomfortable, unless they also took out the apothecaries'
licence. This they felt indisposed to do, and in consequence
of the apothecaries' threats to proceed against them, applied to
the College for assistance. Anxious to defend their licentiates
as far as lay in their power, the surgeons petitioned the Government to remove the monopoly so recently created, which they

said was meant to protect the public from ignorant pretenders, and not to operate against practitioners whose education and professional attainments were perhaps superior to those of the apothecaries. The Faculty of Physicians and Surgeons of Glasgow also intimated their pleasure to co-operate in "this important business."

In the proceedings which ensued against them, the apothecaries made much of the circumstance that, by their laws, no teacher or lecturer should be eligible as an examiner, and that neither the surgeons nor any of the other bodies in Scotland granting diplomas had any similar law. As a matter of fact, although the College had no law to that effect, no lecturer had ever been chosen as an examiner ; but to deprive their opponents of the opportunity of raising this objection such a law was now made.

In 1833, a Conference of the three Surgical Colleges was arranged to be held in London to discuss the question of medical education in general and the assimilation of their several diplomas. Sir George Ballingall and Mr William Wood were appointed to represent the surgeons of Edinburgh, and they were reminded by their College of some of the leading principles by which they had been guided in framing and modifying from time to time their regulations relative to the course of study to be pursued by candidates for their diploma. The first of these was the expediency of confining their attempt to regulate the education of candidates to the period spent by them in attendance at public schools, the portions of each year to be devoted to study, and the value to candidates of previous instruction in the elementary parts of medical science. Lastly, that all who were to exercise the medical profession should be instructed in the elements of all its branches, not only that they might be qualified to follow out all of these or to devote themselves more particularly to one or other branch, but also from the intimate connection which subsists between the principles of the several departments of medicine, and the mutual light which they reflect one upon another.

For this reason the College had embraced in its course of study not only the branches immediately bearing on the practice of surgery and pharmacy—the two departments over which its Charters gave it a more especial supervision—but those also of physic and midwifery. These points the delegates were asked to remember, and also that, although the College had from time to time made such additions to their course of study as the circumstances of the country and the condition of its schools of medicine seemed to warrant, they were far from conceiving that their course was incapable of any further extension or improvement, particularly in the event of the licentiates being secured in the right of practising in every part of the United Kingdom.

Immediately on his return to Edinburgh, Sir George called a meeting of the College and read a series of resolutions which had been adopted by the three Colleges, and also three separate agreements to which they had come with the delegates of the Irish College, viz. : To raise the fees for the diploma, to fix the number of examiners to form a quorum for the examination of students, and to remove, if possible, the obnoxious clauses in the Apothecaries' Act which operate disadvantageously to both Colleges.

With regard to the first of these agreements, Sir George stated that it was with considerable reluctance that he and his co-delegates had been brought to agree to the proposal to raise the diploma fee, but it had been so strenuously insisted on by the Dublin delegates that he feared its rejection might have endangered the whole arrangement. " It was to be observed," he said, "that the expense of a surgical diploma in London was £22, and in Dublin as high as £40. The first suggestion of the Irish delegates had been to raise the Edinburgh diploma to £20, and it was not without difficulty they had been induced to modify it to £15.

The College, in approving of the agreement, expressed an adverse feeling to raising the fee to so great an amount, but they thought that the prospect of ultimate advantage to the profession at large from the agreement, so far concluded with the sister Colleges, might justify it.

In presenting to the College the official documents in connection with the conferences in London, with the conclusions of which all might not agree, Sir George entreated them to remember the difficulties that lay in the way of adjusting a measure of so much importance by three public bodies placed in different circumstances, and having to a certain extent varying and distinct interests, and how essential it was to the formation of a joint measure that each body should make some sacrifice of opinion and feeling.   The agreements entered into by the delegates were then read to the College, who expressed their satisfaction at the prospect of the early introduction of a uniform system of medical legislation for all parts of the British Dominions, established on the basis of equal qualification and reciprocal privileges.   As the result of an exchange of courtesies between the delegates, Sir Benjamin Brodie, one of the representatives of the English College, was made an Honorary Fellow of the Edinburgh College, and Sir George Ballingall received a similar honour from the Irish College.

In 1839, the College met for the purpose of considering and deciding upon certain propositions relative to the education and privileges of medical practitioners, agreed upon by joint committees appointed by the Medical Faculty in the University and by the Royal Colleges of Physicians and Surgeons of Edinburgh.   Before proceeding to discuss the proposals, Mr William Wood explained the situation in which the College was placed in regard to them.   To the general principles of the scheme he said, the College was pledged in honour by the approval which had been given to them in the year 1834, and on several occasions later.   There were some changes, however, both in the general principles of some of the propositions and in the detail ; and these changes, which the joint committee considered improvements, had been made after mature consideration of the views and opinions of various Universities and licensing bodies in England, Scotland, and Ireland.   These changes were now submitted to the members of the College, and were ultimately approved of by them.

The propositions, which ran to some length, refer firstly to practitioners, secondly to teachers, and thirdly to chemists and druggists.   Briefly, it was suggested that the Legislature ought to fix a minimum course of medical education, and that no person should obtain a licence entitling him to act as a general medical practitioner who had not received a competent education in literature and science.   The time to be occupied in the minimum course of education was proposed to be not less than twenty-seven months, in which period should be included three winter sessions, each of six months' duration ;

as the minimum age of a candidate for a diploma or licence twenty-one was suggested.

After enumerating the various courses in detail, it was said that in Edinburgh a final examination might be advantageously conducted by a joint Board of Fellows of the Royal Colleges of Physicians and Surgeons; that all persons having obtained a licence to practise surgery in conformity with these conditions should be entitled to act as general medical practitioners and to dispense medicines in all parts of the British Dominions, provided they had been examined by a competent Board on all the branches of education specified in the curriculum.

In dealing with the University degree in medicine, it was suggested that while a more extended education was necessary, the education should not be raised so high above what was required of the general practitioner as to limit the number of persons who, in order to obtain the honour, might be induced to take a fuller course than was necessary for a simple licence. Further, that a certain portion of the study qualifying for a medical degree should be prosecuted in some University which granted that degree, and that any such University ought to insist on attendance therein during a winter session, as preliminary and requisite to examination.

In regard to teachers, it was proposed that the lectures of no professor or lecturer should be recognised who taught within the same year more than one of the branches required, but that anatomy with practical anatomy, and chemistry with practical chemistry, might be considered as one; while clinical medicine and clinical surgery might be taught, in addition to any of the other branches, by professors, physicians, and surgeons to whom was entrusted the charge of recognised hospitals.

In consequence, however, of a difference of opinion existing among the members of the joint committee in regard to the extent of University monopoly or privilege that should be allowed in regulating the education of candidates for medical degrees, the colleges represented that it was only proper that the greater part of the course of study required of candidates for the highest honours of the medical profession, which were to be granted exclusively by Universities, should be taken under professors. It would be of advantage, however, that a portion of the study should be allowed to be prosecuted under extra-academical teachers.   The minimum extent and duration of study, the minimum age and the minimum proportion of extra-mural study, on the other hand, should be fixed by the Legislature, and not left to be regulated at the discretion of the Universities, either singly or collectively.

The committee representing the University, while agreeing with much of what had been said, strongly dissented from the conclusion that Universities should be prohibited by law from the regulation which had been in force in that of Edinburgh for seventy years, by which every candidate for graduation was required to have studied every branch which was imposed on him by the curriculum in some University, British or foreign, empowered to grant degrees in medicine. They did not wish to impose this law on other Universities, but only desired that the University of Edinburgh might not be prohibited from maintaining it, so long as they should judge it necessary, in order to secure that the Professorships should be an object of ambition to men of talent and of good prospects in the profession.   They also thought it unnecessary to guard against any undue extension of this monopoly in the case of a degree, which, they said, was only an honorary distinction, conferring no exclusive right of practice, and which was equally granted by various Universities openly competing with one another.

With the exception of the above, all the propositions were mutually agreed upon by the three bodies, and upon these terms they entered upon the long and protracted struggle for medical reform.

In 1840, Mr Warburton and Mr Hawes introduced their Bills for the amendment of the Laws relating to the medical profession.   The College having been unsuccessful in a series of attempts during a period of more than twenty years to obtain from Parliament a remedy for the inequalities of education and of privilege which affected the medical profession, rejoiced that there was at length a prospect of this subject being brought under the consideration of the Legislature with such an amount of support from the profession and from the public as to ensure the attainment of some measure of practical good.

In an open letter addressed to the promoters of the Bills,

the College concluded by remarking that they could aver with truth that they had pursued no corporate ends to the public injury, that they had endeavoured to raise the standard of medical acquirement in this school by an enlarged system of education proportionate to the wants of the age, and that they had refrained for a long term of years from making additions to the cost of their diploma. Further, that their examiners had submitted to be greatly underpaid in order to enable the College to maintain their ground without such additions, and that their entire accumulations had been expended in erecting their hall and purchasing a museum, to the accommodation of which the greater part of the building was devoted, and which was accessible to the public and most beneficial to the medical school. Having made such use of their present privileges, the College conceived themselves entitled to claim the credit of disinterestedness in any advice they might offer in reference to medical legislation, and in all that related to that important subject, they most fully admitted the supremacy of the public interest. Let the Medical Incorporations, they said, be compelled to submit to all such regulations as the welfare of the public requires, let their privileges in particular altogether cease to be exclusive and local in their character, but let not an apparatus, so capable of being beneficially employed, be gratuitously and inconsiderately annihilated.

With reference to this open letter, the North of England Medical Association resolved unanimously, . . . " That the cordial thanks of the meeting be given to the Royal College of Surgeons of Edinburgh for their able report on the medical Bills of Messrs Warburton and Hawes, a document which in the opinion of the Council reflects the highest zeal and liberality of the College and (from its appearance at the present moment) is eminently calculated to assist the progress of medical reform."

As soon as the Bills came before Parliament, it was apparent to the College that measures of so general a nature were not likely to be passed into law in the then existing circumstances. In the following session, however, another Bill, having for its principles equality of education, similarity of examinations, and identity of privilege throughout all parts of the United Kingdom, was brought forward by Sir James Graham ; and Mr William Wood was again chosen to represent his

College at a conference of delegates which was to take place in London. Sir James Graham, however, postponed his measure until the next session, and when the time approached for the introduction of the Bill, the College was informed that in all probability an attempt would be made to oppose it by stirring up the jealousy of the English apothecaries, on the ground of their losing the monopoly they had enjoyed under the Act of 1815. The Bill was again postponed owing to the state of public business, but, by May 1845, it had been read a second time in Parliament and was then in Committee.

While the College were pleased to find that some of their suggestions had been adopted in the Bill, they strongly objected to the clause that "none but persons registered as physicians shall use the title of 'doctor.'" At the same time they expressed the hope and most anxious wish that the Bill might be passed at once, with the view to removing the very annoying state of doubt and anxiety in which professional men and medical students were placed with regard to their future status and prospects in the profession.

The progress of the Bill was slow owing to conflicting opinions and interests between English medical men and London Medical Incorporations, and to the imprudent and precipitate manner in which the last amendments were promulgated without consulting the Colleges of Physicians and Surgeons of London. Both these bodies declared themselves hostile to the Bill in its amended form, and it was opposed by a large body of general practitioners, members of the London College of Surgeons. The chemists and druggists were alarmed at the removal of the privileges granted them by the Apothecaries' Act. A strong effort was made by the English teachers, and more especially by those of London University College and King's College, to defeat the great principle of equality of rights which formed the main feature of the Bill, by introducing provisions calculated to secure themselves against competition on the part of the Scottish and Irish Schools. The Bill was therefore wrecked in consequence of the divided opinion of the profession in general.

The matter, however, was not allowed to rest, and, in 1847, Mr Wakely proposed a measure which, if not in all respects such as the College desired, contained the leading principles they had in view. In a petition to the Commons stating their opinions, the College said : " For many years their attention had been directed to the restrictions on the practice of medicine and surgery arising from the faulty state of the laws affecting the medical profession, and they had made every effort in their power to procure a remedy by setting the example of abandoning whatever was invidious or illiberal in their own Chartered Rights, and by frequently pressing upon the Legislature the necessity of a uniform and liberal system of medical legislation. " Ever since the early part of the last century, when Scotland and England were united, the City of Edinburgh has presented advantages for medical instruction which have not been surpassed in any other part of the kingdom or of the world." That these advantages, continued the petition, " have consisted in part in the possession of a University, of extra-academical schools, and of hospitals, dispensaries, libraries, museums, a botanic garden and other similar institutions, but also and chiefly, in the fact that Edinburgh had had the good fortune to secure the services of a succession of medical professors and teachers of such unquestionable celebrity that their names are inseparably associated with the history of the professional advance of medical science, and that very many of them are universally admitted to have been amongst the highest ornaments of the science itself at every period from the origin of the medical school to the present time."

As on former occasions, Mr Wood again proceeded to London to watch over the interests of his College, and, after being examined by the Select Committee, was requested by its Chairman, the Lord Advocate, to remain in London as the expositor of the state of the professional institutions of Scotland. The College, however, soon learned with regret that the hopes which had been entertained of an improvement of the medical profession of Great Britain had been entirely frustrated. The Conference Committee had been broken up, and all its proceedings rendered null and void on " account of the impossibility of reconciling the claims of the Royal College of Surgeons of England and those of the promoters of the intended new Royal College of General Practitioners as to the examination in surgery of general practitioners."

The surgeons of Edinburgh now thought it high time to

take the matter in hand themselves, and, with the object of ascertaining if the medical bodies in Scotland were prepared to act harmoniously with them, sounded the Faculty of Physicians and Surgeons of Glasgow as to how far their sentiments might permit of a joint application for some measure of relief from their grievances. The Faculty seemed quite agreeable, and eventually an arrangement was proposed to enable that body and the College of Surgeons to unite in discharging the duty of examination and licence. It was further understood that the College of Physicians would also join as a third party on the same terms of agreement as formerly, when the two Edinburgh Colleges had the prospect of uniting for the attainment of a similar object.

Affairs went on in this desultory fashion until the year 1854, when Lord Palmerston brought forward a General Medical Reform Bill, which was proposed by the Provincial Medical and Surgical Association. A conference was fixed to take place at the College of Physicians in London in April, and Mr Syme, who at that time was taking a great interest in College affairs, was deputed to attend it.

His report of what took place at the meeting, which is full of interesting particulars showing the divided opinions of the delegates and also the attitude of the College, is given *in extenso* :—

"The meeting," he said, "took place at the Hall of the Royal College of Physicians, and was presided over by the President, Dr Paris. The business was commenced by Mr Hastings of the English Bar, son of Sir Charles Hastings, who gave an account of the origin, progress, and condition of the Bill projected by the Provincial Association. The delegates in a general way stated their views of the measure. Those of Oxford, Cambridge, and the London University gave a qualified assent so far as their personal opinion was concerned. A letter was read from the Secretary of the Royal College of Surgeons of England, intimating that as that body disapproved of the Bill it declined to send representatives. On the part of the University and of the College of Surgeons of Edinburgh, I stated that both of the bodies which I represented disapproved of requiring a double qualification for the licence of general practice, and of maintaining distinction with regard

T

to the right of practice in England, Scotland, and Ireland. I further stated that, upon these grounds, both of the bodies mentioned were resolved by every means in their power to oppose the Bill or any other measure containing similar provisions. Dr Anderson, President of the Faculty of Physicians and Surgeons of Glasgow, and Dr Clarke, delegate of Marischal College, Aberdeen, concurred in the sentiments which I had expressed. Mr Barol, Warden of the Apothecaries' Society of London, stated that the body which he represented entirely disapproved of the Bill on account of its ignoring the assistance of their licentiates. The Dublin apothecaries expressed their approval of the Bill. Dr Renton, on the part of the Royal College of Physicians of Edinburgh, disapproved of the Bill in its present shape and expressed his opinion that it might be amended.

"A conversation then ensued, in the course of which a great variety of views on the subject in question was expressed. On the part of the College, I endeavoured to explain the objects which they had always pursued in their endeavours to obtain a measure of medical reform, viz., equality of privilege to practise, founded upon equality of qualification, and reciprocity of privilege throughout her Majesty's Dominions. While admitting the advantage of a Fellowship with a College which founded its claim to respect, not in possession of exclusive privileges but on the character of its members, I protested against the hardships and inexpediency of enforcing the possession of a diploma in addition to the licence of general practice. I also expressed the surprise with which this College had observed, subsequently to the transmission of their resolutions, that Sir Charles Hastings, in his report to the Provincial Association from their Reform Committee, stated that the College had taken offence at the Bill, and that it had been altered in such a way as seemed to be satisfactory to them. I stated, that, so far as I was aware, there was not a shadow of foundation for these statements. Sir Charles Hastings made no reply.

"From the great diversity of opinion which prevailed, it was obvious that no general agreement could be expected, and it was, therefore, proposed that the further discussion should be confided to a committee. To this proposal I objected, unless the committee were to be limited in its period of action and commissioned to report to the Conference, which could not delegate its deliberative function to a section with powers to represent the whole body. After some discussion it was determined by a show of hands to appoint a committee of unlimited duration, against which I protested as *ultra vires*, and as various members concurred in this view, while none could agree as to the constitution of the committee, the President adjourned the meeting *sine die*.

"Anticipating the falsehood and misrepresentation of the London periodical press, I deemed it right in common with the representatives of Glasgow, Aberdeen, and St Andrews, to record our sentiments in an authentic form, and, therefore, transmitted the following paper to Lord Palmerston."

The paper in question, besides mentioning the insuperable objections entertained by the signatory bodies, contained certain resolutions proposed by Mr Syme as expressive of their sentiments.

The College made strenuous efforts to prevent this Bill from passing. Dr Gairdner and the Secretary were at once despatched to London, where they had an interview with the Prime Minister, who requested them to submit a written memorandum for his consideration.

"It was unfortunate," said Dr Gairdner and his colleague in making their report to the College, "that there were so few of the Scottish peers in London. We saw nearly all of them; of these, the Duke of Argyll took an active part in the House. We saw Lord Eglinton and the Duke of Buccleuch, but the former was obliged to leave London, and the latter, though occasionally in town and remarkably well informed on the subject, was unable to give steady attendance on account of his health.

"Throughout everything which we have done in London, it has been our endeavour, without hostility to any other interests, to maintain the right of the profession and of this College and other similar bodies which are open to that profession and in sympathy with its affairs, and more especially to be the sole judges of the fitness of all future candidates for admission into its ranks as legal practitioners."

As some question arose as to whether the graduates of the old English Universities were not liable to the penalties of

292 ROYAL COLLEGE OF SURGEONS OF EDINBURGH

the Apothecaries' Act, 1815, one of the College delegates took
the trouble to ascertain how this matter was viewed by the
apothecaries themselves. Whereupon he was favoured with
the following extract from Wilcock's *Medical Law*, Chap. 11,
Sec. 1, *Physician* :—

"The first class of Medical Practitioners in rank and legal pre-
eminence, is that of the Physician. They are (by Statute 32 Henry
VIII.) allowed to practise physic in all its branches, among which
Surgery is enumerated. The law, therefore, permits them to compound
and prescribe their medicines, and as well to perform as to superintend
operations in Surgery. Their Privileges are also reserved to them by
the Charters and Statutes relative to the Surgeons and Apothecaries."

In 1855, the University of Edinburgh forwarded to the
Home Secretary a "Draft Bill" for regulating and improving
the medical profession, without so much as even making it
known to the College. The College, therefore, complained
that a Bill for regulating the interests of the whole medical
profession should have been prepared and placed in the
hands of the Government by parties having interests very
different in some respects from that profession, without making
the College aware of its nature or even of its existence.
This was all the more noticeable as all former Bills had been
brought forward and advocated in the most public way. To
this Bill, which endeavoured to show that the Universities of
Scotland could confer rights to practise in any medical department, the College conceived it their duty to offer the most
determined resistance, on the ground of its being in no way
beneficial to the public and, at the same time, full of provisions
injurious to the profession.

Mr Headlam, Member of Parliament for Newcastle, also
introduced about this time a Draft Bill on the same subject,
and some correspondence ensued between that gentleman and
the College which brought out some very interesting points. It
will be remembered that until the passing of the Bill in 1858,
the examination of the College embraced the subjects of
Chemistry, Physics, Materia Medica, Medical Jurisprudence,
Midwifery, and the medical treatment of surgical diseases, and
that its licentiates were in every respect the general practitioners
of the day. It must also be borne in mind that besides the
examinations conducted by the Universities as a condition of

conferring medical honours, viz., the M.D., and an examination conducted by the Royal College of Physicians of Edinburgh in the case of *foreign graduates* applying for admission to their *Fellowship*, the *only* medical examinations in Scotland were those of the College of Surgeons of Edinburgh and the Faculty of Physicians and Surgeons in Glasgow. Now Mr Headlam's Bill, while proposing among other things to give to the Glasgow Faculty the uncontrolled power of licensing surgeons without calling in the aid of any other body, proposed to give to the College of Physicians the right of examining and licensing physicians in Edinburgh, and also, conjointly with the College of Surgeons, the right of examining and licensing surgeons— a right hitherto enjoyed by the latter College alone. The College was unable to see in what way the profession or the public could benefit, by asking the surgeons to surrender the greater part of their privileges. They had ever been forward, they said, in extending their educational requirements and in improving their examinations in proportion to the advancement of medical science. Their diploma had always enjoyed a high reputation, their funds had been devoted to the building of their present Hall, and to the establishment of an extensive anatomical and pathological museum, which was kept up for the benefit of the profession and the public. They considered that amongst their Fellows there was a sufficiency of talent to enable them to conduct their examination in all the departments of medicine, and to entitle them to retain their licensing powers without being obliged to call in extraneous aid.

The latter point was one of the objections the College had to Mr Headlam's Bill, which they thought in the form in which it then appeared was not such as ought to obtain the confidence either of the public or of the profession. The Bill, however, was pushed on and several conferences were held with the physicians regarding the establishment of a Joint Board of Examiners in Scotland in case of its passing.

Dr Andrew Wood and Dr Maclagan then proceeded to London to watch the progress of the Bill, and on their return made a long report to the College, in which occur the following remarks: "The result of this day's proceedings showed more clearly than ever that the great danger to be apprehended is the introduction of amendments benefiting the Universities at the expense of the Colleges, and it became doubly apparent that there was a necessity for concerted action on the part of the Colleges to protect their interests." This led to a "Scottish Branch" being formed by the Faculty and the two Edinburgh Colleges, and to a statement being drawn up and circulated amongst the Members of Parliament protesting against the claim of the Universities to have their M.D. degree recognised as a licence to practise medicine and surgery, which it was averred they had no right to do, and that it would be impolitic to confer it upon them.

In June 1856, the Bill was reported by the Select Committee to the House and was then, in its amended state, more objectionable to the College than in its original form. This fact appealed to them so much that, in their financial report for that year, an expenditure of £150 appears "For resisting an invidious measure of proposed legislation which threatened the College with utter extinction." As it became more and more apparent that the Universities would soon be in a position to grant the full licence to practise, the Edinburgh Colleges along with the Faculty met to consider the constitution of an Examining Board which would enable them to compete with the Universities. At this meeting, a proposal for amalgamation of the three bodies was suggested by the Faculty, whose members were to join *ad eundem* one or other of the Royal Colleges according to their choice—that thus the Colleges would become the Royal Colleges of Scotland, and that from them a branch Board would be appointed to examine in Glasgow. To this the surgeons demurred; the proposal had the approval of the delegates of the physicians. A second plan, very much after the scheme of the present Triple Qualification, was also put forward, and after some debate it was resolved by the delegates to bring both proposals before their respective bodies.

In April 1857, a memorial on behalf of the licentiates of the College, was considered by that body. It indicated the disadvantage under which they as "licentiates" laboured in comparison with those who were "members" of other Colleges. Although a resolution was passed in favour of a change in nomenclature, the opinion of Counsel, for reasons given, was that the College should not adopt the proposed resolution, but should apply to the Crown for a supplementary Charter.

Proposals by the Universities of Edinburgh, Glasgow, and Aberdeen to institute the degree of Bachelor of Medicine were now put forward, and to these the College objected to the utmost. The function of the Universities was to teach and grant honours and not to license to practise. If such a degree was established—carrying with it the licence to practise every branch of the profession—the College saw a serious menace to their own right, and asked if, after having enjoyed for so many years that privilege, unassisted by any other body whatsoever, they could be expected to be content to find themselves stripped of all their most important functions, a proceeding which would render their existence as a College scarcely necessary at all. At last, in July 1858, the Medical Practitioners Bill passed into law and the profession became much what it is at the present day.

Before the establishment of a Medical Register it was difficult to tell who was qualified and who was not, and no doubt amidst much confusion many persons practised without any qualification whatever. Naturally enough this created a desire in the profession to be put on a better footing, but owing to the difficulty of reconciling the different interests and privileges of the Universities and Medical Incorporations it could not be done without legislative enactment; to the same cause may be traced the many abortive attempts at legislation that occurred during the first half of the century. The immediate result to the College was to deprive it of its medical character and to constitute it a College of Surgery pure and simple.

When it became apparent that the College diploma was not a full medical qualification, negotiations were opened with the physicians with the view of instituting a joint examination and conferring a double qualification—viz., one in surgery and one in medicine—and as the Medical Act sanctioned such a course, an arrangement was come to which enabled candidates to pass both examinations at one sitting. At the same time, a proposal by the College to confer with the Senatus Academicus on the subject of granting medical and surgical qualifications was met with a statement that, having made a compact with the other Universities in regard to the institution of a Mastership in Surgery, they were not in a position to enter into any negotiations based upon the abandonment of that degree, a condition which the College stated to be a *sine quâ non* to any negotiations on their part. The College further threatened to dispute the legality of such a step as that proposed by the University, and said it would be the duty of their representative on the General Medical Council to oppose it being done. Meanwhile plans were drawn up for co-operating with the College of Physicians, and although the scheme was strongly opposed by Mr Syme and others it was finally adopted.

In 1884, the Double Qualification gave way to a new scheme which associated the Faculty of Physicians and Surgeons of Glasgow with the two Edinburgh Colleges and thus linked up the three Scottish Corporations into one Examining Board. The Triple Qualification, under which title this combination became known, still flourishes, and has more than fulfilled the great expectations anticipated of it. In 1889, the Conjoint Board instituted a Diploma in Public Health.

The Fellowship Examination.—About the time at which the arrangements for the Triple Qualification were completed, the Laws relating to the Fellowship of the College were also remodelled and put upon a different basis, inasmuch as entrance could now only be obtained after examination. In doing this the College reverted to the method of entrance existing prior to the granting of the Charter of 1851, when admission to the Fellowship could only be obtained after examination and the production of a Thesis on some anatomical or surgical subject, and in addition the compulsory entrance to the Widows' Fund of the College, the cost of which to the non-privileged candidate came to nearly £300.

As the Fellowship was not a qualification to practise and did not confer any special privilege, except to those in Edinburgh who wished to lecture or to obtain hospital appointments, candidates became fewer and fewer and were almost entirely confined to the medical practitioners resident in Edinburgh. In these circumstances, and with a view to establish a closer connection with the profession and to render entrance to its ranks more accessible, the College, in 1851, obtained a new Charter separating all connection between the Fellowship and the Widows' Fund, and reduced the entrance fee to £50. The modern facilities for life insurance had rendered the Fund in a great measure unnecessary. It was felt that a further examination was not essential for the Fellowship, as that which admitted to the licence had always been full and thorough in every department of medicine and surgery. This view was supported at the time by Professor Syme, Mr William Wood, and others, who argued that men who were in practice, and had attained public confidence, should not be submitted to such a test. A Fellowship examination would become merely a student's examination for a higher degree, and could be little else that a repetition of the licentiate's examination, that the expenses connected with it would debar many from taking the Fellowship, and thus maintain, if it did not widen the gulf between the College and the profession. For these reasons the examination was dispensed with.

In 1856, in order to extend the basis of its constitution, the College instituted a non-resident Fellowship, which was open to all surgeons duly qualified and residing ten miles or more from the Hall of the College. Fellows of this class had no voice in the proceedings of the College nor the privilege of attending its meetings. The entrance fee was fixed at £25, and notices of the change were sent to all the licentiates resident in the United Kingdom. From the first this evoked the hostile criticism of the professional press, which culminated, in 1881, in some anonymous articles and letters appearing in the medical journals accusing the College of selling "Bogus Degrees," and stating that any man not guilty of transgressing some of the greater commandments could obtain the Fellowship on payment of £25.

To this the College replied that such statements were not true—that no man, though he kept all the commandments in the Decalogue from his youth up, would even be permitted to apply as a candidate for the Fellowship unless he possessed a diploma from one of the recognised Surgical Corporations of Great Britain or Ireland, and had his professional position vouched by two Fellows of the College, and his application, moreover, subsequently submitted to the scrutiny of the whole College for at least a month before the ballot on his petition took place. The only reason, the College said, why they took note of such statements was because thelatter seemed to have led a member of the House of Parliament to put the following question .to the Vice-President of the Educational Department :—

" To ask the Vice-President of the Council if he is aware that the highest qualification of the Royal College of Surgeons, Edinburgh, viz., the Fellowship, is to be had without examination, and even *in absentiâ*, by persons holding lower qualifications, on payment, and by a process of a vote or ballot."

" If he is aware that the highest qualification of the other two Scottish Medical Corporations, viz., the Royal College of Physicians, Edinburgh, and the Faculty of Physicians and Surgeons, Glasgow, is given on similar terms."

" And if he can inform the House whether such a system has been the subject of representation or remonstrance by the General Medical Council."

This happened in 1881, and although the College then vindicated its position, in 1884 it decided to re-introduce the system of examination, which continues to the present day.

The College and the Extra-Mural School.—The Extra-Mural Section of the Edinburgh Medical School may be said to be as old as the College. In the Seal of Cause of 1505, the teaching of anatomy was provided for when the Town Council granted the Barber-Surgeons a cadaver once in the year on the condition that " ilk ane " should " instruct utheris." From time to time further provision was made for the masters instructing their apprentices, and more anatomical material was provided for the purpose. From what has been said it will be seen that other branches of medical study were gradually developed, until a regular school of teachers was formed under the ægis of the Incorporation. An important stimulus was given to the teaching activities of the surgeons when, in 1697, they erected an anatomical theatre for the purpose of giving public dissections. In the same year Monteith took a lease of the chemical laboratory under the Hall in order to give a course of instruction in chemistry. In 1705, the College elected Robert Eliot to be Professor of Anatomy, and in course of time he was succeeded by two other surgeons—Adam Drummond and John M'Gill. In 1720, the last two, who acted conjointly, resigned in favour of Alexander Monro, who also received his appointment at the hands of the College. In 1764, James Rae lectured in the Hall on Diseases of the Teeth, and in 1772 he commenced a course of lectures on Surgery, which were said to be "useful and necessary to the Students of Physic and Surgery." With the advent of John Bell more attention was given to the teaching of surgery, and in 1787 he was granted the use of the Hall for the purpose of lecturing on Midwifery. In later years the teaching was carried on by Charles Bell, James Barclay, Robert Liston, Robert Knox, and many other distinguished lecturers, and in 1804 the College established its own Chair of Surgery, which was occupied successively by John Thomson, J. W. Turner, and John Lizars.

That the College exercised supervision and control over the lecturers and students of the Extra-Academical School is shown by its providing a hall or theatre for the teaching of anatomy and other subjects, and by its appointing, in 1839, a committee to report upon the attendance of students at the classes of private lecturers, and also to lay down regulations for their guidance. The College fixed the duration of the session and the extent of the holidays, superintended and issued the advertisements of the extra-academical classes, and assumed responsibility for their accuracy. A more stringent method of granting certificates of attendance was also insisted upon, a system of calling the roll was introduced, and the lecturers were obliged to submit their books to the College for inspection. Previous to this, in 1831, a committee had been appointed by the College to consider the subject of improving the discipline of the Edinburgh Medical School. In their report they recommended the College to co-operate with the University and the Town Council, as both of these bodies had an important interest in whatever was calculated to uphold the reputation of the school and to increase the confidence of parents and guardians who sent their young men to study there.

By the College Laws of 1867, all intending lecturers were required to pass an examination, and to satisfy the examiners not only of their competency to teach, but also of having in their possession the means of illustrating their lectures. Later it was entirely due to the interest the College had taken in the success of the school, and without any appeal having been made to them by the body of lecturers, that the recognition of the extra-mural classes by the University was eventually brought about. This was first suggested, in 1839, by James Syme, who in representing to the Town Council the alarming decrease in the numbers of medical students, suggested as a remedy the recognition of extra-mural teaching. This idea though strongly opposed by the Senatus found favour with the Council, and the College heard soon after with satisfaction that some important alterations in the *Statuta Solennia* with respect to the education necessary for candidates for medical degrees were under consideration. It became apparent, however, that while the lectures of some extra-mural teachers in London and Dublin were to be recognised, an invidious distinction was contemplated to the prejudice of private lecturers in Edinburgh. The College considered this unjust, and framed a memorial to the Senatus requesting that their resolution might be reconsidered before it was finally promulgated to the public. The memorial was forwarded to the proper quarter, with the intimation that a copy would be sent to the Royal College of Physicians as the members of that body were greatly interested in the matter, but that no further publicity would then be given to it. Much to the surprise of the College, the University now rescinded its former decision and returned to its strictly exclusive system.

Six years later the new statutes of the University issued by the Town Council, which contained some concessions regarding the system of instruction for the M.D. degree, also recognised the claims of the two Edinburgh Colleges to equal privileges with those of London and Dublin.

This was no sooner done than an alteration, suggested by some members of the Senatus Academicus, was made in the report, to the effect that the fees to be drawn by the extra-mural teachers should in all cases be of the same amount as those charged by the professor of the same subject in the University, and as the College considered that this provision would neutralise the boon which was professed to be granted, it addressed a strong remonstrance on the subject to the Lord Provost.

One of the conditions upon which the Town Council were prepared to make these concessions was that both Colleges should raise the standard of medical instruction given by their lecturers, and upon this subject and that of the equalisation of fees the College said: " When the gentlemen of the two Colleges were called upon to enact laws to raise the standard of qualification of their lecturers, the appeal met with a ready response, for it was obviously right to secure by every reasonable means that those admitted to the enjoyment of an important advantage should be men of capability in their several departments. But the demand for *mere pecuniary protection* made by men who have not scrupled for the promotion of their own emoluments to sacrifice the interests of the Extra-Academical School of this place by withholding from it every title of those privileges which were liberally extended by them twelve months ago to less deserving schools elsewhere, is certainly not entitled to the same favour."

In the meantime the Senatus, which had had no hand in framing the new regulations adopted by the Town Council, decided to resist their introduction and applied to the Court of Session for interdict against their coming into force, on the ground that they alone had the power of making laws for graduation in the University. As a consequence of this the regulations were suspended *ad interim*, and the Senatus raised an action against the Town Council which went from Court to Court until it was finally settled, in 1855, by the House of Lords in favour of the Town Council.

Again, in 1869, when Mr Lister was about to be appointed to the Chair of Clinical Surgery, the College addressed a memorial to the Home Secretary praying that the commission of the new professor might be framed so as to allow his colleagues of the Medical Faculty to give clinical lectures in surgery when they held the office of hospital surgeon ; this would permit of extra-academical teachers who were surgeons to recognised hospitals giving any part of clinical instruction for the medical degrees of the University. The University agreed to receive a deputation from the College and to hear them in support of the memorial, and stated that, as soon as Mr Lister had been inducted into the Professorship, they would have an opportunity of stating their views to the Senatus and also to Mr Lister.

Admission of Women to Medical Classes.—The following year, the students attending at Surgeons' Hall addressed a petition to the College pointing out that several lecturers there had admitted women into their classes without the least endeavour to ascertain the opinion of the male students, and contrary to their desire ; it was further stated that the presence of women at the classes of anatomy and surgery and in the dissecting-room gave rise to various feelings which tended to distract the attention of the students from important subjects of study . . . they requested the College to remove their grievances and thereby restore the uniform good feeling between the students and teachers which previous to the innovation was so prominently manifest. The petition bears the names of sixty-five students. In reply, the College declared it was not a teaching body, and though it recognised and was interested in the success of all extra-academical classes, it had no direct control over them and was not responsible for the decisions of the lecturers. They therefore could not interfere with the teachers who had adopted mixed classes. At the next meeting of the College, however, it was resolved "that in this College it is neither proper nor expedient that males and females should be associated together in the study of medicine either in hospitals or in classes."

CHAPTER XVII

THE OFFICE-BEARERS OF THE COLLEGE

The Kirkmaster, Deacon, or President—The "Boxmaster" or Treasurer— The Clerk or Secretary — The Officer — Fourth Centenary of the College.

THESE notes on the History of the College may fittingly close with a brief reference to the titles and duties of its officials at different periods of its existence.

The Kirkmaster, Deacon, or President.—The first incorporation of a craft in Edinburgh took place in the year 1473, and the title conferred on its master was that of Deacon. The designation was applied to the Masters of all Crafts constituted before 1500, when it was superseded by that of Kirkmaster, an innovation that lasted but a very short time, for, in 1517, the former appellation was again resorted to and continued as long as the Crafts flourished.

The title first borne by the masters of the Chirurgeons was therefore that of Kirkmaster; but from the year 1517 down to the time the Chirurgeons severed their municipal connection they were always known as Deacons, and, as such, were for many years members of the Town Council of the City. The office-bearers were elected at the term of Michaelmas, and to assist the Deacon in his duties there were four masters or councillors, two "keepers of the keys of the box," and a "keeper of the key of the kyst." In the early days the Deacon is usually described as having been elected by the "monyest of his brethrens votes," and upon one occasion, viz., in 1602, the members of the Craft took the following oath : "We all undersubscribers be the faithe of our bodye and under the paine of purjurie and defamation faithfullie promise never hereafter to violet ony point of ye Seal of Cause bot to mentein the samen inviolable and to obey ye said Deacon in all lisome points induring his tyme."

It sometimes happened that the Deacon was elected against his will, and, in 1677, when one was so elected he declared that if the Craft should suffer any prejudice by the want of a member in the Council, whether it was on account of a tender conscience or other ways, that he might be free of any blame and the same to lie at the Calling's own door in respect to their election of him, and upon these terms only he accepted office. A few years later Gideon Elliott refused to accept office as Deacon and was fined by the Town Council. The same thing occurred in 1701, when Robert Clerk was elected but refused to act, alleging that he was not qualified according to law; but on his still refusing to accept office he was prohibited from attending the meetings and suspended from all votings in the affairs of the Calling until he altered his mind. On a new Deacon being elected, however, all his forfeited privileges were restored to him. About the middle of the eighteenth century, the Deacon seems to have been *ex officio* surgeon to the Town Guard, for which duty he received a salary.

When the Incorporation became a Royal College in 1778, its chief officer was designated President.

The " Boxmaster " or Treasurer.—For a considerable period the Treasurer was aptly termed Boxmaster, and to him was entrusted the key of the "kyst." His duties were not laid down until comparatively recent years, although about the year 1650 we find he made "faith *de fideli administratione* in his office as Boxmaster and that he should make just compt reckoning and payment of the Calling's moneys he should meddle and intromett with and that he should be comptable to them for their rights [writs] and securities and all other papers that should be delivered to him by the late Boxmaster."

In 1644, the then Boxmaster, David Kennedy, was relieved of his duties on receiving an Army appointment, and in the following year it is recorded that as "David Kennedy present Boxmaster is employed upon the public service and is presently bound for the North in yis last expedition so that they [the Craft] be destitute of ane Boxmaster unless they depute one in his place,—Andro Walker is deputed Boxmaster till it pleases God to return the said David back again." With reference to this matter, we find in an Act of Parliament dated 27th January

1644, that David Kennedy, James Ker, Thomas Kincaid, and Nehemiah Touch (the first three, Edinburgh surgeons) were appointed surgeons in the Army then about to invade England. Each is to have charge of two regiments joined into one brigade "as they shall be directed by the Lord General and committee with the Army, for which service the Estates modifies the sum of fifteen pounds stg. to be presently paid to each of them for furnishing of the kyst and five shillings stg. of daily allowance to each surgeon and four shillings to his two mates, half a crown daily for maintenance of two baggage horses and three shillings daily for the maintenance of three saddle horses and that there be a month's pay advanced for their outreike and furnishing their horses."

In 1678, the Boxmaster was a certain James Hopkirk, and in the usual order of things he was called upon to produce his accounts for the purpose of auditing. After making various excuses for delay, he at last promised to have them ready by a certain day or go to prison. On their being produced at the appointed hour, they were found to be so complicated that a small committee was formed to deal with them and report to the Incorporation. It was about this time that an Act had been passed prohibiting swearing and cursing at any of the conventions, but at the first meeting of the Auditors such lively scenes were enacted that the Act was disregarded, and the Boxmaster was fined three shillings for swearing. At the next meeting it was the turn of the Auditors, for all of them were fined three shillings for banning; while at the last meeting, a week later, both Auditors and Boxmaster were fined for cursing and banning and for scandalous speeches. Following upon the report of the committee, several items were objected to and were struck out, which the Boxmaster had to make good or else go to the Tolbooth. Amongst these items we find the following: "The hiring of horses to the Lady Elphingston's buriall, there being no authority given." "To deduce twenty shillings from the sum of three pounds five shillings paid to William Daes for wyne and aile, it being clear there were only two pynts of wyne and the aile drunken." "Disallowed the three pounds four shillings for four days' work to the men for ridling of lime, etc., and that for morning and evening drinks because [it was] included in the masons' general discharge."

U

On the election of office-bearers in 1702, an Act was passed that the Boxmaster should in future be named Treasurer, and in 1772 the Deacon and Treasurer first appeared in gowns provided by the Incorporation.

The Clerk or Secretary.—The first Clerk to the Incorporation was a Notary-Public bearing the name of Adam Gibson. He was appointed in May 1587 at a yearly salary of forty shillings, and served as Clerk until the beginning of the following century, when he was succeeded by Mr Quhite. The next to hold the position was David Gibson, and he, in 1637, gave way to Alexander Henryson. Henryson served the Calling for a period of thirty years, during which time he engrossed the whole of the Minutes with his own hand and apparently with the same pen, his caligraphy being deplorable. On the Clerkship becoming vacant in 1671, strange to say the Incorporation passed an Act by which the power of filling it up devolved upon the Lord Provost, Sir Andrew Ramsay, who is described as "an honest abill man." The Act entreats his Lordship to undertake the duty, but not to nominate any Writer to his Majesty's Signet, Sub-Clerk to the Session or any of those whose nomination "breed heat and division amongst us." The Lord Provost eventually recommended Mr Patrick Moubray, Writer, who was appointed Clerk "during all the days of his life tyme." In 1701, the Clerk's fees and emoluments were declared to be as under:—

Official salary	40 merks yearly
For every Intrant Chirurgeon for his Act, the same being written on fair parchment	12 pounds Scots
For every Barber admitted within the burgh and in the Canongate .	6 pounds Scots
For every Barber admitted in Leith and the suburbs	3 pounds 12 shillings Scots
For Indentures made between Chirurgeons and Apprentices . . .	2 rix dollars
For Indentures made between Barbers and their Apprentices . .	1 rix dollar
For booking of Apprentices both to Chirurgeons and Barbers . .	20 shillings Scots
For booking of Servands ditto . .	13 shillings and 4 pence

During the latter part of Mr Moubray's service his health was so bad that he had to be conveyed to the meetings in a chair, for the hire of which, on one occasion, the Incorporation paid fourteen shillings and sixpence. He died in 1708, when the Calling paid to his widow the sum of one hundred pounds Scots upon her delivering up the seals and papers she had belonging to them. In 1717, an Act was passed by the Incorporation allowing the Clerk to dispose of his office to a fit and qualified person approved of by them, but on the sudden death of the gentleman elected under these conditions, the next candidate had to pay to the Calling 3000 merks for his appointment. In 1756, this method was slightly modified, it being then decided to sell it to the highest qualified bidder, when, out of a list of nine candidates, the purchaser turned out to be Mr Alexander Schaw, son of one of the members of the Incorporation, with an offer of £185 stg. Some eighteen years later, when Mr Schaw resigned his office to take up a Government appointment abroad, he resigned his claim of disposing of it in favour of the Incorporation on repayment of £160. The Calling now agreed never again to expose the office for sale, but on selecting a qualified person, to name a moderate sum which he should pay into the hands of the Treasurer, and which, if he demitted office on his own account, the Calling would have power to refund in part or otherwise, at their discretion. Mr Balderston next became Clerk and paid £150 in terms of the new arrangement. In 1825, it was decided that the Clerk should have the title of Secretary, and in all matters relating to the business of the College he was appointed to use and to be designated by that title instead of that of Clerk. It was thought that it would be more consonant with their dignity as a Royal College, and more in keeping with the practice of other Royal Colleges that their principal agent and functionary should be designated Secretary, and that the want of this had been felt on a recent occasion when the Clerk was in London on the business of the College. Ten years later the salary and emoluments of the Clerk or Secretary were readjusted. With a considerable increase to the former, all the fees, with the exception of those payable on indentures and on the admission of Fellows, were discontinued and no extra payment was allowed except his professional charges when employed by the College on special business.

These arrangements in turn gave way to others in 1861, when it became a law of the College that the Secretary should in future be a Fellow of the College and that he should have the nomination of a Clerk, subject to the approval of the College, whose duties should be performed under the Secretary's superintendence. A legal gentleman was also appointed, to whom the College might refer all legal questions at an ordinary rate of remuneration. Since that time no important alterations in the position of the Secretary has taken place.

The Officer.—The position of Officer to the Incorporation dates from the granting of the Seal of Cause in 1505, and the Officer is now the only College official who retains his original designation. His duties in the early days were to collect "oure quarter payments and oulklie [weekly] pennies and to pass before us on Corpus Christi day and the oatanis thairof and all aither generall processionis and gatheringis siclike as utheris craftis hes within this burgh." In 1603, each apprentice on being booked was ordered to pay to the Officer three shillings and fourpence and, in 1614, Alexander Thomson was elected Officer at a yearly salary of four pounds Scots, and to receive from each master at his admission six shillings and eightpence, "providit alwayes that at the admission of the first freeman to be made master, that last master who is to be admitted shall be Officer." He was also by common consent of the Craft to "poind for unlawis" those persons who should be absent from the meetings without consent. From this it will be seen that the last joined master of the Craft performed the duties of Officer until relieved by a junior. In 1650, the Officer having accepted office in consequence of the absence in Spain of two younger members was fined ten merks for refusing to convene a meeting of the Craft at the Deacon's request. This probably raised the question of the expediency of the duties being performed by a master, for at the next meeting a certain Samivel Campbell was elected to the post and was ordered by the Deacon to receive out of the box "twenty pounds of fee yearly and all other casualties belonging to the office, and forty-eight shillings for a pair of shoes out of their gratitude." In 1664, in consequence of some members of the Incorporation having become apothecaries, a botanic garden on a small scale was instituted and a professional gardener named George Cathcart was employed to look after it and also to perform the duties of Officer. Cathcart served the Incorporation over thirty years, and would have served them longer had they not, in 1698, decided that their Officer should wear a livery coat with a silver badge bearing their arms. This proved too much, for on the coat and badge being offered to him he indignantly refused to wear them, with the result that the post of Gardener-Officer was again vacant. Andrew Raeburn who had served as gardener "to many gentlemen in the neighbourhood to their entire satisfaction" was the next comer, and having received from Cathcart "his gudewill and blessing," he offered his services to the Calling, and promised "with the assistance of God to do his duty as honestly and as faithfully as was possible for him to do." In 1771, the Officer was superannuated through sickness and placed in the workhouse, and, he being a freeman barber, his daughter was elected to a vacancy in the Trades Maiden Hospital. His successor also died in indigent circumstances, leaving a family of four children, one of whom, a girl, being deprived of the use of her limbs by disease, was allowed by the College a quarterly pension of thirty shillings.

John Dodds was Officer at the time the new Hall was built, and he for one seems not to have appreciated the change of quarters. In 1833, in stating some grievances to the College, he said he regretted the loss of a perquisite in the shape of the ground lying behind the old Hall where he kept a few fowls and two or three sheep. His predecessor, he explained, who enjoyed the same salary as himself, had time for doing a little business upon his own account by buying grain on commission and renting grass parks. Upon one occasion he said, " I acted as one of the referees in a dispute which he had about part of the grazings of the King's Park, where he was engaged to the extent of an annual rent of £180." In 1847, in consequence of failing health, Mr Dodds was awarded an annuity of £30 a year, and as Mr Hamlin Lee, the Conservator of the Museum, was willing and desirous to devote his time and attention more exclusively to the service of the College, he agreed to combine the Officer's duties along with his own, conditionally that the house, salary, and perquisites of the Officer were granted to him. Five years later the Museum Committee reported that this arrangement was unsatisfactory, and recommended the College to declare both of these offices vacant and to be filled up by separate parties, which was done.

The Fourth Centenary of the College.—In July 1905 the College celebrated the fourth centenary of its incorporation. The most important of the ceremonies on this occasion was the conferring of the Honorary Fellowship upon thirty-six of the most distinguished surgeons of the day from all parts of the world.

The proceedings commenced on the evening of 19th July, when the President and Fellows welcomed the Honorary Fellows Elect at a Reception in the College. A Commemoration Service in St Giles Cathedral, the next morning, was attended by the Honorary Fellows, Fellows, Guests, and Delegates from the different learned bodies, and by a large number of the general public. A most impressive service in the old Kirk, with which the College was so intimately connected in its earliest days, was followed by a luncheon given in the City Chambers by the Lord Provost, Magistrates, and Council of the City, to a company of nearly a hundred. After lunch came the function at the M'Ewan Hall, when the Honorary Fellowship was conferred upon those whom the College had selected to receive the highest honour they had in their power to bestow. A Reception in the Royal Scottish Museum was held in the evening and was attended by some 2000 guests. Hospitality, in the shape of a luncheon given by the President and Fellows of the Royal College of Physicians in their Hall, was continued the next day, and in the afternoon the guests of the College met at a garden party in the grounds of George Heriot's Hospital. The same evening the functions concluded with a banquet in the Music Hall. The Chair was taken by Sir Patrick Heron Watson, LL.D., the President of the College, and amongst the learned and distinguished guests was his Excellency the French Ambassador, M. Paul Cambon.

INDEX

Royal Infirmary, management of, 211
  origin of, 209
  Royal Charter of, 211
  substitute surgeons, 219
  surgeons to, 209, 217, 221, 229
Royal Medical Society Hall, 60, 65, 66
Russell, Professor James, 64, 83, 222,
  228, 234, 239, 252

SABBATH observance, 30
St Giles, Kirk of, altar in, 2
  celebration of Mass in, 6
School of Medicine, Surgeons' Hall,
  95
Seal of Cause, 2
Secretary, the, 276, 306
Servants, laws regarding, 137
Smith, Dr, Honorary Fellow, 174
Social gatherings, 149
South Bridge, erection of, 260
Spence, James, 85
Struthers, John, 96
Surgeon-Apothecaries, 36, 112
Surgeons (see also Royal College of
    Surgeons), admission to, 35
  association with Barbers, 130
  duties of, 112, 116
  licence granted to country surgeons,
    122
  meeting places of, 46
  new Charter of, 119, 121
  revised Constitution of, 136
  separation from Barbers, 124
Surgeons' jurisdiction extended to
    the three Lothians, 122
Surgeons' Hall, School of Medicine, 96
  Hospital, 209, 212, 229; coalition
    with Royal Infirmary, 213, 214
  Square, 47; disposal of, 65

Surgery, mastership in, 295
  Professorship of, 235, 239, 247
Syme, James, 83, 174, 231, 247, 248,
  250, 263, 289

TAYLOR, "Dr," the itinerant oculist,
  108
Thatcher, Dr, recognition of lectures
  by, 176
Thomson, John, 240, 246
Town Council, association of College
  with, 256
  separation of College of Surgeons
    from, 264
Trades Maiden Hospital, the, 155
Trained Bands, the, 21
Treasurer, the, 304
Triple qualification, 296
Turner, John William, 245, 247

UNIVERSITY degree in medicine,
  284
  museum, 81
  transfer of College Library to, 86

VACCINATION, public, 165
Valentine, Daniel, barber, 106, 128

WEIR, John, Honorary Fellow, 172
Widows' Fund, the, 157, 276
Wigmaker fined, 125
Women, admission of, to medical
  classes, 301
Wood, Alexander, 150
  Thomas, 163
  William, 64, 180

PRINTED BY
OLIVER AND BOYD
EDINBURGH